MW01076354

<u>Legal Notice</u>

For information on bulk purchases and licensing agreements, please email

support@SATPrepGet800.com

ISBN-13: 978-0999811764

Acknowledgements

The author would like to thank Dan Seabold for his helpful input during the creation of this book. Special thanks also go to Joel David Hamkins and Simon Thomas for introducing this subject to the author and for their inspiration.

Also Available from Dr. Steve Warner

CONNECT WITH DR. STEVE WARNER

www.facebook.com/SATPrepGet800

www.youtube.com/TheSATMathPrep

www.twitter.com/SATPrepGet800

www.linkedin.com/in/DrSteveWarner

www.pinterest.com/SATPrepGet800

plus.google.com/+SteveWarnerPhD

Set Theory
for Beginners

A Rigorous Introduction to Sets, Relations, Partitions, Functions, Induction, Ordinals, Cardinals, Martin's Axiom, and Stationary Sets

Dr. Steve Warner

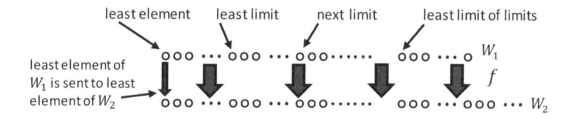

iii

Table of Contents

INTRODUCTION
SET THEORY

This book was written to provide a basic but rigorous introduction to set theory. Additionally, a few more advanced topics are presented later in the book.

For students: There are no prerequisites for this book. The content is completely self-contained. Students with a bit of mathematical knowledge may have an easier time getting through some of the material, but no such knowledge is necessary to read this book.

More important than mathematical knowledge is "mathematical maturity." Although there is no single agreed upon definition of mathematical maturity, one reasonable way to define it is as "one's ability to analyze, understand, and communicate mathematics." A student with a higher level of mathematical maturity will be able to move through this book more quickly than a student with a lower level of mathematical maturity.

Whether your level of mathematical maturity is low or high, if you are just starting out in set theory, then you're in the right place. If you read this book the "right way," then your level of mathematical maturity will continually be increasing. This increased level of mathematical maturity will not only help you to succeed in advanced math courses, but it will improve your general problem solving and reasoning skills. This will make it easier to improve your performance in college, in your professional life, and on standardized tests.

So, what is the "right way" to read this book? Simply reading each lesson from end to end without any further thought and analysis is not the best way to read the book. You will need to put in some effort to have the best chance of absorbing and retaining the material. When a new theorem is presented, don't just jump right to the proof and read it. Think about what the theorem is saying. Try to describe it in your own words. Do you believe that it is true? If you do believe it, can you give a convincing argument that it is true? If you do not believe that it is true, try to come up with an example that shows it is false, and then figure out why your example does not contradict the theorem. Pick up a pen or pencil. Draw some pictures, come up with your own examples, and try to write your own proof.

You may find that this book goes into more detail than other set theory books when explaining examples, discussing concepts, and proving theorems. This was done so that any student can read this book, and not just students that are naturally gifted in mathematics. So, it is up to you as the student to try to answer questions before they are answered for you. When a new definition is given, try to think of your own examples before looking at those presented in the book. And when the book provides an example, do not just accept that it satisfies the given definition. Convince yourself. Prove it.

Each lesson is followed by a Problem Set. The problems in each Problem Set have been organized into five levels of difficulty, followed by one or more Challenge Problems. Level 1 problems are the easiest and Level 5 problems are the most difficult, except for the Challenge Problems. If you want to get just a small taste of set theory, then you can work on the easier problems. If you want to achieve a deeper understanding of the material, take some time to struggle with the harder problems.

For instructors: This book can be used as an undergraduate text or an introductory graduate text in set theory. The subject is developed slowly with an emphasis early on of developing skill with proof writing.

Lessons 1 through 7 provide a complete introduction to nonaxiomatic set theory. All the basics of sets, subsets, set operations, relations, partitions, functions, and equinumerosity are included. Set theoretic definitions of the natural numbers, integers, rationals, and reals are provided in Lessons 5 and 6. The formal treatments of these number systems can be included or omitted, depending on the taste of each individual instructor.

Lesson 8 covers induction and recursion on the natural numbers. This lesson can be skipped over in more advanced courses, as transfinite induction and recursion are covered in Lesson 12.

Lessons 9 and 10 provide introductions to propositional logic and first-order logic, respectively. These lessons can be skipped by instructors that do not wish to get caught up in too much logic.

Lesson 11 gives a development of ZFC axiomatically, providing a rigorous treatment of all the axioms. Lessons 9 and 10 are not essential to understanding this lesson.

Lessons 12 and 13 contain a full treatment of the ordinals and cardinals. Most instructors will want to include these lessons in their course.

Lessons 14 through 16 contain a few more advanced topics, such as Martin's Axiom, the completeness of the reals, and clubs and stationary sets.

Students will have access to solutions to all problems in the Problem Sets at the end of each lesson, except for the Challenge Problems. These Challenge Problems can be used for graded assignments. I would recommend giving students at least several days to a week to work on each one. Most students will find them quite difficult.

The author welcomes all feedback from instructors. Any suggestions will be considered for future editions of the book. The author would also love to hear about the various courses that are created using these lessons. Feel free to email Dr. Steve Warner with any feedback at

steve@SATPrepGet800.com

LESSON 1
SETS

Describing Sets

A **set** is simply a collection of "objects." These objects can be numbers, letters, colors, animals, funny quotes, or just about anything else you can imagine. We will usually refer to the objects in a set as the **members** or **elements** of the set.

If a set consists of a small number of elements, we can describe the set simply by listing the elements in the set in curly braces, separating elements by commas.

Example 1.1:

1. {cat, dog} is the set consisting of two elements: *cat* and *dog.*

2. {red, green, purple, teal} is the set consisting of four elements: *red*, *green*, *purple*, and *teal.*

3. {baseball, football, basketball, tennis, airplane, piano} is the set consisting of six elements: *baseball, football, basketball*, *tennis, airplane*, and *piano.*

4. $\{1, 2, 3, 4, 5\}$ is the set consisting of five elements: 1, 2, 3, 4, and 5. The elements in this set happen to be *numbers.*

A set is determined by its elements, and not the order in which the elements are presented. For example, the set $\{2, 1, 4, 3, 5\}$ is the same as the set $\{1, 2, 3, 4, 5\}$.

Also, the set $\{1, 1, 2, 3, 4, 5, 5, 5\}$ is the same as the set $\{1, 2, 3, 4, 5\}$. If we are describing a set by listing its elements, the most natural way to do this is to list each element just once.

We will usually name sets using capital letters such as A, B, and C. For example, we might write $A = \{a, b, c\}$. So, A is the set consisting of the elements a, b, and c.

Example 1.2: Consider the sets $A = \{x, y\}$, $B = \{y, x\}$, $C = \{x, y, x\}$. Then A, B, and C all represent the same set. We can write $A = B = C$.

We use the symbol $\in$ for the membership relation (we will define the term "relation" more carefully in Lesson 4). So, $x \in A$ means "x is an element of A," whereas $x \notin A$ means "x is **not** an element of A." We will often simply say "x is in A," and "x is not in A," respectively.

Example 1.3: Let $A = \{c, z, 8, \Delta, \square\}$. Then $c \in A$, $z \in A$, $8 \in A$, $\Delta \in A$, and $\square \in A$.

If a set consists of many elements, we can use **ellipses** (...) to help describe the set. For example, the set consisting of the natural numbers between 25 and 3168, inclusive, can be written $\{25, 26, 27, \ldots, 3167, 3168\}$ ("inclusive" means that we include 25 and 3168). The ellipses between 27 and 3167 are there to indicate that there are elements in the set that we are not explicitly mentioning.

9

Ellipses can also be used to help describe **infinite sets**. The set of **natural numbers** can be written $\mathbb{N} = \{0, 1, 2, 3, \dots\}$, and the set of **integers** can be written $\mathbb{Z} = \{\dots, -4, -3, -2, -1, 0, 1, 2, 3, 4, \dots\}$. (We will see more formal definitions of $\mathbb{N}$ and $\mathbb{Z}$ in Lesson 5.)

Note: Some mathematicians exclude 0 from the set of natural numbers. We will never do this here.

Example 1.4:

1. The even natural numbers can be written $\mathbb{E} = \{0, 2, 4, 6, \dots\}$.

2. The odd natural numbers can be written $\mathbb{O} = \{1, 3, 5, \dots\}$.

3. The even integers can be written $2\mathbb{Z} = \{\dots, -6, -4, -2, 0, 2, 4, 6, \dots\}$.

4. The primes can be written $\mathbb{P} = \{2, 3, 5, 7, 11, 13, 17, \dots\}$.

A set can also be described by a certain property P that all its elements have in common. In this case, we can use the **set-builder notation** $\{x | P(x)\}$ to describe the set. The expression $\{x | P(x)\}$ can be read "the set of all x such that the property $P(x)$ is true." Note that the symbol "|" is read as "such that."

Example 1.5: Let's look at a few different ways that we can describe the set $\{2, 4, 6, 8, 10, 12, 14\}$. We have already seen that reordering and/or repeating elements does not change the set. For example, $\{2, 2, 6, 4, 10, 8, 14, 14, 12\}$ describes the same set. Here are a few more descriptions using set-builder notation:

- $\{n \mid n \text{ is an even positive integer less than or equal to } 14\}$

- $\{n \in \mathbb{Z} \mid n \text{ is even}, 0 < n \leq 14\}$

- $\{2k \mid k = 1, 2, 3, 4, 5, 6, 7\}$

The first expression in the bulleted list can be read "the set of n such that n is an even positive integer less than or equal to 14." The second expression can be read "the set of integers n such that n is even and n is between 0 and 14, including 14, but excluding 0. Note that the abbreviation "$n \in \mathbb{Z}$" can be read "n is in the set of integers," or more succinctly, "n is an integer." The third expression can be read "the set of $2k$ such that k is 1, 2, 3, 4, 5, 6, or 7."

The **empty set** is the unique set with no elements. We use the symbol $\emptyset$ to denote the empty set (some authors use the symbol $\{\ \}$ instead).

A set may contain other sets as elements. For example, the set $A = \{a, \{b, c\}\}$ is the set consisting of the two elements a and $\{b, c\}$. It's worth emphasizing that b and c are **not** elements of the set A. Using the membership relation, we have $a \in A$, $\{b, c\} \in A$, $b \notin A$, and $c \notin A$.

Example 1.6:

1. $X = \{\{a\}\}$ is the set consisting of one element: $\{a\}$. Note that $a \notin X$, while $\{a\} \in X$.

2. $Y = \{\{0\}, \{1\}\}$ is the set consisting of two elements: $\{0\}$ and $\{1\}$. Note that $0 \notin Y$ and $1 \notin Y$, while $\{0\} \in Y$ and $\{1\} \in Y$.

3. $Z = \{\emptyset, \{\emptyset\}\}$ is the set consisting of two elements: $\emptyset$ and $\{\emptyset\}$.

Cardinality of a Finite Set

If A is a finite set, we define the **cardinality** of A, written $|A|$, to be the number of elements of A. For example, $|\{a, b\}| = 2$. In Lesson 13, we will extend the notion of cardinality to also include infinite sets.

Example 1.7: Let $A = \{\text{painting}, \text{tree}, \text{diamond}\}$, $B = \{y, z, z\}$, and $C = \{25, 26, 27, \ldots, 3167, 3168\}$. Then $|A| = 3$, $|B| = 2$, and $|C| = 3144$.

Notes: (1) The set A consists of the three elements "painting," "tree," and "diamond."

(2) The set B consists of just two elements: y and z. Remember that $\{y, z, z\} = \{y, z\}$.

(3) The number of consecutive integers from m to n, inclusive, is $\boldsymbol{n - m + 1}$. For set C, we have $m = 25$ and $n = 3168$. Therefore, $|C| = 3168 - 25 + 1 = 3144$.

(4) I call the formula "$n - m + 1$" the **fence-post formula**. If you construct a 3-foot fence by placing a fence-post every foot, then the fence will consist of 4 fence-posts ($3 - 0 + 1 = 4$).

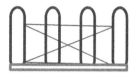

Example 1.8: Let $X = \{x, \{x\}\}$, $Y = \{\{x\}, \{x, x\}, \{x, x, x\}\}$, and $Z = \{\emptyset, \{\emptyset\}, \{\emptyset, \{\emptyset\}\}\}$. Then $|X| = 2$, $|Y| = 1$, and $|Z| = 3$.

Notes: (1) The set X consists of the two elements x and $\{x\}$.

(2) Since $\{x, x\} = \{x\}$ and $\{x, x, x\} = \{x\}$, it follows that $Y = \{\{x\}, \{x\}, \{x\}\} = \{\{x\}\}$. So, Y consists of the single element $\{x\}$.

(3) The set Z consists of the three elements $\emptyset$, $\{\emptyset\}$, and $\{\emptyset, \{\emptyset\}\}$.

Problem Set 1

Full solutions to these problems are available for free download here:

www.SATPrepGet800.com/STFBYKG

LEVEL 1

1. Determine whether each of the following statements is true or false:

    (i) $k \in \{k\}$

    (ii) $0 \in \{0, 1, 2\}$

    (iii) $-1 \in \{1\}$

    (iv) $3 \in \mathbb{N}$

    (v) $-72 \in \mathbb{Z}$

2. Determine the cardinality of each of the following sets:

    (i) $\{a, b, c\}$

    (ii) $\{0, 1, 2, 3, 4, 5\}$

    (iii) $\{1, 2, \ldots, 72\}$

LEVEL 2

3. Determine whether each of the following statements is true or false:

    (i) $2 \in \emptyset$

    (ii) $\emptyset \in \{1, 2\}$

    (iii) $\emptyset \in \{\emptyset\}$

    (iv) $\{\emptyset\} \in \emptyset$

    (v) $\{\emptyset\} \in \{\emptyset\}$

4. Determine the cardinality of each of the following sets:

    (i) $\{1, 2, 3, 4, 3, 2, 1\}$

    (ii) $\{\emptyset, \{a, b, c\}\}$

    (iii) $\{3, 4, 5, \ldots, 4031, 4032\}$

LEVEL 3

5. Determine whether each of the following statements is true or false:

   (i) $\emptyset \in \emptyset$

   (ii) $\emptyset \in \{\emptyset, \{\emptyset\}\}$

   (iii) $1 \in \{2k \mid k = 1, 2, 3, 4, 5, 6\}$

   (iv) $12 \in \{3t \mid t = 1, 2, 3, 4, 5\}$

   (v) $\{a, b, c\} \in \{a, b, c\}$

6. Determine the cardinality of each of the following sets:

   (i) $\Big\{\{\{\emptyset, \{\emptyset\}\}\}\Big\}$

   (ii) $\Big\{\{0, 1\}, \emptyset, \{\emptyset\}, \{\emptyset, \{\emptyset, a, b\}\}\Big\}$

   (iii) $\Big\{\emptyset, \{\emptyset\}, \{\{\emptyset\}\}, \{\emptyset, \{\emptyset\}, \{\{\emptyset\}\}\}\Big\}$

LEVEL 4

7. Determine whether each of the following statements is true or false:

   (i) $c \in \{a, \{c\}\}$

   (ii) $\{\Delta\} \in \{\delta, \Delta\}$

   (iii) $\{1\} \in \{1, a, 2, b\}$

   (iv) $\emptyset \in \{\{\emptyset\}\}$

   (v) $\{\{\emptyset\}\} \in \emptyset$

8. Let $C = \Big\{\{\emptyset\}, \{\emptyset, \{\emptyset\}\}\Big\}$ and $D = \{\emptyset, \{\emptyset\}\}$. Is $C \in D$? Is $D \in C$?

LEVEL 5

9. Determine the cardinality of $\Big\{a, \{a\}, \{a, a\}, \{a, a, a, a\}, \{a, a, \{a\}\}, \{a, \{a\}, \{a\}\}\Big\}$.

13

10. We say that a set A is **transitive** if whenever $y \in x$ and $x \in A$, it follows that $y \in A$. Determine if each of the following sets is transitive:

    (i) $\emptyset$

    (ii) $\{\emptyset\}$

    (iii) $\{\{\emptyset\}\}$

    (iv) $\{\emptyset, \{\emptyset\}\}$

    (v) $\{\emptyset, \{\emptyset\}, \{\{\emptyset\}\}\}$

    (vi) $\{\{\emptyset\}, \{\emptyset, \{\emptyset\}\}\}$

CHALLENGE PROBLEM

11. Provide an example of an infinite transitive set (see Problem 10 above for the definition of a transitive set).

LESSON 2
SUBSETS

Subsets and Proper Subsets

We say that a set A is a **subset** of a set B, written $A \subseteq B$, if every element of A is an element of B.

Example 2.1:

1. Let $A = \{0, 1\}$ and $B = \{0, 1, 2\}$. The only elements of A are 0 and 1. Since 0 and 1 are also elements of B, we see that $A \subseteq B$.

    Notice that $B \nsubseteq A$ (B is **not** a subset of A) because $2 \in B$, but $2 \notin A$.

2. Let $\mathbb{N} = \{0, 1, 2, 3, \dots\}$ be the set of natural numbers and let $\mathbb{Z} = \{\dots, -3, -2, -1, 0, 1, 2, 3, 4, \dots\}$ be the set of integers. Since every natural number is an integer, $\mathbb{N} \subseteq \mathbb{Z}$.

To the right we see a physical representation of $A \subseteq B$. This figure is called a **Venn diagram**. These types of diagrams are very useful to help visualize relationships among sets. Notice that set A lies completely inside set B. We assume that all the elements of A and B lie in some **universal set** U.

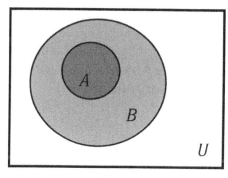

$A \subseteq B$

As an example, let's let U be the set of all species of animals. If we let A be the set of species of cats and we let B be the set of species of mammals, then we have $A \subseteq B \subseteq U$, and we see that the Venn diagram to the right gives a visual representation of this situation. (Note that every cat is a mammal and every mammal is an animal.)

We say that A is a **proper subset** of B, written $A \subset B$ (or sometimes $A \subsetneq B$), if $A \subseteq B$, but $A \neq B$. For example, $\mathbb{N} \subset \mathbb{Z}$, whereas $\mathbb{N} \not\subset \mathbb{N}$ (although $\mathbb{N} \subseteq \mathbb{N}$).

Note: The definition of proper subset is not very important. It just gives us a convenient way to discuss all the subsets of a specific set except for the set itself. For example, it is quite cumbersome to say "Find all subsets of A, but exclude the set A." It's nice to be able to rephrase this as "Find all proper subsets of A."

Let's look at the definition of $\subseteq$ (subset) in a bit more detail.

Once again, we write $A \subseteq B$ if every element of A is an element of B. That is, $A \subseteq B$ if, for every x, $x \in A$ implies $x \in B$. Symbolically, we can write the following:

$$\forall x(x \in A \to x \in B)$$

Notes: (1) The symbol $\forall$ is called a **universal quantifier**, and it is pronounced "For all."

(2) The logical expression $\forall x(x \in A \to x \in B)$ can be translated into English as "For all x, if x is an element of A, then x is an element of B."

15

(3) To show that a set A is a subset of a set B, we need to show that the expression $\forall x(x \in A \rightarrow x \in B)$ is true. If the set A is finite and the elements are listed, we can just check that each element of A is also an element of B. However, if the set A is described by a property, say $A = \{x | P(x)\}$, we may need to craft an argument more carefully. We can begin by taking an **arbitrary but specific element** a from A and then arguing that this element a is in B.

What could we possibly mean by an arbitrary but specific element? Aren't the words "arbitrary" and "specific" antonyms? Well, by arbitrary, we mean that we don't know which element we are choosing – it's just some element a that satisfies the property P. So, we are just assuming that $P(a)$ is true. However, once we choose this element a, we use this same a for the rest of the argument, and that is what we mean by it being specific.

(4) "$p \rightarrow q$" is an example of a **statement** in **propositional logic** (see Lesson 9 for a detailed review of this subject). It is usually read as "if p, then q" or "p implies q." The letters p and q are called **propositional variables**, and we will generally assign a truth value of T (for true) or F (for false) to each propositional variable. Formally, we define a **truth assignment** of a list of propositional variables to be a choice of T or F for each propositional variable in the list.

The symbol $\rightarrow$ is called a **conditional** or **implication**. It is one example of a **logical connective** (it *connects* two propositional variables). The rules for determining the truth value for $p \rightarrow q$ are given by the following truth table:

p	q	$p \rightarrow q$
T	T	T
T	F	F
F	T	T
F	F	T

For example, if p and q are both assigned the truth value T, then the truth value of $p \rightarrow q$ is also T, as can be seen by the first row of the above truth table. We can write $T \rightarrow T \equiv T$. The symbol "$\equiv$" can be read "**is logically equivalent to**."

Observe from the truth table above that the only time $p \rightarrow q$ can be false is if p is true and q is false. So, one way to prove that $p \rightarrow q$ is true is to assume that p is true and then provide a logically correct argument that q must also be true.

If we let p represent the statement "$x \in A$" and we let q represent the statement "$x \in B$," then $p \rightarrow q$ represents the statement "if $x \in A$, then $x \in B$." As stated in the last paragraph, one way to prove that this statement is true is to assume that $x \in A$ is true and then provide a logically correct argument that $x \in B$ must also be true.

Basic Theorems Involving Subsets

Let's try to prove our first theorem using the definition of a subset together with Note 3 above about arbitrary but specific elements.

Theorem 2.1: Every set A is a subset of itself.

Analysis: Before writing the proof, let's think about our strategy. We want to prove $A \subseteq A$. In other words, we want to show $\forall x (x \in A \rightarrow x \in A)$. So, we will take an arbitrary but specific $a \in A$ and then argue that $a \in A$. But that's pretty obvious, isn't it? In this case, the property we're describing is precisely the conclusion we are looking for. Here are the details.

Proof of Theorem 2.1: Let A be a set and let $a \in A$. Then $a \in A$. So, $a \in A \rightarrow a \in A$ is true. Since a was an arbitrary element of A, $\forall x (x \in A \rightarrow x \in A)$ is true. Therefore, $A \subseteq A$. $\qquad \square$

Notes: (1) The proof begins with the **opening statement** "Let A be a set and let $a \in A$." In general, the opening statement states what is given in the problem and/or fixes any arbitrary but specific objects that we will need.

(2) The proof ends with the **closing statement** "Therefore, $A \subseteq A$." In general, the closing statement states the result.

(3) Everything between the opening statement and the closing statement is known as the **argument**.

(4) We place the symbol $\square$ at the end of the proof to indicate that the proof is complete.

(5) Consider the logical statement $p \rightarrow p$. This statement is always true ($\mathrm{T} \rightarrow \mathrm{T} \equiv \mathrm{T}$ and $\mathrm{F} \rightarrow \mathrm{F} \equiv \mathrm{T}$). $p \rightarrow p$ is an example of a tautology. A **tautology** is a statement that is true for every possible truth assignment of the propositional variables.

(6) If we let p represent the statement $a \in A$, by Note 5, we see that $a \in A \rightarrow a \in A$ is always true.

Alternate proof of Theorem 2.1: Let A be a set and let $a \in A$. Since $p \rightarrow p$ is a tautology, we have that $a \in A \rightarrow a \in A$ is true. Since a was arbitrary, $\forall x (x \in A \rightarrow x \in A)$ is true. Therefore, $A \subseteq A$. $\qquad \square$

Let's prove another basic but important theorem.

Theorem 2.2: The empty set is a subset of every set.

Analysis: This time we want to prove $\emptyset \subseteq A$. In other words, we want to show $\forall x (x \in \emptyset \rightarrow x \in A)$. Since $x \in \emptyset$ is always false (the empty set has no elements), $x \in \emptyset \rightarrow x \in A$ is always true.

In general, if p is a false statement, then we say that $p \rightarrow q$ is **vacuously true**.

Proof of Theorem 2.2: Let A be a set. The statement $x \in \emptyset \rightarrow x \in A$ is vacuously true for any x, and so, $\forall x (x \in \emptyset \rightarrow x \in A)$ is true. Therefore, $\emptyset \subseteq A$. $\qquad \square$

Note: The opening statement is "Let A be a set," the closing statement is "Therefore, $\emptyset \subseteq A$," and the argument is everything in between.

Example 2.2: Let $C = \{a, b, c\}$, $D = \{a, c\}$, $E = \{b, c\}$, $F = \{b, d\}$, and $G = \emptyset$. Then $D \subseteq C$ and $E \subseteq C$. Also, since **the empty set is a subset of every set**, we have $G \subseteq C$, $G \subseteq D$, $G \subseteq E$, $G \subseteq F$, and $G \subseteq G$. **Every set is a subset of itself**, and so, $C \subseteq C$, $D \subseteq D$, $E \subseteq E$, and $F \subseteq F$.

Note: Below are possible Venn diagrams for this problem. The diagram on the left shows the relationship between the sets C, D, E, and F. Notice how D and E are both subsets of C, whereas F is not a subset of C. Also, notice how D and E overlap, E and F overlap, but there is no overlap between D and F (they have no elements in common). The diagram on the right shows the proper placement of the elements. Here, I chose the universal set to be $U = \{a, b, c, d, e, f, g\}$. This choice for the universal set is somewhat arbitrary. Any set containing $\{a, b, c, d\}$ would do.

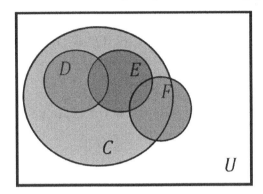 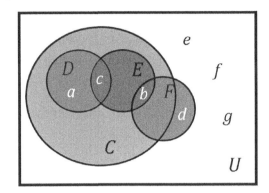

Power Sets

If A is a set, then the **power set** of A, written $\mathcal{P}(A)$, is the set of all subsets of A. In set-builder notation, we write $\mathcal{P}(A) = \{B \mid B \subseteq A\}$.

Example 2.3: The set $A = \{a, b\}$ has 2 elements and 4 subsets. The subsets of A are $\emptyset$, $\{a\}$, $\{b\}$, and $\{a, b\}$. It follows that $\mathcal{P}(A) = \{\emptyset, \{a\}, \{b\}, \{a, b\}\}$.

The set $B = \{a, b, c\}$ has 3 elements and 8 subsets. The subsets of B are $\emptyset$, $\{a\}$, $\{b\}$, $\{c\}$, $\{a, b\}$, $\{a, c\}$, $\{b, c\}$, and $\{a, b, c\}$. It follows that $\mathcal{P}(B) = \{\emptyset, \{a\}, \{b\}, \{c\}, \{a, b\}, \{a, c\}, \{b, c\}, \{a, b, c\}\}$.

Let's draw a **tree diagram** for the subsets of each of the sets A and B.

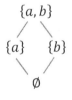 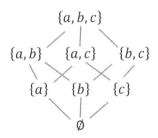

The tree diagram on the left is for the subsets of the set $A = \{a, b\}$. We start by writing the set $A = \{a, b\}$ at the top. On the next line we write the subsets of cardinality 1 ($\{a\}$ and $\{b\}$). On the line below that we write the subsets of cardinality 0 (just $\emptyset$). We draw a line segment between any two sets when the smaller (lower) set is a subset of the larger (higher) set. So, we see that $\emptyset \subseteq \{a\}$, $\emptyset \subseteq \{b\}$, $\{a\} \subseteq \{a, b\}$, and $\{b\} \subseteq \{a, b\}$. There is actually one more subset relationship, namely $\emptyset \subseteq \{a, b\}$ (and of course each set displayed is a subset of itself). We didn't draw a line segment from $\emptyset$ to $\{a, b\}$ to avoid unnecessary clutter. Instead, we can simply trace the path from $\emptyset$ to $\{a\}$ to $\{a, b\}$ (or from $\emptyset$ to $\{b\}$ to $\{a, b\}$). We are using a property called **transitivity** here (see Theorem 2.3 below).

The tree diagram on the right is for the subsets of $B = \{a, b, c\}$. Observe that from top to bottom we write the subsets of B of size 3, then 2, then 1, and then 0. We then draw the appropriate line segments, just as we did for $A = \{a, b\}$.

How many subsets does a set of cardinality n have? Let's start by looking at some examples.

Example 2.4: A set with 0 elements must be $\emptyset$, and this set has exactly 1 subset (the only subset of the empty set is the empty set itself).

A set with 1 element has 2 subsets, namely $\emptyset$ and the set itself.

In the last example, we saw that a set with 2 elements has 4 subsets, and we also saw that a set with 3 elements has 8 subsets.

Do you see the pattern yet? $1 = 2^0$, $2 = 2^1$, $4 = 2^2$, $8 = 2^3$. So, we see that a set with 0 elements has 2^0 subsets, a set with 1 element has 2^1 subsets, a set with 2 elements has 2^2 subsets, and a set with 3 elements has 2^3 subsets. A reasonable guess would be that a set with n elements has $\mathbf{2^n}$ subsets. You will be asked to prove this result later (Problem 10 in Problem Set 8). We can also say that if $|A| = n$, then $|\mathcal{P}(A)| = 2^n$.

Transitivity of the Subset Relation

Let's get back to the transitivity mentioned above in our discussion of tree diagrams.

Theorem 2.3: Let A, B, and C be sets such that $A \subseteq B$ and $B \subseteq C$. Then $A \subseteq C$.

Proof: Suppose that A, B, and C are sets with $A \subseteq B$ and $B \subseteq C$, and let $a \in A$. Since $A \subseteq B$ and $a \in A$, it follows that $a \in B$. Since $B \subseteq C$ and $a \in B$, it follows that $a \in C$. Since a was an arbitrary element of A, we have shown that every element of A is an element of C. That is, $\forall x(x \in A \rightarrow x \in C)$ is true. Therefore, $A \subseteq C$. □

Note: To the right we have a Venn diagram illustrating Theorem 2.3.

Theorem 2.3 tells us that the relation $\subseteq$ is **transitive**. Since $\subseteq$ is transitive, we can write things like $A \subseteq B \subseteq C \subseteq D$, and without explicitly saying it, we know that $A \subseteq C$, $A \subseteq D$, and $B \subseteq D$.

Example 2.5: The membership relation $\in$ is an example of a relation that is **not** transitive. For example, let $A = \{0\}$, $B = \{0, 1, \{0\}\}$, and $C = \{x, y, \{0, 1, \{0\}\}\}$. Observe that $A \in B$ and $B \in C$, but $A \notin C$.

$A \subseteq B \subseteq C$

$\{0\} \in \{0, 1, \{0\}\} \in \{x, y, \{0, 1, \{0\}\}\}$

Notes: (1) The set A has just 1 element, namely 0.

(2) The set B has 3 elements, namely 0, 1, and $\{0\}$. But wait! $A = \{0\}$. So, $A \in B$. The set A is circled twice in the above image.

19

(3) The set C also has 3 elements, namely, x, y, and $\{0,1,\{0\}\}$. But wait! $B = \{0, 1, \{0\}\}$. So, $B \in C$. The set B has a rectangle around it twice in the above image.

(4) Since $A \neq x$, $A \neq y$, and $A \neq \{0, 1, \{0\}\}$, we see that $A \notin C$.

(5) Is it clear that $\{0\} \notin C$? $\{0\}$ is in a set that's in C (namely, B), but $\{0\}$ is not itself in C.

(6) Here is a more basic example showing that $\in$ is not transitive: $\emptyset \in \{\emptyset\} \in \{\{\emptyset\}\}$, but $\emptyset \notin \{\{\emptyset\}\}$
The only element of $\{\{\emptyset\}\}$ is $\{\emptyset\}$.

Equality of Sets

Two sets A and B are **equal**, written $A = B$, if they have the same elements. Symbolically, we can write the following:

$$\forall x(x \in A \leftrightarrow x \in B)$$

Notes: (1) "$p \leftrightarrow q$" is another example of a **statement** in **propositional logic** (once again, see Lesson 9 for a detailed review of this subject). It is usually read as "p if and only if q."

The logical connective $\leftrightarrow$ is called a **biconditional**. The rules for determining the truth value for $p \leftrightarrow q$ are given by the following truth table:

p	q	$p \leftrightarrow q$
T	T	T
T	F	F
F	T	F
F	F	T

In other words, $p \leftrightarrow q$ is true when p and q have the same truth value (both T or both F) and false when p and q have opposite truth values (one T and the other F).

If we let p represent the statement "$x \in A$" and we let q represent the statement "$x \in B$," then $p \leftrightarrow q$ represents the statement "$x \in A$ if and only if $x \in B$."

(2) In addition to the conditional ($\rightarrow$) and biconditional ($\leftrightarrow$), there are three more commonly used logical connectives: the **conjunction** ($\wedge$), the **disjunction** ($\vee$), and the **negation** ($\neg$). They have the following truth tables:

p	q	$p \wedge q$
T	T	T
T	F	F
F	T	F
F	F	F

p	q	$p \vee q$
T	T	T
T	F	T
F	T	T
F	F	F

p	$\neg p$
T	F
F	T

These logical connectives are discussed in detail in Lesson 9.

In addition, we will see in Lesson 9 that we can use statements in place of propositional variables to form compound statements (see the discussion right before Example 9.2)

(3) We say that two statements are **logically equivalent** if every truth assignment of the propositional variables appearing in either statement (or both statements) leads to the same truth value for both statements.

It is easy to verify that $p \leftrightarrow q$ is logically equivalent to $(p \rightarrow q) \wedge (q \rightarrow p)$. To see this, we check that all possible truth assignments for p and q lead to the same truth value for the two statements. For example, if p and q are both true, then

$$p \leftrightarrow q \equiv \mathrm{T} \leftrightarrow \mathrm{T} \equiv \mathrm{T} \quad \text{and} \quad (p \rightarrow q) \wedge (q \rightarrow p) \equiv (\mathrm{T} \rightarrow \mathrm{T}) \wedge (\mathrm{T} \rightarrow \mathrm{T}) \equiv \mathrm{T} \wedge \mathrm{T} \equiv \mathrm{T}.$$

The reader should check the other three truth assignments for p and q, or draw the entire truth table for both statements (see Lesson 9 for more details on both of these methods).

(4) Letting p be the statement $x \in A$, letting q be the statement $x \in B$, and replacing $p \leftrightarrow q$ by the logically equivalent statement $(p \rightarrow q) \wedge (q \rightarrow p)$ gives us

$$\forall x(x \in A \leftrightarrow x \in B) \text{ if and only if } \forall x\big((x \in A \rightarrow x \in B) \wedge (x \in B \rightarrow x \in A)\big).$$

(5) It is also true that $\forall x\big(p(x) \wedge q(x)\big)$ is logically equivalent to $\forall x\big(p(x)\big) \wedge \forall x\big(q(x)\big)$ (this can be proved using the theory developed in Lesson 10). And so, we have

$$\forall x(x \in A \leftrightarrow x \in B) \text{ if and only if } \forall x(x \in A \rightarrow x \in B) \text{ and } \forall x(x \in B \rightarrow x \in A).$$

In other words, to show that $A = B$, we can instead show that $A \subseteq B$ and $B \subseteq A$.

The statement "$A = B$ if and only if $A \subseteq B$ and $B \subseteq A$" is usually called the **Axiom of Extensionality**. It is often easiest to prove that two sets are equal by showing that each one is a subset of the other.

Example 2.6: Let $A = \{n \in \mathbb{N} \mid n < 100\}$ and let $B = \{n \in \mathbb{Z} \mid 0 \leq n \leq 99\}$. Let's use the Axiom of Extensionality to prove that $A = B$.

Note: We are assuming that $<$ and $\leq$ are defined in the usual way on $\mathbb{N}$ and $\mathbb{Z}$. In the proof, we will freely use the properties of these relations that we know to be true. For example, 0 is the least element of $\mathbb{N}$ with respect to $<$ and $\leq$. As another example, in both $\mathbb{N}$ and $\mathbb{Z}$, we have $n < k + 1$ if and only if $n \leq k$.

Proof: We first prove that $A \subseteq B$. Let $n \in A$. Then $n \in \mathbb{N}$ and $n < 100$. Since $n \in \mathbb{N}$ and $\mathbb{N} \subseteq \mathbb{Z}$, it follows that $n \in \mathbb{Z}$. Since $n \in \mathbb{N}$ and the least element of $\mathbb{N}$ is 0, $0 \leq n$. Since $n < 100$ and $n \in \mathbb{N}$, we have $n \leq 99$. Therefore, $n \in B$. Since $n \in A$ was arbitrary, $\forall n(n \in A \rightarrow n \in B)$. Therefore, we have shown $A \subseteq B$.

We now prove that $B \subseteq A$. Let $n \in B$. Then $n \in \mathbb{Z}$ and $0 \leq n \leq 99$. Since $n \in \mathbb{Z}$ and $0 \leq n$, it follows that $n \in \mathbb{N}$. Since $n \leq 99$ and $99 < 100$, it follows that $n < 100$. Therefore, $n \in A$. Since $n \in B$ was arbitrary, $\forall n(n \in B \rightarrow n \in A)$. Therefore, we have shown $B \subseteq A$.

Since $A \subseteq B$ and $B \subseteq A$, we have $A = B$. □

Problem Set 2

Full solutions to these problems are available for free download here:
www.SATPrepGet800.com/STFBYKG

LEVEL 1

1. Determine whether each of the following statements is true or false:

   (i) $\emptyset \subseteq \{a, b\}$

   (ii) $\{\Delta\} \subseteq \{\delta, \Delta\}$

   (iii) $\{1, 2, 3\} \subseteq \{1, 2, 3\}$

   (iv) $\{1, c, \{5, k\}\} \subseteq \{1, c, 5, k\}$

2. Provide a single example of a set A with the following properties: (i) $A \subset \mathbb{Z}$ (A is a *proper* subset of $\mathbb{Z}$); (ii) A is infinite; (iii) A contains both positive and negative integers; (iv) A contains both even and odd integers.

LEVEL 2

3. Determine whether each of the following statements is true or false:

   (i) $\emptyset \subseteq \emptyset$

   (ii) $\emptyset \subseteq \{\emptyset\}$

   (iii) $\{\emptyset\} \subseteq \emptyset$

   (iv) $\{\emptyset\} \subseteq \{\emptyset\}$

4. Compute the power set of each of the following sets:

   (i) $\emptyset$

   (ii) $\{\delta, \Delta\}$

   (iii) $\{\emptyset, \{\emptyset\}\}$

   (iv) $\{\{\emptyset\}\}$

LEVEL 3

5. How many subsets does $\{a, b, c, d\}$ have? Draw a tree diagram for the subsets of $\{a, b, c, d\}$.

6. Let A, B, C, D, and E be sets such that $A \subseteq B$, $B \subseteq C$, $C \subseteq D$, and $D \subseteq E$. Prove that $A \subseteq E$.

LEVEL 4

7. A relation R is **reflexive** if $\forall x(xRx)$ and **symmetric** if $\forall x \forall y(xRy \rightarrow yRx)$. For example, the relation "$=$" is reflexive and symmetric because $\forall x(x = x)$ and $\forall x \forall y(x = y \rightarrow y = x)$. Show that $\subseteq$ is reflexive, but $\in$ is not. Then decide if each of $\subseteq$ and $\in$ is symmetric.

8. A set A is **transitive** if $\forall x(x \in A \rightarrow x \subseteq A)$ (in words, every element of A is also a subset of A). Prove that if A is a transitive set, then $\mathcal{P}(A)$ is also a transitive set.

LEVEL 5

9. Let $P(x)$ be the property $x \notin x$. Prove that $\{x | P(x)\}$ cannot be a set.

10. Let $A = \{a, b, c, d\}$, $B = \{X \mid X \subseteq A \wedge d \notin X\}$, and $C = \{X \mid X \subseteq A \wedge d \in X\}$. Show that there is a natural **one-to-one correspondence** (see definition below) between the elements of B and the elements of C. Then generalize this result to a set with $n + 1$ elements for $n > 0$.

   Definition: Informally, a **one-to-one correspondence** between two sets is a pairing so that each element of the first set is matched up with exactly one element of the second set, and vice versa.

   Formally, a **one-to-one correspondence** is a function that is bijective. Functions (and in particular, bijective functions) will be defined rigorously in Lesson 6.

CHALLENGE PROBLEM

11. Let A and B be sets with $A \subseteq B$ and B transitive. Prove that $\mathcal{P}(A) \subseteq \mathcal{P}(\mathcal{P}(B))$. (See Problem 8 above for the definition of a transitive set.)

Basic Set Operations

The **union** of the sets A and B, written $A \cup B$, is the set of elements that are in A or B (or both).

$$A \cup B = \{x \mid x \in A \text{ or } x \in B\}$$

The **intersection** of A and B, written $A \cap B$, is the set of elements that are simultaneously in A and B.

$$A \cap B = \{x \mid x \in A \text{ and } x \in B\}$$

The following Venn diagrams for the union and intersection of two sets can be useful for visualizing these operations.

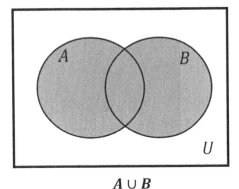

$A \cup B$

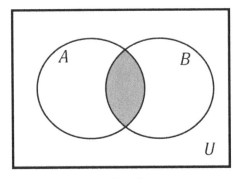

$A \cap B$

The **difference** $A \setminus B$ is the set of elements that are in A and not in B.

$$A \setminus B = \{x \mid x \in A \text{ and } x \notin B\}$$

The **symmetric difference** between A and B, written $A \, \Delta \, B$, is the set of elements that are in A or B, but not both.

$$A \, \Delta \, B = (A \setminus B) \cup (B \setminus A)$$

Let's also look at Venn diagrams for the difference and symmetric difference of two sets.

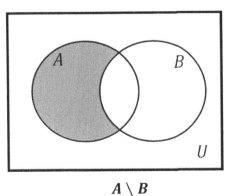

$A \setminus B$

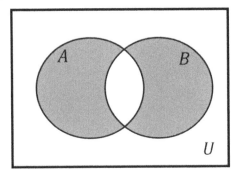

$A \, \Delta \, B$

Example 3.1: Let $A = \{0, 1, 2, 3, 4\}$ and $B = \{3, 4, 5, 6\}$. We have

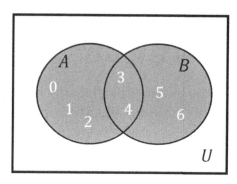

1. $A \cup B = \{0, 1, 2, 3, 4, 5, 6\}$.
2. $A \cap B = \{3, 4\}$.
3. $A \setminus B = \{0, 1, 2\}$.
4. $B \setminus A = \{5, 6\}$.
5. $A \mathbin{\Delta} B = \{0, 1, 2\} \cup \{5, 6\} = \{0, 1, 2, 5, 6\}$.

Example 3.2: Recall that the set of natural numbers is $\mathbb{N} = \{0, 1, 2, 3, \dots\}$ and the set of integers is $\mathbb{Z} = \{\dots, -4, -3, -2, -1, 0, 1, 2, 3, 4, \dots\}$. Observe that in this case, $\mathbb{N} \subseteq \mathbb{Z}$. We have

1. $\mathbb{N} \cup \mathbb{Z} = \mathbb{Z}$.
2. $\mathbb{N} \cap \mathbb{Z} = \mathbb{N}$.
3. $\mathbb{N} \setminus \mathbb{Z} = \emptyset$.
4. $\mathbb{Z} \setminus \mathbb{N} = \{\dots, -4, -3, -2, -1\} = \mathbb{Z}^-$. ($\mathbb{Z}^-$ is "the set of negative integers.")
5. $\mathbb{N} \mathbin{\Delta} \mathbb{Z} = \emptyset \cup \mathbb{Z}^- = \mathbb{Z}^-$.

Note: Whenever A and B are sets and $B \subseteq A$, then $A \cup B = A$, $A \cap B = B$, and $B \setminus A = \emptyset$. We will prove the first and third of these three facts in Theorems 3.2 and 3.3 below, respectively. You will be asked to prove the second in Problem 7 below.

Example 3.3: Let $\mathbb{E} = \{0, 2, 4, 6, \dots\}$ be the set of even natural numbers and let $\mathbb{O} = \{1, 3, 5, 7, \dots\}$ be the set of odd natural numbers. We have

1. $\mathbb{E} \cup \mathbb{O} = \{0, 1, 2, 3, 4, 5, 6, 7, \dots\} = \mathbb{N}$.
2. $\mathbb{E} \cap \mathbb{O} = \emptyset$.
3. $\mathbb{E} \setminus \mathbb{O} = \mathbb{E}$.
4. $\mathbb{O} \setminus \mathbb{E} = \mathbb{O}$.
5. $\mathbb{E} \mathbin{\Delta} \mathbb{O} = \mathbb{E} \cup \mathbb{O} = \mathbb{N}$.

In general, we say that sets A and B are **disjoint** or **mutually exclusive** if $A \cap B = \emptyset$. Below is a Venn diagram for disjoint sets.

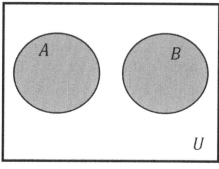

$A \cap B = \emptyset$

Let's prove some theorems involving unions of sets. You will be asked to prove the analogous results for intersections of sets in Problems 6 and 7 below.

Theorem 3.1: If A and B are sets, then $A \subseteq A \cup B$.

Before going through the proof, look once more at the Venn diagram above for $A \cup B$ and convince yourself that this theorem should be true.

Proof of Theorem 3.1: Suppose that A and B are sets and let $x \in A$. Then $x \in A$ or $x \in B$. Therefore, $x \in A \cup B$. Since x was an arbitrary element of A, we have shown that every element of A is an element of $A \cup B$. That is, $\forall x (x \in A \rightarrow x \in A \cup B)$ is true. Therefore, $A \subseteq A \cup B$. $\qquad \square$

Note: If p is a true statement, then $p \vee q$ (p or q) is true no matter what the truth value of q is. In the second sentence of the proof above, we are using this fact with p being the statement $x \in A$ and q being the statement $x \in B$.

We will use this same reasoning in the second paragraph of the next proof as well.

Theorem 3.2: $B \subseteq A$ if and only if $A \cup B = A$.

Before going through the proof, it's a good idea to draw a Venn diagram for $B \subseteq A$ and convince yourself that this theorem should be true.

Proof of Theorem 3.2: Suppose that $B \subseteq A$ and let $x \in A \cup B$. Then $x \in A$ or $x \in B$. If $x \in A$, then $x \in A$ (trivially). If $x \in B$, then since $B \subseteq A$, it follows that $x \in A$. Since x was an arbitrary element of $A \cup B$, we have shown that every element of $A \cup B$ is an element of A. That is, $\forall x (x \in A \cup B \rightarrow x \in A)$ is true. Therefore, $A \cup B \subseteq A$. By Theorem 3.1, $A \subseteq A \cup B$. Since $A \cup B \subseteq A$ and $A \subseteq A \cup B$, it follows that $A \cup B = A$.

Now, suppose that $A \cup B = A$ and let $x \in B$. Since $x \in B$, it follows that $x \in A$ or $x \in B$. Therefore, $x \in A \cup B$. Since $A \cup B = A$, we have $x \in A$. Since x was an arbitrary element of B, we have shown that every element of B is an element of A. That is, $\forall x (x \in B \rightarrow x \in A)$. Therefore, $B \subseteq A$. $\qquad \square$

Theorem 3.3: Let A and B be sets. If $B \subseteq A$, then $B \setminus A = \emptyset$.

We will use an **indirect proof** to prove Theorem 3.3. Specifically, we will use a **proof by contrapositive**.

The contrapositive of the conditional statement $p \rightarrow q$ is the statement $\neg q \rightarrow \neg p$. These two statements are logically equivalent. To see this, we check that all possible truth assignments for p and q lead to the same truth value for the two statements. For example, if p and q are both true, then $p \rightarrow q \equiv T \rightarrow T \equiv T$ and $\neg q \rightarrow \neg p \equiv F \rightarrow F \equiv T$. The reader should check the other three truth assignments for p and q, or draw the entire truth table for both statements (see Lesson 9).

The contrapositive of the statement "If $B \subseteq A$, then $B \setminus A = \emptyset$" is "If $B \setminus A \neq \emptyset$, then $B \not\subseteq A$." So, we will prove Theorem 3.3 by assuming that $B \setminus A \neq \emptyset$ and using this to show that $B \not\subseteq A$.

Proof of Theorem 3.3: Let A and B be sets such that $B \setminus A \neq \emptyset$. Since $B \setminus A \neq \emptyset$, there is $a \in B \setminus A$. Then $a \in B$ and $a \notin A$. So, $\forall x (x \in B \rightarrow x \in A)$ is false. Therefore, $B \not\subseteq A$. $\qquad \square$

Properties of Unions and Intersections

Unions, intersections, and set differences have many nice algebraic properties such as

1. **Commutativity:** $A \cup B = B \cup A$ and $A \cap B = B \cap A$.

2. **Associativity:** $(A \cup B) \cup C = A \cup (B \cup C)$ and $(A \cap B) \cap C = A \cap (B \cap C)$.

3. **Distributivity:** $A \cap (B \cup C) = (A \cap B) \cup (A \cap C)$ and $A \cup (B \cap C) = (A \cup B) \cap (A \cup C)$.

4. **De Morgan's Laws:** $C \setminus (A \cup B) = (C \setminus A) \cap (C \setminus B)$ and $C \setminus (A \cap B) = (C \setminus A) \cup (C \setminus B)$.

5. **Idempotent Laws:** $A \cup A = A$ and $A \cap A = A$.

As an example, let's prove that the operation of forming unions is associative. You will be asked to prove that the other properties hold in the problems below.

Theorem 3.4: The operation of forming unions is associative.

Note: Before beginning the proof, let's draw Venn diagrams of the situation to convince ourselves that the theorem is true.

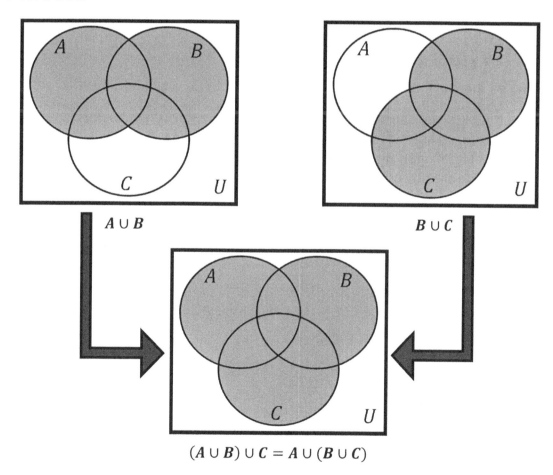

$$(A \cup B) \cup C = A \cup (B \cup C)$$

Proof of Theorem 3.4: Let A, B, and C be sets, and let $x \in (A \cup B) \cup C$. Then $x \in A \cup B$ or $x \in C$. If $x \in C$, then $x \in B$ or $x \in C$. So, $x \in B \cup C$. Then $x \in A$ or $x \in B \cup C$. So, $x \in A \cup (B \cup C)$. If, on the other hand, $x \in A \cup B$, then $x \in A$ or $x \in B$. If $x \in A$, then $x \in A$ or $x \in B \cup C$. So, $x \in A \cup (B \cup C)$. If $x \in B$, then $x \in B$ or $x \in C$. So, $x \in B \cup C$. Then $x \in A$ or $x \in B \cup C$. So, $x \in A \cup (B \cup C)$. Since x was arbitrary, we have shown $\forall x \big(x \in (A \cup B) \cup C \rightarrow x \in A \cup (B \cup C) \big)$. Therefore, we have shown that $(A \cup B) \cup C \subseteq A \cup (B \cup C)$.

A similar argument can be used to show $A \cup (B \cup C) \subseteq (A \cup B) \cup C$ (the reader should write out the details).

Since $(A \cup B) \cup C \subseteq A \cup (B \cup C)$ and $A \cup (B \cup C) \subseteq (A \cup B) \cup C$, $(A \cup B) \cup C = A \cup (B \cup C)$, and therefore, the operation of forming unions is associative. $\square$

Remember that associativity allows us to drop parentheses. So, we can now simply write $A \cup B \cup C$ when taking the union of the three sets A, B, and C.

Arbitrary Unions and Intersections

We will often be interested in taking unions and intersections of more than two sets. Therefore, we make the following more general definitions.

Let $\boldsymbol{X}$ be a nonempty set of sets.

$$\cup \boldsymbol{X} = \{y \mid \text{there is } Y \in X \text{ with } y \in Y\} \qquad \text{and} \qquad \cap \boldsymbol{X} = \{y \mid \text{for all } Y \in X, y \in Y\}.$$

If you're having trouble understanding what these definitions are saying, you're not alone. The notation probably looks confusing, but the ideas behind these definitions are very simple. You have a whole bunch of sets (possibly infinitely many). To take the union of all these sets, you simply throw all the elements together into one big set. To take the intersection of all these sets, you take only the elements that are in every single one of those sets.

Example 3.4:

1. Let A and B be sets and let $\boldsymbol{X} = \{A, B\}$. Then

$$\cup \boldsymbol{X} = \{y \mid \text{there is } Y \in X \text{ with } y \in Y\} = \{y \mid y \in A \text{ or } y \in B\} = A \cup B.$$
$$\cap \boldsymbol{X} = \{y \mid \text{for all } Y \in X, y \in Y\} = \{y \mid y \in A \text{ and } y \in B\} = A \cap B.$$

2. Let A, B, and C be sets, and let $\boldsymbol{X} = \{A, B, C\}$. Then

$$\cup \boldsymbol{X} = \{y \mid \text{there is } Y \in X \text{ with } y \in Y\} = \{y \mid y \in A, y \in B, \text{ or } y \in C\} = A \cup B \cup C.$$
$$\cap \boldsymbol{X} = \{y \mid \text{for all } Y \in X, y \in Y\} = \{y \mid y \in A, y \in B, \text{ and } y \in C\} = A \cap B \cap C.$$

3. Let $\boldsymbol{X} = \big\{\{-n, \ldots, -3, -2, -1, 0, 1, 2, 3, 4, \ldots, n\} \mid n \in \mathbb{N}\big\}$. Then

$$\cup \boldsymbol{X} = \{y \mid \text{there is } Y \in X \text{ with } y \in Y\}$$
$$= \big\{y \mid \text{there is } n \in \mathbb{N} \text{ with } y \in \{-n, \ldots, -3, -2, -1, 0, 1, 2, 3, 4, \ldots, n\}\big\} = \mathbb{Z}.$$
$$\cap \boldsymbol{X} = \{y \mid \text{for all } Y \in X, y \in Y\}$$
$$= \big\{y \mid \text{for all } n \in \mathbb{N}, y \in \{-n, \ldots, -3, -2, -1, 0, 1, 2, 3, 4, \ldots, n\}\big\} = \{0\}.$$

Notes: (1) Examples 1 and 2 give a good idea of what $\bigcup X$ and $\bigcap X$ look like when X is finite. More generally, if $X = \{A_1, A_2, \ldots, A_n\}$, then $\bigcup X = A_1 \cup A_2 \cup \cdots \cup A_n$ and $\bigcap X = A_1 \cap A_2 \cap \cdots \cap A_n$.

(2) As a specific example of Note 1, let $A_1 = \{\ldots, -3, -2, -1, 0, 1, 2, 3, 4, 5\}$, $A_2 = \{0, 1, 2, 3, 4, 5\}$, $A_3 = \{2, 3, 4, 5\}$, and $A_4 = \{4, 5, 6, 7, \ldots, 98, 99\}$. Let $X = \{A_1, A_2, A_3, A_4\}$. Then

$$\bigcup X = A_1 \cup A_2 \cup A_3 \cup A_4 = \{\ldots, -3, -2, -1, 0, 1, 2, 3, , \ldots, 98, 99\}.$$

$$\bigcap X = A_1 \cap A_2 \cap A_3 \cap A_4 = \{4, 5\}.$$

If you have trouble seeing how to compute the intersection, it may help to take the intersections two at a time:

$A_1 \cap A_2 = A_2 = \{0, 1, 2, 3, 4, 5\}$ because $A_2 \subseteq A_1$.

$\{0, 1, 2, 3, 4, 5\} \cap A_3 = A_3 = \{2, 3, 4, 5\}$ because $A_3 \subseteq \{0, 1, 2, 3, 4, 5\}$.

$\{2, 3, 4, 5\} \cap A_4 = \{2, 3, 4, 5\} \cap \{4, 5, 6, 7, \ldots, 98, 99\} = \{4, 5\}$.

(3) Let's prove carefully that $\{y \mid \text{there is } n \in \mathbb{N} \text{ with } y \in \{-n, \ldots, -3, -2, -1, 0, 1, 2, 3, 4, \ldots, n\}\} = \mathbb{Z}$.

For convenience, let's let $A = \{y \mid \text{there is } n \in \mathbb{N} \text{ with } y \in \{-n, \ldots, -3, -2, -1, 0, 1, 2, 3, 4, \ldots, n\}\}$.

If $y \in A$, then there is $n \in \mathbb{N}$ with $y \in \{-n, \ldots, -3, -2, -1, 0, 1, 2, 3, 4, \ldots, n\}$. In particular, $y \in \mathbb{Z}$. Since $y \in A$ was arbitrary, we have shown that $A \subseteq \mathbb{Z}$.

Let $y \in \mathbb{Z}$. Then $y \in \{-n, \ldots, -3, -2, -1, 0, 1, 2, 3, 4, \ldots, n\}$, where $n = y$ if $y \geq 0$ and $n = -y$ if $y < 0$ (in other words, n is the **absolute value** of y, written $n = |y|$). So, $y \in A$. Since $y \in \mathbb{Z}$ was arbitrary, we have shown that $\mathbb{Z} \subseteq A$.

Since $A \subseteq \mathbb{Z}$ and $\mathbb{Z} \subseteq A$, it follows that $A = \mathbb{Z}$.

(4) Let's also prove carefully that $\{y \mid \text{for all } n \in \mathbb{N}, y \in \{-n, \ldots, -3, -2, -1, 0, 1, 2, 3, 4, \ldots, n\}\} = \{0\}$.

For convenience, let's let $B = \{y \mid \text{for all } n \in \mathbb{N}, y \in \{-n, \ldots, -3, -2, -1, 0, 1, 2, 3, 4, \ldots, n\}\}$.

If $y \in B$, then for all $n \in \mathbb{N}$, $y \in \{-n, \ldots, -3, -2, -1, 0, 1, 2, 3, 4, \ldots, n\}$. In particular, $y \in \{0\}$. Since $y \in B$ was arbitrary, we have shown that $B \subseteq \{0\}$.

Now, let $y \in \{0\}$. Then $y = 0$. For all $n \in \mathbb{N}$, $0 \in \{-n, \ldots, -3, -2, -1, 0, 1, 2, 3, 4, \ldots, n\}$. So, $y \in B$. It follows that $\{0\} \subseteq B$.

Since $B \subseteq \{0\}$ and $\{0\} \subseteq B$, it follows that $B = \{0\}$.

(5) Note that the empty union is empty. Indeed, we have $\bigcup \emptyset = \{y \mid \text{there is } Y \in \emptyset \text{ with } y \in Y\} = \emptyset$.

If X is a nonempty set of sets, we say that X is **disjoint** if $\bigcap X = \emptyset$. We say that X is **pairwise disjoint** if for all $A, B \in X$ with $A \neq B$, A and B are disjoint. For example, if we let $X = \{(n, n + 1) \mid n \in \mathbb{Z}\}$, then X is both disjoint and pairwise disjoint.

Are the definitions of disjoint and pairwise disjoint equivalent? You will be asked to answer this question in Problem 5 below.

Problem Set 3

Full solutions to these problems are available for free download here:
www.SATPrepGet800.com/STFBYKG

LEVEL 1

1. Let $A = \{a, b, \Delta, \delta\}$ and $B = \{b, c, \delta, \gamma\}$. Determine each of the following:

    (i) $A \cup B$

    (ii) $A \cap B$

    (iii) $A \setminus B$

    (iv) $B \setminus A$

    (v) $A \Delta B$

2. Draw Venn diagrams for $(A \setminus B) \setminus C$ and $A \setminus (B \setminus C)$. Are these two sets equal for all sets A, B, and C? If so, prove it. If not, provide a counterexample.

LEVEL 2

3. Let $A = \left\{\emptyset, \{\emptyset, \{\emptyset\}\}\right\}$ and $B = \{\emptyset, \{\emptyset\}\}$. Compute each of the following:

    (i) $A \cup B$

    (ii) $A \cap B$

    (iii) $A \setminus B$

    (iv) $B \setminus A$

    (v) $A \Delta B$

4. Prove the following:

    (i)   The operation of forming unions is commutative.

    (ii) The operation of forming intersections is commutative.

    (iii) The operation of forming intersections is associative.

LEVEL 3

5. Prove or provide a counterexample:

    (i)   Every pairwise disjoint set of sets is disjoint.

    (ii) Every disjoint set of sets is pairwise disjoint.

6. Let A and B be sets. Prove that $A \cap B \subseteq A$.

LEVEL 4

7. Prove that $B \subseteq A$ if and only if $A \cap B = B$.

8. Let A, B, and C be sets. Prove each of the following:

    (i) $A \cap (B \cup C) = (A \cap B) \cup (A \cap C)$.

    (ii) $A \cup (B \cap C) = (A \cup B) \cap (A \cup C)$.

    (iii) $C \setminus (A \cup B) = (C \setminus A) \cap (C \setminus B)$.

    (iv) $C \setminus (A \cap B) = (C \setminus A) \cup (C \setminus B)$.

LEVEL 5

9. Let X be a nonempty set of sets. Prove the following:

    (i)   For all $A \in X$, $A \subseteq \bigcup X$.

    (ii)   For all $A \in X$, $\bigcap X \subseteq A$.

10. Let A be a set and let X be a nonempty collection of sets. Prove each of the following:

    (i) $A \cap \bigcup X = \bigcup \{A \cap B \mid B \in X\}$

    (ii) $A \cup \bigcap X = \bigcap \{A \cup B \mid B \in X\}$

    (iii) $A \setminus \bigcup X = \bigcap \{A \setminus B \mid B \in X\}$

    (iv) $A \setminus \bigcap X = \bigcup \{A \setminus B \mid B \in X\}$.

CHALLENGE PROBLEMS

11. Let X be a nonempty collection of sets. Prove that $\mathcal{P}(\bigcap X) = \bigcap \{\mathcal{P}(A) \mid A \in X\}$.

12. Let X be a nonempty collection of sets. Prove that $\mathcal{P}(\bigcup X) = \bigcup \{\mathcal{P}(A) \mid A \in X\}$ if and only if $\bigcup X \in X$.

LESSON 4
RELATIONS

Cartesian Products

An **unordered pair** is a set with 2 elements. Recall, that a set doesn't change if we write the elements in a different order or if we write the same element multiple times. For example, $\{0, 1\} = \{1, 0\}$ and $\{0, 0\} = \{0\}$.

We now define the **ordered pair** (x, y) in such a way that (y, x) will **not** be the same as (x, y). The simplest way to define a set with this property is as follows:

$$(x, y) = \{\{x\}, \{x, y\}\}$$

Let's show that with this definition, the ordered pair behaves as we would expect.

Theorem 4.1: $(x, y) = (z, w)$ if and only if $x = z$ and $y = w$.

Part of the proof of this theorem is a little trickier than expected. Assuming that $(x, y) = (z, w)$, there are actually two cases to consider: $x = y$ and $x \neq y$. If $x = y$, then (x, y) is a set with just one element. Indeed, $(x, x) = \{\{x\}, \{x, x\}\} = \{\{x\}, \{x\}\} = \{\{x\}\}$. So, the only element of (x, x) is $\{x\}$. Watch carefully how this plays out in the proof.

Proof of Theorem 4.1: First suppose that $x = z$ and $y = w$. Then by direct substitution, $\{x\} = \{z\}$ and $\{x, y\} = \{z, w\}$. So, $(x, y) = \{\{x\}, \{x, y\}\} = \{\{z\}, \{z, w\}\} = (z, w)$.

Conversely, suppose that $(x, y) = (z, w)$. Then $\{\{x\}, \{x, y\}\} = \{\{z\}, \{z, w\}\}$. There are two cases to consider.

Case 1: If $x = y$, then $\{\{x\}, \{x, y\}\} = \{\{x\}\}$. So, $\{\{x\}\} = \{\{z\}, \{z, w\}\}$. It follows that $\{z\} = \{x\}$ and $\{z, w\} = \{x\}$. Since $\{z, w\} = \{x\}$, we must have $z = x$ and $w = x$. Therefore, $x, y, z,$ and w are all equal. In particular, $x = z$ and $y = w$.

Case 2: If $x \neq y$, then $\{x, y\}$ is a set with two elements. So, $\{x, y\}$ cannot be equal to $\{z\}$ (because $\{z\}$ has just one element). Therefore, we must have $\{x, y\} = \{z, w\}$. It then follows that $\{x\} = \{z\}$. So, we have $x = z$. Since $x = z$ and $\{x, y\} = \{z, w\}$, we must have $y = w$. □

Note: (x, y) is an abbreviation for the set $\{\{x\}, \{x, y\}\}$. In the study of Set Theory, every object can be written as a set like this. It's often convenient to use abbreviations, but we should always be aware that if necessary, we can write any object in its unabbreviated form.

We can extend the idea of an ordered pair to an **ordered k-tuple**. An ordered 3-tuple (also called an **ordered triple)** is defined by $(x, y, z) = ((x, y), z)$, an ordered 4-tuple is $(x, y, z, w) = ((x, y, z), w)$, and so on.

Example 4.1: Let's write the ordered triple (x, y, z) in its unabbreviated form (take a deep breath!).

$$(x, y, z) = ((x, y), z) = \{\{(x, y)\}, \{(x, y), z\}\} = \Big\{\big\{\{\{x\}, \{x, y\}\}\big\}, \big\{\{\{x\}, \{x, y\}\}, z\big\}\Big\}$$

The **Cartesian product** of the sets A and B, written $A \times B$ is the set of ordered pairs (a, b) with $a \in A$ and $b \in B$. Symbolically, we have

$$A \times B = \{(a, b) \mid a \in A \wedge b \in B\}.$$

Observe that if A and B are finite sets with $|A| = m$ and $|B| = n$, then $|A \times B| = mn$.

Example 4.2:

1. Let $A = \{0, 1, 2\}$ and $B = \{a, b\}$. Then $A \times B = \{(0, a), (0, b), (1, a), (1, b), (2, a), (2, b)\}$. Note that $|A| = 3$, $|B| = 2$, and $|A \times B| = 3 \cdot 2 = 6$.

2. Let $C = \emptyset$ and $D = \{a, b, c, d\}$. Then $C \times D = \emptyset$ (since there are no elements in C, there can be no elements in $C \times D$). Note that $|C| = 0$, $|D| = 4$, and $|C \times D| = 0 \cdot 4 = 0$.

3. Let $E = \{\emptyset\}$ and $F = \{\Delta, *\}$. Then $E \times F = \{(\emptyset, \Delta), (\emptyset, *)\}$. Note that $|E| = 1$, $|F| = 2$, and $|E \times F| = 1 \cdot 2 = 2$.

4. $\mathbb{N} \times \mathbb{Z} = \{(m, n) \mid m \in \mathbb{N} \wedge n \in \mathbb{Z}\}$. For example, $(5, -3) \in \mathbb{N} \times \mathbb{Z}$, whereas $(-3, 5) \notin \mathbb{N} \times \mathbb{Z}$ (although it is in $\mathbb{Z} \times \mathbb{N}$). We can visualize $\mathbb{N} \times \mathbb{Z}$ as follows:

$$..., (0, -3), (0, -2), (0, -1), (0, 0), (0, 1), (0, 2), (0, 3), ...$$
$$..., (1, -3), (1, -2), (1, -1), (1, 0), (1, 1), (1, 2), (1, 3), ...$$
$$..., (2, -3), (2, -2), (2, -1), (2, 0), (2, 1), (2, 2), (2, 3), ...$$
$$\vdots \qquad\qquad \vdots \qquad\qquad \vdots$$

We can extend the definition of the Cartesian product to more than two sets in the obvious way:

$$A \times B \times C = \{(a, b, c) \mid a \in A \wedge b \in B \wedge c \in C\}$$
$$A \times B \times C \times D = \{(a, b, c, d) \mid a \in A \wedge b \in B \wedge c \in C \wedge d \in D\}$$

Observe that if A, B, and C are finite sets with $|A| = m$, $|B| = n$, and $|C| = k$, then we have $|A \times B \times C| = mnk$. This result generalizes to more than 3 sets in the obvious way.

Example 4.3:

1. $\{\Delta\} \times \{1\} \times \{a\} \times \{\propto\} = \{(\Delta, 1, a, \propto)\}$.

   Note that $|\{\Delta\} \times \{1\} \times \{a\} \times \{\propto\}| = |\{\Delta\}| \cdot |\{1\}| \cdot |\{a\}| \cdot |\{\propto\}| = 1 \cdot 1 \cdot 1 \cdot 1 = 1$.

2. $\{0\} \times \{0, 1\} \times \{1\} \times \{0, 1\} \times \{0\} = \{(0, 0, 1, 0, 0), (0, 0, 1, 1, 0), (0, 1, 1, 0, 0), (0, 1, 1, 1, 0)\}$.

   Note that $|\{0\} \times \{0, 1\} \times \{1\} \times \{0, 1\} \times \{0\}| = 1 \cdot 2 \cdot 1 \cdot 2 \cdot 1 = 4$.

3. $\{0\} \times \mathbb{Z} \times \mathbb{N} = \{(0, m, n) \mid m \in \mathbb{Z} \wedge n \in \mathbb{N}\}$.

We abbreviate Cartesian products of sets with themselves using exponents.

$$A^2 = A \times A \qquad A^3 = A \times A \times A \qquad A^4 = A \times A \times A \times A$$

Example 4.4:

1. $\mathbb{Z}^2 = \mathbb{Z} \times \mathbb{Z} = \{(x, y) \mid x, y \in \mathbb{Z}\}$ is the set of ordered pairs of integers.

2. $\mathbb{N}^5 = \mathbb{N} \times \mathbb{N} \times \mathbb{N} \times \mathbb{N} \times \mathbb{N} = \{(a, b, c, d, e) \mid a, b, c, d, e \in \mathbb{N}\}$ is the set of ordered 5-tuples of natural numbers.

3. $\{0, 1\}^2 = \{0, 1\} \times \{0, 1\} = \{(0, 0), (0, 1), (1, 0), (1, 1)\}$.

4. $\{0, 1\}^3 = \{0, 1\} \times \{0, 1\} \times \{0, 1\}$
   $$= \{(0, 0, 0), (0, 0, 1), (0, 1, 0), (0, 1, 1), (1, 0, 0), (1, 0, 1), (1, 1, 0), (1, 1, 1)\}.$$

Binary Relations

A **binary relation** on a set A is a subset of $A^2 = A \times A$. Symbolically, we have

$$R \text{ is a binary relation on } A \text{ if and only if } R \subseteq A \times A.$$

We will usually abbreviate $(a, b) \in R$ as aRb.

Remark: The statement $R \subseteq A \times A$ is equivalent to the statement $R \in \mathcal{P}(A \times A)$. It follows that for a finite set A, the number of binary relations on A is $|\mathcal{P}(A \times A)|$.

Example 4.5:

1. Let $R = \{(a, b) \in \mathbb{N} \times \mathbb{N} \mid a < b\}$. For example, we have $(0, 1) \in R$ because $0 < 1$. However, $(1, 1) \notin R$ because $1 \not< 1$. We abbreviate $(0, 1) \in R$ by $0R1$.

   Observe that $R \subseteq \mathbb{N} \times \mathbb{N}$, and so, R is a binary relation on $\mathbb{N}$.

   We would normally use the name $<$ for this relation R. So, we have $(0, 1) \in <$, which we abbreviate as $0 < 1$, and we have $(1, 1) \notin <$, which we abbreviate as $1 \not< 1$.

2. There are binary relations $<, \leq, >, \geq$ defined on $\mathbb{N}$ and $\mathbb{Z}$. For example, if we consider $> \subseteq \mathbb{Z}^2$, we have $(13, -7) \in >$, or equivalently, $13 > -7$.

3. Let $A = \{0\}$. Since $|A| = 1$, we have $|A \times A| = 1 \cdot 1 = 1$. So, $|\mathcal{P}(A \times A)| = 2^1 = 2$. So, there are 2 binary relations on A. They are $R_1 = \emptyset$ and $R_2 = \{(0, 0)\}$.

4. Let $B = \{0, 1\}$. Since $|B| = 2$, we have $|B \times B| = 2 \cdot 2 = 4$. So, $|\mathcal{P}(B \times B)| = 2^4 = 16$. So, there are 16 binary relations on B. A few examples are $R_1 = \emptyset$, $R_2 = \{(0, 0)\}$, $R_3 = \{(0, 1)\}$, and $R_4 = \{(0, 0), (0, 1)\}$. Can you list the rest of them?

5. Let A be a set and let R be the binary relation on A defined by $R = \{(a, b) \in A \times A \mid a \in b\}$. R is known as the **membership relation**, and it is usually denoted by $\in$. So, if $a, b \in A$ and a is a member of b, we can write $(a, b) \in \in$, which we will usually abbreviate as $a \in b$.

6. Let $R = \{((a, b), (c, d)) \in (\mathbb{Z} \times \mathbb{Z}^*)^2 \mid ad = bc\}$. (Recall that $\mathbb{Z}^*$ is the set of *nonzero* integers.) Then R is a binary relation on $\mathbb{Z} \times \mathbb{Z}^*$. For example, $(1, 2)R(2, 4)$ because $1 \cdot 4 = 2 \cdot 2$. However, $(1, 2)\not{R}(2, 5)$ because $1 \cdot 5 \neq 2 \cdot 2$.

The **domain** of a binary relation R, written dom R, is $\{x \mid \exists y(xRy)\}$. The **range** of a binary relation, written ran R, is $\{y \mid \exists x(xRy)\}$. The **field** of a binary relation R is dom $R \cup$ ran R.

Notes: (1) The symbol $\exists$ is called an **existential quantifier**, and it is pronounced "There exists" or "There is."

(2) The expression $\exists y(xRy)$ can be translated into English as "There exists a y such that xRy." Similarly, the expression $\exists x(xRy)$ can be translated into English as "There exists an x such that xRy." In general, if P is some property, then the expression $\exists x(P)$ can be translated into English as "There exists an x such that P."

Example 4.6:

1. Let $R = \{(a, b) \in \mathbb{N} \times \mathbb{N} \mid a < b\}$. Then dom $R = \mathbb{N}$, ran $R = \mathbb{N}$, and field $R = \mathbb{N} \cup \mathbb{N} = \mathbb{N}$.

2. Let $B = \{0, 1, 2\}$ and $R = \{(0,1), (0,2), (1,2)\}$. Then dom $R = \{0, 1\}$, ran $R = \{1, 2\}$, and field $R = \{0, 1\} \cup \{1, 2\} = \{0, 1, 2\} = B$.

3. Let $R = \{\big((a, b), (c, d)\big) \in (\mathbb{Z} \times \mathbb{Z}^*)^2 \mid ad = bc\}$. Then dom $R = \mathbb{Z} \times \mathbb{Z}^*$, ran $R = \mathbb{Z} \times \mathbb{Z}^*$, and field $R = (\mathbb{Z} \times \mathbb{Z}^*) \cup (\mathbb{Z} \times \mathbb{Z}^*) = \mathbb{Z} \times \mathbb{Z}^*$.

We say that a binary relation R on A is

- **reflexive** if for all $a \in A$, aRa.

- **symmetric** if for all $a, b \in A$, aRb implies bRa.

- **transitive** if for all $a, b, c \in A$, aRb and bRc imply aRc.

- **antireflexive** if for all $a \in A$, $a\cancel{R}a$.

- **antisymmetric** if for all $a, b \in A$, aRb and bRa imply $a = b$.

Example 4.7:

1. Let A be any set and let $R = \{(a, b) \in A^2 \mid a = b\}$. Then R is reflexive ($a = a$), symmetric (if $a = b$, then $b = a$), transitive (if $a = b$ and $b = c$, then $a = c$), and antisymmetric (trivially). If $A \neq \emptyset$, then this relation is not antireflexive because $a \neq a$ is false for any $a \in A$.

2. The binary relations $\leq$ and $\geq$ defined in the usual way on $\mathbb{Z}$ are transitive (if $a \leq b$ and $b \leq c$, then $a \leq c$, and similarly for $\geq$), reflexive ($a \leq a$ and $a \geq a$), and antisymmetric (if $a \leq b$ and $b \leq a$, then $a = b$, and similarly for $\geq$). These relations are not symmetric. For example, $1 \leq 2$, but $2 \nleq 1$). These relations are not antireflexive. For example, $1 \leq 1$ is true.

   Any relation that is transitive, reflexive, and antisymmetric is called a **partial ordering**.

3. The binary relations $<$ and $>$ defined on $\mathbb{Z}$ are transitive (if $a < b$ and $b < c$, then $a < c$, and similarly for $>$), antireflexive ($a \nless a$ and $a \ngtr a$), and antisymmetric (this is vacuously true because $a < b$ and $b < a$ can never occur). These relations are not symmetric (for example, $1 < 2$, but $2 \nless 1$). These relations are not reflexive (for example, $1 < 1$ is false).

   Any relation that is transitive, antireflexive, and antisymmetric is called a **strict partial ordering**.

4. Let $R = \{(0,0),(0,2),(2,0),(2,2),(2,3),(3,2),(3,3)\}$ be a binary relation on $\mathbb{N}$. Then it is easy to see that R is symmetric. R is not reflexive because $1 \in \mathbb{N}$, but $(1,1) \notin R$ (however, if we were to consider R as a relation on $\{0,2,3\}$ instead of on $\mathbb{N}$, then R **would** be reflexive). R is not transitive because we have $(0,2),(2,3) \in R$, but $(0,3) \notin R$. R is not antisymmetric because we have $(2,3),(3,2) \in R$ and $2 \neq 3$. R is not antireflexive because $(0,0) \in R$.

n-ary Relations

We can extend the idea of a binary relation on a set A to an **n-ary relation** on A. For example, a 3-ary relation (or **ternary relation**) on A is a subset of $A^3 = A \times A \times A$. More generally, we have that R is an n-ary relation on A if and only if $R \subseteq A^n$. A **1-ary relation** (or **unary relation**) on A is just a subset of A.

Example 4.8:

1. $\mathbb{N}$ is a unary relation on $\mathbb{Z}$ because $\mathbb{N} \subseteq \mathbb{Z}$.

2. Let $R = \{(x,y,z) \in \mathbb{Z}^3 \mid x + y = z\}$. Then R is a ternary (or 3-ary) relation on $\mathbb{Z}$. We have, for example, $(1,2,3) \in R$ (because $1 + 2 = 3$) and $(1,2,4) \notin R$ (because $1 + 2 \neq 4$).

3. Let C be the set of all colors. For example, blue $\in C$, pink $\in C$, and violet $\in C$. Let $S = \{(a,b,c) \in C^3 \mid$ when a and b are combined in equal quantities, the result is $c\}$. Then S is a ternary relation on C. We have, for example, (red, yellow, orange) $\in S$.

4. Let $T = \{(a,b,c,d,e) \in \mathbb{N}^5 \mid ab + c = de\}$. Then T is a 5-ary relation on $\mathbb{N}$. We have, for example, $(1,2,8,5,2) \in T$ $(1 \cdot 2 + 8 = 5 \cdot 2)$ and $(1,1,1,1,1) \notin T$ $(1 \cdot 1 + 1 \neq 1 \cdot 1)$.

Orderings

A binary relation $\leq$ on a set A is a **partial ordering** on A if $\leq$ is reflexive, antisymmetric, and transitive on A. If we replace "reflexive" by "antireflexive," then we call the relation a **strict partial ordering** on A (we would normally use the symbol $<$ instead of $\leq$ for a strict partial ordering).

A **partially ordered set** (or **poset**) is a pair $(A, \leq)$, where A is a set and $\leq$ is a partial ordering on A. Similarly, a **strict poset** is a pair $(A, <)$, where A is a set and $<$ is a strict partial ordering on A.

Example 4.9:

1. The usual ordering $\leq$ on $\mathbb{Z} = \{\dots, -3, -2, -1, 0, 1, 2, 3, \dots\}$ is a partial ordering, and the ordering $<$ on $\mathbb{Z}$ is a strict partial ordering. See Example 4.7 (parts 2 and 3).

2. If A is a set, then $(\mathcal{P}(A), \subseteq)$ is a poset. Since every set is a subset of itself, $\subseteq$ is reflexive (see Theorem 2.1). If $X, Y \in \mathcal{P}(A)$ with $X \subseteq Y$ and $Y \subseteq X$, then $X = Y$ (see the end of Lesson 2). So, $\subseteq$ is antisymmetric. By Theorem 2.3, $\subseteq$ is transitive.

    See the tree diagrams at the end of Example 2.3 from Lesson 2 for visual representations of this poset when $A = \{a, b\}$ and $A = \{a, b, c\}$.

3. Let $(A, \leq_A)$ be a partially ordered set, $B \subseteq A$, and $\leq_B = \{(x,y) \mid x, y \in B \land x \leq_A y\}$. Then $(B, \leq_B)$ is also a partially ordered set. Let's check this carefully.

    To see that $\leq_B$ is transitive on B, let $x, y, z \in B$ with $x \leq_B y$ and $y \leq_B z$. Then $x \leq_A y$ and $y \leq_A z$. Since $\leq_A$ is transitive on A, $x \leq_A z$. Since $x, z \in B$, $x \leq_B z$.

To see that $\leq_B$ is reflexive on B, let $x \in B$. Since $B \subseteq A$, $x \in A$. Since $\leq_A$ is reflexive on A, $x \leq_A x$. Since $x \in B$, $x \leq_B x$.

Finally, to see that $\leq_B$ is antisymmetric on B, let $x, y \in B$ with $x \leq_B y$ and $y \leq_B x$. Then $x \leq_A y$ and $y \leq_A x$. Since $\leq_A$ is antisymmetric on A, $x = y$.

Let $(A, \leq)$ be a poset. We say that $a, b \in A$ are **comparable** if $a \leq b$ or $b \leq a$. The poset satisfies the **comparability condition** if every pair of elements in A are comparable. A poset that satisfies the comparability condition is called a **linearly ordered set** (or **totally ordered set**). Similarly, a **strict linearly ordered set** $(A, <)$ satisfies **trichotomy**: If $a, b \in A$, then $a < b$, $a = b$, or $b < a$.

Note: If $<$ is a strict partial ordering on a set A, then $\forall a, b \in A (a < b \rightarrow b \not< a)$. To see this, let $a < b$. Since $<$ is antireflexive, $a \neq b$. Since $<$ is antisymmetric, $b < a$ would lead to the contradiction $a = b$.

Example 4.10:

1. $(\mathbb{N}, \leq)$ and $(\mathbb{Z}, \leq)$ are linearly ordered sets. Similarly, $(\mathbb{N}, <)$ and $(\mathbb{Z}, <)$ are strict linearly ordered sets.

2. If A has at least two elements, then $(\mathcal{P}(A), \subseteq)$ is **not** linearly ordered. Indeed, if $a, b \in A$ with $a \neq b$, then $\{a\} \not\subseteq \{b\}$ and $\{b\} \not\subseteq \{a\}$. See either of the tree diagrams at the end of Example 2.3 from Lesson 2.

We can modify a partial ordering slightly to get a strict partial ordering. We do this as follows:

Theorem 4.2: Let A be a set and let $\leq_A$ be a partial ordering on A. Define the binary relation $<_A$ on A by $a <_A b$ if and only if $a \leq_A b$ and $a \neq b$. Then $<_A$ is a strict partial ordering on A.

Proof: Suppose that $a <_A b$ and $b <_A c$. Then $a \leq_A b$ and $b \leq_A c$. Since $\leq_A$ is transitive, $a \leq_A c$. Also, $a \neq b$ and $b \neq c$. Suppose toward contradiction that $a = c$. Since $b \leq_A c$, we have $b \leq_A a$. Since $\leq_A$ is antisymmetric, $a = b$, contrary to our assumption. Therefore, $a \neq c$. Since $a \leq_A c$ and $a \neq c$, we have $a <_A c$. This shows that $<_A$ is transitive. Now, suppose that $a <_A b$ and $b <_A a$. Then $a \leq_A b$ and $b \leq_A a$. Since $\leq_A$ is antisymmetric, $a = b$. Therefore, $<_A$ is antisymmetric. Finally, by definition, $a <_A a$ is false. Therefore, $<_A$ is antireflexive. Since $<_A$ is transitive, antisymmetric, and antireflexive, $<_A$ is a strict partial ordering on A. □

Similarly, we can modify a strict partial ordering to get a partial ordering.

Theorem 4.3: Let A be a set and let $<_A$ be a strict partial ordering on A. Define the binary relation $\leq_A$ on A by $a \leq_A b$ if and only if $a <_A b$ or $a = b$. Then $\leq_A$ is a partial ordering on A.

Proof: Suppose that $a \leq_A b$ and $b \leq_A c$. If $a = b$, then we have $a \leq_A c$ by direct substitution. Similarly, if $b = c$, we have $a \leq_A c$ by direct substitution. If $a <_A b$ and $b <_A c$, then $a <_A c$ because $<_A$ is transitive. It follows that $a \leq_A c$. This shows that $\leq_A$ is transitive. Now, suppose that $a \leq_A b$ and $b \leq_A a$. Assume toward contradiction that $a \neq b$. Then $a <_A b$ and $b <_A a$. Since $<_A$ is antisymmetric, $a = b$, contrary to our assumption. Therefore, $\leq_A$ is antisymmetric. Finally, by definition, $a \leq_A a$ is true. Therefore, $\leq_A$ is reflexive. Since $\leq_A$ is transitive, antisymmetric, and reflexive, $\leq_A$ is a partial ordering on A. □

Problem Set 4

Full solutions to these problems are available for free download here:
www.SATPrepGet800.com/STFBYKG

LEVEL 1

1. List the elements of $\{\Delta, \gamma, \tau\} \times \{z, t\}$.

2. For each set A below, evaluate (i) A^2; (ii) A^3; (iii) $\mathcal{P}(A)$.

   1. $A = \emptyset$ 2. $A = \{\emptyset\}$ 3. $A = \mathcal{P}(\{\emptyset\})$

LEVEL 2

3. Compute each of the following:

   (i) $\{0, 1, 2\}^3$

   (ii) $\{a, b\}^4$

4. Find the domain, range, and field of each of the following relations:

   (i) $R = \{(a, b), (c, d), (e, f), (f, a)\}$

   (ii) $S = \{(2k, 2t + 1) \mid k, t \in \mathbb{Z}\}$

LEVEL 3

5. Let A, B, C, and D be sets with $A \subseteq B$ and $C \subseteq D$. Prove that $A \times C \subseteq B \times D$.

6. Prove that there do not exist sets A and B such that the relation $<$ on $\mathbb{Z}$ is equal to $A \times B$.

LEVEL 4

7. Let A, B, C, and D be sets. Determine if each of the following statements is true or false. If true, provide a proof. If false, provide a counterexample.

   (i) $(A \times B) \cap (C \times D) = (A \cap C) \times (B \cap D)$

   (ii) $(A \times B) \cup (C \times D) = (A \cup C) \times (B \cup D)$

8. Prove that $(x, y, z) = (t, u, v)$ if and only if $x = t$, $y = u$, and $z = v$.

LEVEL 5

9. For $a, b \in \mathbb{N}$, we will say that a divides b, written $a|b$, if there is a natural number k such that $b = ak$. Notice that $|$ is a binary relation on $\mathbb{N}$. Prove that $(\mathbb{N}, |)$ is a partially ordered set, but it is not a linearly ordered set.

10. Let R be a relation on a set A. Determine if each of the following statements is true or false. If true, provide a proof. If false, provide a counterexample.

    (i)   If R is symmetric and transitive on A, then R is reflexive on A.

    (ii)   If R is antisymmetric on A, then R is not symmetric on A.

CHALLENGE PROBLEM

11. Let $k, t, m \in \mathbb{N}$, let A and B be finite sets with $|A| = k$ and $|B| = t$, let $C = \big(\mathcal{P}(A \times B)\big)^m$, and let X be the set of relations on $A \times B \times C$. Evaluate $|X|$.

LESSON 5
EQUIVALENCE RELATIONS AND PARTITIONS

Equivalence Relations

A binary relation R on a set A is an **equivalence relation** if R is reflexive, symmetric, and transitive.

Example 5.1:

1. The most basic equivalence relation on a set A is the relation $R = \{(a, b) \in A^2 \mid a = b\}$ (the **equality relation**). We already saw in part 1 of Example 4.7 that this relation is reflexive, symmetric and transitive.

2. Another trivial equivalence relation on a set A is the set A^2. Since every ordered pair (a, b) is in A^2, reflexivity, symmetry, and transitivity can never fail. We will refer to A^2 as the **trivial equivalence relation** on A.

3. We say that integers a and b have the same **parity** if they are both even or both odd. Define $\equiv_2$ on $\mathbb{Z}$ by $\equiv_2 = \{(a, b) \in \mathbb{Z}^2 \mid a \text{ and } b \text{ have the same parity}\}$. It is easy to see that $\equiv_2$ is reflexive ($a \equiv_2 a$ because every integer has the same parity as itself), $\equiv_2$ is symmetric (if $a \equiv_2 b$, then a has the same parity as b, so b has the same parity as a, and therefore, $b \equiv_2 a$), and $\equiv_2$ is transitive (if $a \equiv_2 b$ and $b \equiv_2 c$, then a, b, and c all have the same parity, and so, $a \equiv_2 c$). Therefore, $\equiv_2$ is an equivalence relation.

4. An integer n is **divisible** by an integer m, written $m|n$, if there is another integer k such that $n = km$. Another way to say that a and b have the same parity is to say that $b - a$ is divisible by 2, or equivalently, $2|b - a$. This observation allows us to generalize the notion of having the same parity. For example, $\equiv_3 = \{(a, b) \in \mathbb{Z}^2 \mid 3|b - a\}$ is an equivalence relation, and more generally, for each $n \in \mathbb{Z}^+$, $\equiv_n = \{(a, b) \in \mathbb{Z}^2 \mid n|b - a\}$ is an equivalence relation. I leave the proof that $\equiv_n$ is reflexive, symmetric, and transitive on $\mathbb{Z}$ as an exercise (see Problem 3 in the problem set below).

5. Consider the relation $R = \{((a, b), (c, d)) \in (\mathbb{Z} \times \mathbb{Z}^*)^2 \mid ad = bc\}$ defined in part 6 of Example 4.5. Since $ab = ba$, we see that $(a, b)R(a, b)$, and therefore, R is reflexive. If $(a, b)R(c, d)$, then $ad = bc$. Therefore, $cb = da$, and so, $(c, d)R(a, b)$. Thus, R is symmetric. Finally, suppose that $(a, b)R(c, d)$ and $(c, d)R(e, f)$. Then $ad = bc$ and $cf = de$. So, $adcf = bcde$. Therefore, $cd(af - be) = adcf - bcde = 0$. If $a = 0$, then $bc = 0$, and so, $c = 0$ (because $b \neq 0$). So, $de = 0$, and therefore, $e = 0$ (because $d \neq 0$). So, $af = be$ (because they're both 0). If $a \neq 0$, then $c \neq 0$. Therefore, $af - be = 0$, and so, $af = be$. Since $a = 0$ and $a \neq 0$ both lead to $af = be$, we have $(a, b)R(e, f)$. So, R is transitive. Since R is reflexive, symmetric, and transitive, it follows that R is an equivalence relation.

Let $\sim$ be an equivalence relation on a set S. If $x \in S$, the **equivalence class** of x, written $[x]$, is the set

$$[x] = \{y \in S \mid x \sim y\}.$$

Example 5.2:

1. Let A be a set and let $R = \{(a,b) \in A^2 \mid a = b\}$ be the equality relation. Then for each $a \in A$, $[a] = \{a\}$.

2. Let A be a set and let $R = A^2$ be the trivial equivalence relation. Then for each $a \in A$, $[a] = A$.

3. Consider the equivalence relation $\equiv_2 = \{(a,b) \in \mathbb{Z}^2 \mid a \text{ and } b \text{ have the same parity}\}$ on $\mathbb{Z}$. Let $\mathbb{E} = \{2k \mid k \in \mathbb{Z}\}$ be the set of even integers and let $\mathbb{O} = \{2k + 1 \mid k \in \mathbb{Z}\}$ be the set of odd integers. We have $[0] = \{y \in \mathbb{Z} \mid 0 \equiv_2 y\} = \mathbb{E}$. Observe that $[2] = [0]$, and in fact, if n is any even integer, then $[n] = [0] = \mathbb{E}$. Similarly, if n is any odd integer, then $[n] = [1] = \mathbb{O}$.

Partitions

Recall: (1) If X is a nonempty set of sets, we say that X is **pairwise disjoint** if for all $A, B \in X$ with $A \neq B$, A and B are disjoint ($A \cap B = \emptyset$).

(2) If X is a nonempty set of sets, then **union** X is defined by $\bigcup X = \{y \mid \text{there is } Y \in X \text{ with } y \in Y\}$.

A **partition** of a set S is a set of pairwise disjoint nonempty subsets of S whose union is S. Symbolically, X is a partition of S if and only if

$$\forall A \in X(A \neq \emptyset \wedge A \subseteq S) \wedge \forall A, B \in X(A \neq B \rightarrow A \cap B = \emptyset) \wedge \bigcup X = S.$$

Example 5.3:

1. Let $\mathbb{E} = \{2k \mid k \in \mathbb{Z}\}$ be the set of even integers and let $\mathbb{O} = \{2k + 1 \mid k \in \mathbb{Z}\}$ be the set of odd integers. Then $X = \{\mathbb{E}, \mathbb{O}\}$ is a partition of $\mathbb{Z}$. We can visualize this partition as follows:

$$\mathbb{Z} = \{\ldots, -4, -2, 0, 2, 4, \ldots\} \cup \{\ldots, -3, -1, 1, 3, 5, \ldots\}$$

2. Let $A = \{3k \mid k \in \mathbb{Z}\}$, $B = \{3k + 1 \mid k \in \mathbb{Z}\}$, and $C = \{3k + 2 \mid k \in \mathbb{Z}\}$. Then $X = \{A, B, C\}$ is a partition of $\mathbb{Z}$. We can visualize this partition as follows:

$$\mathbb{Z} = \{\ldots, -6, -3, 0, 3, 6, \ldots\} \cup \{\ldots, -5, -2, 1, 4, 7, \ldots\} \cup \{\ldots, -4, -1, 2, 5, 8, \ldots\}$$

3. For each $n \in \mathbb{N}$, let $A_n = \{2n, 2n + 1\}$. Then $X = \{A_n \mid n \in \mathbb{N}\}$ is a partition of $\mathbb{N}$. We can visualize this partition as follows:

$$\mathbb{N} = \{0, 1\} \cup \{2, 3\} \cup \{4, 5\} \cup \{6, 7\} \cup \{8, 9\} \cup \cdots$$

4. For each $n \in \mathbb{Z}$, let $A_n = \{(n, m) \mid m \in \mathbb{Z}\}$. Then $X = \{A_n \mid n \in \mathbb{Z}\}$ is a partition of $\mathbb{Z} \times \mathbb{Z}$. We can visualize this partition as follows:

$$\vdots \qquad \vdots \qquad \vdots$$

$$A_{-2} = \{\ldots, (-2, -3), (-2, -2), (-2, -1), (-2, 0), (-2, 1), (-2, 2), (-2, 3), \ldots\}$$
$$A_{-1} = \{\ldots, (-1, -3), (-1, -2), (-1, -1), (-1, 0), (-1, 1), (-1, 2), (-1, 3), \ldots\}$$
$$A_0 = \{\ldots, (0, -3), (0, -2), (0, -1), (0, 0), (0, 1), (0, 2), (0, 3), \ldots\}$$
$$A_1 = \{\ldots, (1, -3), (1, -2), (1, -1), (1, 0), (1, 1), (1, 2), (1, 3), \ldots\}$$
$$A_2 = \{\ldots, (2, -3), (2, -2), (2, -1), (2, 0), (2, 1), (2, 2), (2, 3), \ldots\}$$

$$\vdots \qquad \vdots \qquad \vdots$$

5. The only partition of the one element set $\{a\}$ is $\{\{a\}\}$. The partitions of the two element set $\{a, b\}$ with $a \neq b$ are $\{\{a\}, \{b\}\}$ and $\{\{a, b\}\}$.

We will now explore the relationship between equivalence relations and partitions. Let's begin with an example.

Example 5.4: Consider the equivalence relation $\equiv_2$ from part 3 of Example 5.1, defined by $a \equiv_2 b$ if and only if a and b have the same parity, and the partition $\{\mathbb{E}, \mathbb{O}\}$ of $\mathbb{Z}$ from part 1 of Example 5.3. For this partition, we are thinking of $\mathbb{Z}$ as the union of the even and odd integers:

$$\mathbb{Z} = \{\ldots, -4, -2, 0, 2, 4, \ldots\} \cup \{\ldots, -3, -1, 1, 3, 5, \ldots\}$$

Observe that a and b are in the same member of the partition if and only if $a \equiv_2 b$ if and only if $[a] = [b]$. If n is any even integer, then $[n] = [0] = \mathbb{E}$ and if n is any odd integer, then $[n] = [1] = \mathbb{O}$.

Example 5.5: Recall that the **power set** of A, written $\mathcal{P}(A)$, is the set consisting of all subsets of A.

$$\mathcal{P}(A) = \{X \mid X \subseteq A\}$$

For example, if $A = \{a, b, c\}$, then $\mathcal{P}(A) = \{\emptyset, \{a\}, \{b\}, \{c\}, \{a, b\}, \{a, c\}, \{b, c\}, \{a, b, c\}\}$. We can define a binary relation $\sim$ on $\mathcal{P}(A)$ by $X \sim Y$ if and only if $|X| = |Y|$ (X and Y have the same number of elements). It is easy to see that $\sim$ is an equivalence relation on $\mathcal{P}(A)$. There are four equivalence classes.

$$[\emptyset] = \{\emptyset\}$$
$$[\{a\}] = \{\{a\}, \{b\}, \{c\}\}$$
$$[\{a, b\}] = \{\{a, b\}, \{a, c\}, \{b, c\}\}$$
$$[\{a, b, c\}] = \{\{a, b, c\}\}$$

Notes: (1) $\{a\} \sim \{b\} \sim \{c\}$ because each of these sets has one element. It follows that $\{a\}$, $\{b\}$, and $\{c\}$ are all in the same equivalence class. Above, we chose to use $\{a\}$ as the **representative** for this equivalence class. This is an arbitrary choice. In fact, $[\{a\}] = [\{b\}] = [\{c\}]$.

Similarly, $[\{a, b\}] = [\{a, c\}] = [\{b, c\}]$.

(2) The empty set is the only subset of A with 0 elements. Therefore, the equivalence class of $\emptyset$ contains only itself. Similarly, the equivalence class of $A = \{a, b, c\}$ contains only itself.

(3) Notice that the four equivalence classes are pairwise disjoint, nonempty, and their union is $\mathcal{P}(A)$. In other words, the equivalence classes form a partition of $\mathcal{P}(A)$.

Theorem 5.1: Let P be a partition of a set S. Then there is an equivalence relation $\sim$ on S for which the elements of P are the equivalence classes of $\sim$. Conversely, if $\sim$ is an equivalence relation on a set S, then the equivalence classes of $\sim$ form a partition of S.

You will be asked to prove Theorem 5.1 in Problems 9 and 10 below.

Important note: We will sometimes want to define relations on equivalence classes. When we do this, we must be careful that what we are defining is **well-defined**. If E is a set of equivalence classes on a set A and R is a relation on A, then we say that R is **well-defined** on E if for all $x, y, z, w \in A$ with $[x] = [z]$ and $[y] = [w]$, xRy if and only if zRw. If R is in fact well-defined on E, then we can define the relation $R^* = \{([x], [y]) \mid xRy\}$. We often identify R and R^* and say that R^* is well-defined on E.

For example, consider the equivalence relation $\equiv_2$ on $\mathbb{Z}$, and let $E = \{[0], [1]\}$ be the set of equivalence classes. Now, consider the relation $<$ on $\mathbb{Z}$. Is $<$ well-defined on E? Well, we have $0 \equiv_2 2$, $0 < 1$ and $2 \not< 1$. It follows that $<$ is **not** well-defined on E. Therefore, if we attempt to define the "relation" $<^*$ on E by $[x] <^* [y]$ if and only if $x < y$, we get something that does not make any sense. Therefore, this definition cannot be made.

Let's define the relation R on $\mathbb{Z}$ by $R = \{(x, y) \mid x$ is even and y is odd$\}$. This is an example of a relation that is well-defined on E. Indeed, suppose that $x, y, z, w \in \mathbb{Z}$ with $[x] = [z]$ and $[y] = [w]$ and let xRy. Then x is even and y is odd. Since $[x] = [z]$, z must be even. Since $[y] = [w]$, w must be odd. Therefore, by the definition of R, zRw. A symmetrical argument shows that zRw implies xRy. It follows that we can define R^* on E by $[x]R^*[y]$ if and only if xRy and the definition of R^* makes sense.

In practice, we would usually just define R on E by $[x]R[y]$ if and only if x is even and y is odd. Of course, we should then use the argument given in the last paragraph to verify that R is well-defined.

Natural Numbers and Integers

At this point, let's provide more formal definitions of the sets of natural numbers and integers (see Lesson 8 for an even more rigorous treatment of the natural numbers).

We define the following:

$$0 = \emptyset$$
$$1 = \{\emptyset\} = \{0\}$$
$$2 = \{\emptyset, \{\emptyset\}\} = \{0, 1\}$$
$$3 = \{\emptyset, \{\emptyset\}, \{\emptyset, \{\emptyset\}\}\} = \{0, 1, 2\}$$

In general, we let $n = \{0, 1, 2, \ldots, n-1\}$. We define the **successor** of n to be $n^+ = n \cup \{n\}$.

We now define the set of **natural numbers** to be $\mathbb{N} = \{0, 1, 2, \ldots\}$. More formally, $\mathbb{N}$ is the unique set such that (i) $\emptyset \in \mathbb{N}$, (ii) $n \in \mathbb{N}$ implies $n^+ \in \mathbb{N}$, and (iii) if X is any set satisfying (i) and (ii), then $\mathbb{N} \subseteq X$.

We define the ordering $<_{\mathbb{N}}$ on $\mathbb{N}$ by $n <_{\mathbb{N}} m$ if and only if $n \in m$.

With this definition, $<_{\mathbb{N}}$ is a strict linear ordering on $\mathbb{N}$. You will be asked to prove this as part of Problem 4 in Problem Set 12.

We add the natural numbers m and n as follows:

(i) If $n = 0$, then $m + n = m$.
(ii) If $n = k^+$, then $m + n = (m + k)^+$.

We multiply the natural numbers m and n as follows:

(i) If $n = 0$, then $mn = 0$.
(ii) If $n = k^+$, then $mn = (mk) + m$.

Notes: (1) Whenever it will not cause confusion, we will use the usual order of operations that we learned in elementary school. So, for example, we can abbreviate $(mk) + m$ as $mk + m$.

(2) Addition and multiplication of natural numbers are examples of **recursive definitions**. See Lesson 8 for a description of how to justify these definitions.

Example 5.6:

1. $0 + 0 = 0$ by the first part of the definition of addition of natural numbers.

2. $0 + 1 = 0 + 0^+ = (0 + 0)^+ = 0^+ = 0 \cup \{0\} = \emptyset \cup \{\emptyset\} = \{\emptyset\} = 1$.

3. $0 + 2 = 0 + 1^+ = (0 + 1)^+ = 1^+ = 1 \cup \{1\} = \{0\} \cup \{1\} = \{0, 1\} = 2$.

4. $2 + 0 = 2$ by the first part of the definition of addition of natural numbers.

5. $2 + 1 = 2 + 0^+ = (2 + 0)^+ = 2^+ = 2 \cup \{2\} = \{0, 1\} \cup \{2\} = \{0, 1, 2\} = 3$.

6. $2 + 2 = 2 + 1^+ = (2 + 1)^+ = 3^+ = 3 \cup \{3\} = \{0, 1, 2\} \cup \{3\} = \{0, 1, 2, 3\} = 4$.

7. $2 \cdot 0 = 0$ by the first part of the definition of multiplication of natural numbers.

8. $2 \cdot 1 = 2 \cdot 0^+ = 2 \cdot 0 + 2 = 0 + 2 = 2$ (by part 3 above).

9. $2 \cdot 2 = 2 \cdot 1^+ = 2 \cdot 1 + 2 = 2 + 2 = 4$ (by part 6 above).

To motivate the definition of the integers, note that we can think of every integer as a difference of two natural numbers. For example, the integer -3 can be thought of as $1 - 4$. However, -3 can also be thought of as $2 - 5$. So, we must insist that $1 - 4 = 2 - 5$, or equivalently, $1 + 5 = 2 + 4$.

We define a relation R on $\mathbb{N} \times \mathbb{N}$ by $R = \{((a, b), (c, d)) \in (\mathbb{N} \times \mathbb{N})^2 \mid a + d = b + c\}$. In Problem 4 below, you will be asked to show that this relation is an equivalence relation. We can now define the set of integers to be $\mathbb{Z} = \{[(a, b)] \mid (a, b) \in \mathbb{N} \times \mathbb{N}\}$.

We identify the integer $[(n, 0)]$ with the natural number n. In this way, we have $\mathbb{N} \subseteq \mathbb{Z}$.

We define the ordering $<_{\mathbb{Z}}$ on $\mathbb{Z}$ by $[(a, b)] <_{\mathbb{Z}} [(c, d)]$ if and only if $a + d <_{\mathbb{N}} b + c$, where $<_{\mathbb{N}}$ is the usual ordering on $\mathbb{N}$ ($n <_{\mathbb{N}} m$ if and only if $n \in m$).

In Problem 5 below, you will be asked to show that $<_{\mathbb{Z}}$ is a well-defined strict linear ordering on $\mathbb{Z}$.

We add and multiply two integers using the following rules:

$$[(a, b)] + [(c, d)] = [(a + c, b + d)]$$
$$[(a, b)] \cdot [(c, d)] = [(ac + bd, ad + bc)]$$

In Problems 7 and 12 below, you will be asked to show that these two operations are well-defined.

Notes: (1) We will generally drop the subscript from $<_{\mathbb{N}}$ and $<_{\mathbb{Z}}$, and simply write $<$. It will almost always be clear from the context which ordering we are talking about.

(2) We will usually use the more familiar notation to describe integers. For example, the integer $[(2,7)]$ will be written as -5. In this way, we can describe an arbitrary integer using a single variable name such as n instead of the more tedious notation $[(a, b)]$.

Example 5.7:

1. $[(k, k)] = [(0, 0)]$ for all $k \in \mathbb{N}$ because $k + 0 = k + 0$.

2. $[(5, 0)] = [(6, 1)]$ because $5 + 1 = 0 + 6$. Similarly, we have $[(5, 0)] = [(7, 2)] = [(8, 3)]$, and in general $[(5, 0)] = [(5 + k, k)]$ for any natural number k. $[(5, 0)]$ is the most "natural" way to express the natural number 5 as an integer. More generally, the natural number n can be expressed as an integer as $[(n, 0)]$.

3. We usually abbreviate the integer $[(0, k)]$ as $- k$. For example, $- 3$ is an abbreviation for $[(0, 3)]$. We can also write $- 3$ as $[(1, 4)]$ because $1 + 3 = 4 + 0$.

4. $[(0, 0)] < [(4, 0)]$ because $0 + 0 < 0 + 4$. More generally, for any natural number $k \neq 0$, we have $[(0, 0)] < [(k, 0)]$ because $0 + 0 < 0 + k$. This shows that for any natural number $k \neq 0$, the natural number k satisfies $0 < k$.

5. $[(0, 4)] < [(0, 0)]$ because $0 + 0 < 4 + 0$. More generally, for any natural number $k \neq 0$, we have $[(0, k)] < [(0, 0)]$ because $0 + 0 < k + 0$. This shows that for any natural number $k \neq 0$, the integer $- k$ satisfies $- k < 0$.

6. $7 + (-2) = [(7, 0)] + [(0, 2)] = [(7, 2)] = [(5, 0)] = 5$.

7. $-3 \cdot 5 = [(0, 3)] \cdot [(5, 0)] = [(0 \cdot 5 + 3 \cdot 0, 0 \cdot 0 + 3 \cdot 5)] = [(0, 15)] = -15$.

The Rational Numbers

In part 5 of Example 5.1, we showed that $R = \{((a, b), (c, d)) \in (\mathbb{Z} \times \mathbb{Z}^*)^2 \mid ad = bc\}$ is an equivalence relation on $\mathbb{Z} \times \mathbb{Z}^*$. For each $a \in \mathbb{Z}$ and $b \in \mathbb{Z}^*$, we define the **rational number** $\frac{a}{b}$ to be the equivalence class of (a, b). So, $\frac{a}{b} = [(a, b)]$, and we have $\frac{a}{b} = \frac{c}{d}$ if and only if $(a, b)R(c, d)$ if and only if $ad = bc$. The set of rational numbers is $\mathbb{Q} = \left\{ \frac{a}{b} \mid a \in \mathbb{Z} \wedge b \in \mathbb{Z}^* \right\}$. In words, $\mathbb{Q}$ is "the set of quotients a over b such that a and b are integers and b is not zero."

We identify the rational number $\frac{a}{1}$ with the integer a. In this way, we have $\mathbb{Z} \subseteq \mathbb{Q}$.

We define $<_\mathbb{Q}$ on $\mathbb{Q}$ by $\frac{a}{b} <_\mathbb{Q} \frac{c}{d}$ if and only if $ad <_\mathbb{Z} bc$, where $<_\mathbb{Z}$ is the usual ordering on $\mathbb{Z}$.

In Problem 11 below, you will be asked to show that $<_\mathbb{Q}$ is a well-defined strict linear ordering on $\mathbb{Q}$.

We add and multiply two rational numbers using the following rules:

$$\frac{a}{b} + \frac{c}{d} = \frac{a \cdot d + b \cdot c}{b \cdot d} \qquad\qquad \frac{a}{b} \cdot \frac{c}{d} = \frac{a \cdot c}{b \cdot d}$$

In Problem 8 below, you will be asked to show that these two operations are well-defined.

Example 5.8:

1. $\frac{2}{3} < \frac{5}{4}$ because $2 \cdot 4 < 3 \cdot 5$. Also, $\frac{2}{3} + \frac{5}{4} = \frac{2 \cdot 4 + 3 \cdot 5}{3 \cdot 4} = \frac{23}{12}$ and $\frac{2}{3} \cdot \frac{5}{4} = \frac{2 \cdot 5}{3 \cdot 4} = \frac{10}{12} = \frac{5}{6}$ (because $10 \cdot 6 = 12 \cdot 5$).

2. $\frac{-3}{4} < \frac{-5}{7}$ because $-3 \cdot 7 < 4(-5)$, $\frac{-3}{4} + \frac{-5}{7} = \frac{-3 \cdot 7 + 4(-5)}{4 \cdot 7} = \frac{-41}{28}$, and $\frac{-3}{4} \cdot \frac{-5}{7} = \frac{-3(-5)}{4 \cdot 7} = \frac{15}{28}$.

45

Problem Set 5

LEVEL 1

1. Find all partitions of the three-element set $\{a, b, c\}$ and the four-element set $\{a, b, c, d\}$.

2. Let $A = \{1, 2, 3, 4\}$ and let $R = \{(1, 1), (1, 3), (2, 2), (2, 4), (3, 1), (3, 3), (4, 2), (4, 4)\}$. Note that R is an equivalence relation on A. Find the equivalence classes of R.

LEVEL 2

3. Prove that for each $n \in \mathbb{Z}^+$, $\equiv_n$ (see part 4 of Example 5.1) is an equivalence relation on $\mathbb{Z}$.

4. Prove that $R = \{((a, b), (c, d)) \in (\mathbb{N} \times \mathbb{N})^2 \mid a + d = b + c\}$ is an equivalence relation on $\mathbb{N} \times \mathbb{N}$.

LEVEL 3

5. Prove that $<_{\mathbb{Z}}$ is a well-defined strict linear ordering on $\mathbb{Z}$. You may use the fact that $<_{\mathbb{N}}$ is a well-defined strict linear ordering on $\mathbb{N}$ that is compatible with addition.

6. Let X be a set of equivalence relations on a nonempty set A. Prove that $\cap X$ is an equivalence relation on A.

LEVEL 4

7. Prove that addition of integers is well-defined.

8. Prove that addition and multiplication of rational numbers are well-defined.

LEVEL 5

9. Let P be a partition of a set S. Prove that there is an equivalence relation $\sim$ on S for which the elements of P are the equivalence classes of $\sim$.

10. Let $\sim$ be an equivalence relation on a set S. Prove that the equivalence classes of $\sim$ form a partition of S.

CHALLENGE PROBLEMS

11. Prove that $<_{\mathbb{Q}}$ is a well-defined strict linear ordering on $\mathbb{Q}$.

12. Prove that multiplication of integers is well-defined.

LESSON 6
FUNCTIONS

Function Basics

Let A and B be sets. f is a **function** from A to B, written $f: A \to B$, if the following two conditions hold.

1. $f \subseteq A \times B$.

2. For all $a \in A$, there is a unique $b \in B$ such that $(a, b) \in f$.

Notes: (1) A function $f: A \to B$ is a binary relation on $A \cup B$.

(2) Not every binary relation on $A \cup B$ is a function from A to B. See part 2 of Example 6.1 below.

(3) The uniqueness in the second clause in the definition of a function above is equivalent to the statement "if $(a, b), (a, c) \in f$, then $b = c$."

(4) When we know that f is a function, we will abbreviate $(a, b) \in f$ by $f(a) = b$.

If $f: A \to B$, the **domain** of f, written dom f, is the set A, and the **range** of f, written ran f, is the set $\{f(a) \mid a \in A\}$. Observe that ran $f \subseteq B$. The set B is sometimes called the **codomain** of f.

Example 6.1:

1. $f = \{(0, a), (1, a)\}$ is a function with dom $f = \{0, 1\}$ and ran $f = \{a\}$. Instead of $(0, a) \in f$, we will usually write $f(0) = a$. Similarly, instead of $(1, a) \in f$, we will write $f(1) = a$. Here is a visual representation of this function.

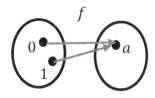

This function $f: \{0, 1\} \to \{a\}$ is called a **constant function** because the range of f consists of a single element.

Note also that f is a binary relation on the set $\{0, 1, a\}$.

2. If $a \neq b$, then $g = \{(0, a), (0, b)\}$ is **not** a function because it violates the second clause in the definition of being a function. It is, however, a binary relation on $\{0, a, b\}$.

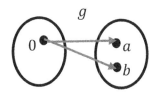

A function with domain $\mathbb{N}$ is called an **infinite sequence**. For example, let $b: \mathbb{N} \to \{0, 1\}$ be defined by $b(n) = \begin{cases} 0 & \text{if } n \text{ is even.} \\ 1 & \text{if } n \text{ is odd.} \end{cases}$ A nice way to visualize an infinite sequence is to list the "outputs" of the sequence in order in parentheses. So, we may write b as $(0, 1, 0, 1, 0, 1, \dots)$. In general, if A is a nonempty set and $f: \mathbb{N} \to A$ is a sequence, then we can write f as $(f(0), f(1), f(2), \dots)$.

Similarly, a **finite sequence** is a function with domain $n = \{0, 1, \dots, n-1\}$ for some n. For example, the sequence $(0, 2, 4, 6, 8, 10)$ is the function $h: 6 \to \mathbb{N}$ defined by $h(k) = 2k$. If the domain of a finite sequence is n, we say that n is the **length** of the sequence.

Observe how a finite sequence with domain n and range A looks just like an n-tuple in A^n. In fact, it's completely natural to identify a finite sequence of length n with the corresponding n-tuple. So, $(0, 2, 4, 6, 8, 10)$ can be thought of as a 6-tuple from $\mathbb{N}^6$, or as the function $h: 6 \to \mathbb{N}$ defined by $h(k) = 2k$.

Informally, we can think of an infinite sequence as an infinite length tuple. As one more example, $(1, 2, 4, 8, 16, 32, \dots)$ represents the sequence $k: \mathbb{N} \to \mathbb{N}$ defined by $k(n) = 2^n$. If $f: \mathbb{N} \to X$ is defined by $f(n) = x_n$, then we may represent the sequence f using the notation $(x_n)_{n \in \mathbb{N}}$ or simply (x_n). For example, the sequence k can be represented as $(2^n)_{n \in \mathbb{N}}$ or (2^n). x_n is called the nth term of the sequence. The 0th term of the sequence k is 1, the first term of the sequence k is 2, and so on. In general, the nth term of the sequence k is 2^n.

Example 6.2:

1. The infinite sequence $\left(\frac{1}{n+1}\right)$ is a function from $\mathbb{N}$ to $\mathbb{Q}$. The nth term of this sequence is $\frac{1}{n+1}$. If we name this function f, then we have that $f: \mathbb{N} \to \mathbb{Q}$ and f is defined by $f(n) = \frac{1}{n+1}$. This function f is an example of a *rational-valued function* (or *$\mathbb{Q}$-valued function*) because the codomain of f consists of only rational numbers. Since the "outputs" of f take on only positive values, we can "shrink" the codomain of f to $\mathbb{Q}^+$, the set of positive rational numbers. So, we can write $f: \mathbb{N} \to \mathbb{Q}^+$. We can visualize this sequence as follows:

$$\left(1, \frac{1}{2}, \frac{1}{3}, \frac{1}{4}, \frac{1}{5}, \dots\right)$$

2. The infinite sequence $(0, -1, 2, -3, 4, -5, \dots)$ is a function from $\mathbb{N}$ to $\mathbb{Z}$. If we name this function g, then we have that $g: \mathbb{N} \to \mathbb{Z}$ and g is defined by $g(n) = (-1)^n n$. So, the nth term of the sequence g is $(-1)^n n$ and we can represent the sequence as $((-1)^n n)$. In this example, g is an example of an *integer-valued function* (or *$\mathbb{Z}$-valued function*) because the codomain of g consists of only integers. Note that every integer-valued function is also a rational-valued function.

3. There is exactly one finite sequence of length 0, namely the empty sequence, $\emptyset$. The empty sequence can be described using function notation as $f: 0 \to X$, where X is any set.

The Real Numbers

There are several equivalent ways to define the set of real numbers. We will define this set here as equivalence classes of **Cauchy sequences** (see Problem 24 from Problem Set 15 for another approach). Informally, a Cauchy sequence is a rational-valued sequence whose values get "closer and closer to each other" as we go further out into the sequence.

We can recognize a Cauchy sequence as one that seems to be "converging" to a fixed value.

For example, it looks like the sequence $(x_n) = \left(\frac{1}{n+1}\right) = \left(1, \frac{1}{2}, \frac{1}{3}, \frac{1}{4}, \frac{1}{5}, \dots\right)$ from part 1 of Example 6.2 is a Cauchy sequence, as it seems to be converging to 0. The sequence $(x_n) = (n) = (0, 1, 2, 3, 4, 5, \dots)$ does not seem to be a Cauchy sequence, as it does not seem to be converging to a fixed number. See Example 6.3 below for more details.

Let's now define Cauchy sequence more formally. We first make a few preliminary definitions.

If $n = [(k, m)]$ is an integer, we define $-n$ to be the integer $[(m, k)]$. With this definition, we have $-(-n) = n$. Indeed, if $n = [(k, m)]$, then $-(-n) = -(-[(k, m)]) = -[(m, k)] = [(k, m)] = n$.

If $x = \frac{a}{b}$ is a rational number, then we define $-x$ to be $\frac{-a}{b}$.

The **absolute value** of the rational number x is then defined by $|x| = \begin{cases} x & \text{if } x \geq 0. \\ -x & \text{if } x < 0. \end{cases}$

For example, we have $\left|\frac{2}{3}\right| = \frac{2}{3}$, $|0| = 0$, and $\left|\frac{-5}{7}\right| = -\left(\frac{-5}{7}\right) = \frac{-(-5)}{7} = \frac{5}{7}$.

The **distance** between rational numbers x and y is $|x - y|$. For example, the distance between 3 and 5 is $|3 - 5| = |-2| = 2$ and the distance between $\frac{1}{5}$ and $\frac{1}{7}$ is $\left|\frac{1}{5} - \frac{1}{7}\right| = \left|\frac{7-5}{5\cdot7}\right| = \left|\frac{2}{35}\right| = \frac{2}{35}$.

Notice that the distance between 5 and 3 is the same as the distance between 3 and 5. Indeed, we also have $|5 - 3| = |2| = 2$. In general, for rational numbers x and y, we have $|x - y| = |y - x|$.

Let $f = (x_n)$ be a rational-valued sequence. We say that f is a **Cauchy sequence** if

for every $k \in \mathbb{N}^+$, there is $K \in \mathbb{N}$ such that $m \geq n > K$ implies $|x_m - x_n| < \frac{1}{k}$.

The idea is that we can make the distance between any two terms of the sequence as small as we choose by deleting a finite portion of the beginning of the sequence. If we wish to make the distance between any two terms less than $\frac{1}{k}$, we delete the first $K + 1$ terms of the sequence.

Example 6.3:

1. The sequence $(x_n) = \left(\frac{1}{n+1}\right)$ from part 1 of Example 6.2 is a Cauchy sequence. To see this, let $k \in \mathbb{N}^+$, let $K = k$, and let $m \geq n > K$. Then

$$|x_m - x_n| = \left|\frac{1}{m+1} - \frac{1}{n+1}\right| = \left|\frac{n-m}{(m+1)(n+1)}\right| \leq \left|\frac{m}{(m+1)(n+1)}\right| = \left|\frac{m}{mn+m+n+1}\right| \leq \left|\frac{m}{mn}\right| = \frac{1}{n} < \frac{1}{K} = \frac{1}{k}.$$

2. The sequence $(x_n) = ((-1)^n n)$ from part 2 of Example 6.2 is **not** a Cauchy sequence. To see this, let $k = 1$ and let $K \in \mathbb{N}$. Then $K + 2 \geq K + 1 > K$, and

$$|x_{K+2} - x_{K+1}| = |(-1)^{K+1}(K+1) - (-1)^{K+2}(K+2)| = |(K+2) + (K+1)| = 2K + 3 \geq 3.$$

But $\frac{1}{k} = \frac{1}{1} = 1$ and $3 \not< 1$.

3. For each $q \in \mathbb{Q}$, the **constant sequence** $(x_n) = (q)$ is a Cauchy sequence. To see this, let $k \in \mathbb{N}$, let $K = 0$, and let $m \geq n > 0$. Then

$$|x_m - x_n| = |q - q| = |0| = 0 < \frac{1}{k}.$$

Next, we would like to identify Cauchy sequences that seem to be converging to the same value. For example, we will identify the Cauchy sequences $(x_n) = \left(\frac{1}{n+1}\right)$ and $(y_n) = (0)$.

An equivalent way of saying that (x_n) and (y_n) converge to the same value is to say that $(x_n - y_n)$ converges to 0.

Let $A = \{(x_n) \mid (x_n)$ is a Cauchy sequence of rational numbers$\}$. We define a relation R on A as follows:

$(x_n)R(y_n)$ if and only if for every $k \in \mathbb{N}^+$, there is $K \in \mathbb{N}$ such that $n > K$ implies $|x_n - y_n| < \frac{1}{k}$.

In Problem 8 below, you will be asked to show that R is an equivalence relation on A.

Note: To show that R is transitive, you will need to use the **Triangle Inequality**. The Triangle Inequality says that if $a, b \in \mathbb{Q}$, then $|a + b| \leq |a| + |b|$.

One way to prove the Triangle Inequality is to analyze several cases separately. As an example of one such case, suppose that a and b are both nonnegative. Then $|a| = a$, $|b| = b$, and $|a + b| = a + b$. So, we get $|a + b| = a + b = |a| + |b|$ (in this case we get equality). I leave it to the reader to describe the other cases and to prove that the Triangle Inequality is true for each of these cases.

We can now define the set of real numbers as follows:

$$\mathbb{R} = \{[(x_n)] \mid (x_n) \text{ is a Cauchy sequence of rational numbers}\}.$$

We identify the real number $[(q)]$ with the rational number q. In this way, we have $\mathbb{Q} \subseteq \mathbb{R}$.

We define the ordering $\leq_\mathbb{R}$ on $\mathbb{R}$ by

$$[(x_n)] \leq_\mathbb{R} [(y_n)] \text{ if and only if there is } K \in \mathbb{N} \text{ such that } n > K \text{ implies } x_n \leq y_n.$$

We can then define $<_\mathbb{R}$ on $\mathbb{R}$ by $[(x_n)] <_\mathbb{R} [(y_n)]$ if and only if $[(x_n)] \leq_\mathbb{R} [(y_n)]$ and $[(x_n)] \neq [(y_n)]$.

In Problem 12 below, you will be asked to show that $<_\mathbb{R}$ is a well-defined strict linear ordering on $\mathbb{R}$.

We add and multiply two real numbers using the following rules:

$$[(x_n)] + [(y_n)] = [(x_n + y_n)]$$
$$[(x_n)] \cdot [(y_n)] = [(x_n \cdot y_n)]$$

In Problems 10 and 11 below, you will be asked to show that $+$ and $\cdot$ are well-defined operations on the real numbers and that the sum and product of two real numbers are real numbers.

Notes: We will generally drop the subscript from $<_\mathbb{R}$ and simply write $<$.

A set I of real numbers is called an **interval** if any real number that lies between two numbers in I is also in I. Symbolically, we can write

$$\forall x, y \in I \; \forall z \in \mathbb{R} \; (x < z < y \to z \in I).$$

The expression above can be read "For all x, y in I and all $z \in \mathbb{R}$, if x is less than z and z is less than y, then z is in I."

Example 6.4:

1. The set $A = \{0, 1\}$ is **not** an interval. A consists of just the two real numbers 0 and 1. There are infinitely many real numbers between 0 and 1. For example, the real number $\frac{1}{2}$ satisfies $0 < \frac{1}{2} < 1$, but $\frac{1}{2} \notin A$.

2. $\mathbb{R}$ is an interval. This follows trivially from the definition. If we replace I by $\mathbb{R}$, we get $\forall x, y \in \mathbb{R} \; \forall z \in \mathbb{R} \; (x < z < y \to z \in \mathbb{R})$. In other words, if we start with two real numbers, and take a real number between them, then that number is a real number (which we already said).

When we are thinking of $\mathbb{R}$ as an interval, we sometimes use the notation $(-\infty, \infty)$ and refer to this as **the real line**. The following picture gives the standard geometric interpretation of the real line.

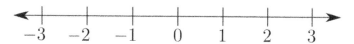

In addition to the real line, there are 8 other types of intervals.

Open Interval: $(a, b) = \{x \in \mathbb{R} \mid a < x < b\}$

Closed Interval: $[a, b] = \{x \in \mathbb{R} \mid a \leq x \leq b\}$

Half-open Intervals: $(a, b] = \{x \in \mathbb{R} \mid a < x \leq b\}$ $[a, b) = \{x \in \mathbb{R} \mid a \leq x < b\}$

Infinite Open Intervals: $(a, \infty) = \{x \in \mathbb{R} \mid x > a\}$ $(-\infty, b) = \{x \in \mathbb{R} \mid x < b\}$

Infinite Closed Intervals: $[a, \infty) = \{x \in \mathbb{R} \mid x \geq a\}$ $(-\infty, b] = \{x \in \mathbb{R} \mid x \leq b\}$

Example 6.5:

1. The half-open interval $(-2, 1] = \{x \in \mathbb{R} \mid -2 < x \leq 1\}$ has the following graph:

51

2. The infinite open interval $(0, \infty) = \{x \in \mathbb{R} \mid x > 0\}$ has the following graph:

Example 6.6:

1. $h = \{(a, b) \mid a, b \in \mathbb{R} \land a > 0 \land a^2 + b^2 = 2\}$ is a relation on $\mathbb{R}$ that is **not** a function. $(1, 1)$ and $(1, -1)$ are both elements of h, violating the second clause in the definition of a function. See the figure below on the left. Notice how a vertical line hits the graph twice.

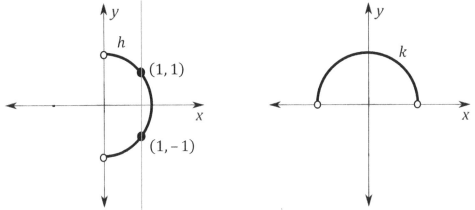

2. $k = \{(a, b) \mid a, b \in \mathbb{R} \land b > 0 \land a^2 + b^2 = 2\}$ **is** a function. See the figure above on the right. To see that the second clause in the definition of a function is satisfied, suppose that (a, b) and (a, c) are both in f. Then $a^2 + b^2 = 2$, $a^2 + c^2 = 2$, and b and c are both positive. It follows that $b^2 = c^2$, and since b and c are both positive, we have $b = c$.

   We have dom $k = \left(-\sqrt{2}, \sqrt{2}\right)$ and ran $k = \left(0, \sqrt{2}\right]$. So, $k: \left(-\sqrt{2}, \sqrt{2}\right) \to \left(0, \sqrt{2}\right]$.

Notes: (1): If $a \in \mathbb{R}$, then $a^2 = a \cdot a$ and $\sqrt{b} = a$ if $a \geq 0$ and $a^2 = b$.

(2) It is unfortunate that the same notation is used for points (ordered pairs of real numbers) and open intervals. Normally this isn't an issue, but in part 2 of Example 6.6 above, both usages of this notation appear. Take another look at the example and note that (a, b) and (a, c) are points, whereas $\left(-\sqrt{2}, \sqrt{2}\right)$ is an open interval.

Injections, Surjections, and Bijections

A function $f: A \to B$ is **injective** (or **one-to-one**), written $f: A \hookrightarrow B$, if for all $a, b \in A$, if $a \neq b$, then $f(a) \neq f(b)$. In this case, we call f an **injection**.

Notes: (1) The contrapositive of the conditional statement $p \to q$ is the statement $\neg q \to \neg p$. These two statements are logically equivalent. See the analysis after the statement of Theorem 3.3 from Lesson 3 for an explanation and see Lesson 9 for more details.

(2) The contrapositive of the statement "If $a \neq b$, then $f(a) \neq f(b)$" is "If $f(a) = f(b)$, then $a = b$." So, we can say that a function $f: A \to B$ is injective if for all $a, b \in A$, if $f(a) = f(b)$, then $a = b$.

A function $f: A \to B$ is **surjective** (or **onto B**), written $f: A \twoheadrightarrow B$, if for all $b \in B$, there is an $a \in A$ such that $f(a) = b$. In this case, we call f a **surjection**.

A function $f: A \rightarrow B$ is **bijective**, written $f: A \cong B$ if f is both injective and surjective. In this case, we call f a **bijection**.

Example 6.7:

1. $f = \{(0, a), (1, a)\}$ from part 1 of Example 6.1 is **not** an injective function because $f(0) = a$, $f(1) = a$, and $0 \neq 1$. If we think of f as $f: \{0, 1\} \rightarrow \{a\}$, then f is surjective. However, if we think of f as $f: \{0, 1\} \rightarrow \{a, b\}$, then f is **not** surjective. So, surjectivity depends upon the codomain of the function.

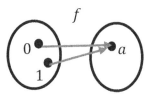

2. $k = \{(a, b) \mid a, b \in \mathbb{R} \wedge b > 0 \wedge a^2 + b^2 = 2\}$ from part 2 of Example 6.6 is **not** an injective function. For example, $(1, 1) \in k$ because $1^2 + 1^2 = 1 + 1 = 2$ and $(-1, 1) \in k$ because $(-1)^2 + 1^2 = 1 + 1 = 2$. Notice how a horizontal line hits the graph twice. If we think of k as a function from $(-\sqrt{2}, \sqrt{2})$ to $\mathbb{R}^+$, then k is **not** surjective. For example, $2 \notin \operatorname{ran} k$ because for any $a \in \mathbb{R}$, $a^2 + 2^2 = a^2 + 4 \geq 4$, and so, $a^2 + 2^2$ cannot be equal to 2. However, if instead we consider k as a function with codomain $(0, \sqrt{2}]$, that is $k: (-\sqrt{2}, \sqrt{2}) \rightarrow (0, \sqrt{2}]$, then k **is** surjective. Indeed, if $0 < b \leq \sqrt{2}$, then $0 < b^2 \leq 2$, and so, $a^2 = 2 - b^2 \geq 0$. Therefore, $a = \sqrt{2 - b^2}$ is a real number such that $k(a) = b$.

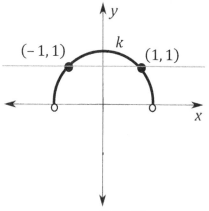

3. Define $g: \mathbb{R} \rightarrow \mathbb{R}$ by $g(x) = 7x - 3$. Then g is injective because if $g(a) = g(b)$, we then have $7a - 3 = 7b - 3$. Adding 3 to each side of this equation, we get $7a = 7b$, and then multiplying each side of this last equation by $\frac{1}{7}$, we get $a = b$ (see Lesson 15 for justification of these cancellation rules). Also, g is surjective because if $b \in \mathbb{R}$, then $\frac{b+3}{7} \in \mathbb{R}$ and

$$g\left(\frac{b+3}{7}\right) = 7\left(\frac{b+3}{7}\right) - 3 = (b + 3) - 3 = b + (3 - 3) = b + 0 = b$$

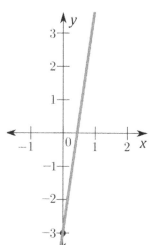

Therefore, g is bijective. See the image to the right for a visual representation of $\mathbb{R}^2$ and the graph of the function g.

Notice that any vertical line will hit the graph of g exactly once because g is a function with domain $\mathbb{R}$. Also, any horizontal line will hit the graph exactly once because g is bijective. Injectivity ensures that each horizontal line hits the graph *at most* once and surjectivity ensures that each horizontal line hits the graph *at least* once.

Inverse Functions

If $f: A \to B$ is bijective, we define $f^{-1}: B \to A$, the **inverse** of f, by $f^{-1} = \{(b, a) \mid (a, b) \in f\}$. In other words, for each $b \in B$, $f^{-1}(b) =$ "the unique $a \in A$ such that $f(a) = b$."

Notes: (1) Let $f: A \to B$ be bijective. Since f is surjective, for each $b \in B$, there is an $a \in A$ such that $f(a) = b$. Since f is injective, there is only one such value of a.

(2) The inverse of a bijective function is also bijective.

Example 6.8:

1. Define $f: \{0, 1\} \to \{a, b\}$ by $f = \{(0, a), (1, b)\}$. Then f is a bijection and $f^{-1}: \{a, b\} \to \{0, 1\}$ is defined by $f^{-1} = \{(a, 0), (b, 1)\}$. Observe that f^{-1} is also a bijection.

2. Let $\mathbb{E} = \{0, 2, 4, 6, 8, \dots\}$ be the set of even natural numbers and let $\mathbb{O} = \{1, 3, 5, 7, 9 \dots\}$ be the set of odd natural numbers. The function $f: \mathbb{E} \to \mathbb{O}$ defined by $f(n) = n + 1$ is a bijection with inverse $f^{-1}: \mathbb{O} \to \mathbb{E}$ defined by $f(n) = n - 1$.

3. If X and Y are sets, we define ^{X}Y to be the set of functions from X to Y. Symbolically, we have

$$^{X}Y = \{f \mid f: X \to Y\}$$

   For example, if $A = \{a, b\}$ and $B = \{0, 1\}$, then ^{A}B has 4 elements (each element is a function from A to B). The elements are $f_1 = \{(a, 0), (b, 0)\}$, $f_2 = \{(a, 0), (b, 1)\}$, $f_3 = \{(a, 1), (b, 0)\}$, and $f_4 = \{(a, 1), (b, 1)\}$. Here is a visual representation of these four functions.

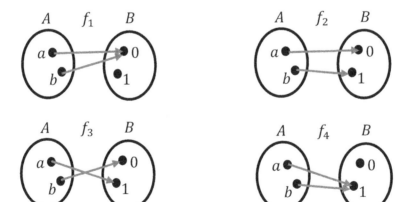

   Define $F: {}^{A}B \to \mathcal{P}(A)$ by $F(f) = \{x \in A \mid f(x) = 1\}$.

   So, $F(f_1) = \emptyset$, $F(f_2) = \{b\}$, $F(f_3) = \{a\}$, and $F(f_4) = \{a, b\}$.

   Since $\mathcal{P}(A) = \{\emptyset, \{a\}, \{b\}, \{a, b\}\}$, we see that F is a bijection from ^{A}B to $\mathcal{P}(A)$.

   The inverse of F is the function $F^{-1}: \mathcal{P}(A) \to {}^{A}B$ defined by $F^{-1}(C)(x) = \begin{cases} 0 & \text{if } x \notin C. \\ 1 & \text{if } x \in C. \end{cases}$

   So, we see that $F^{-1}(\emptyset) = f_1$, $F^{-1}(\{b\}) = f_2$, $F^{-1}(\{a\}) = f_3$, and $F^{-1}(\{a, b\}) = f_4$.

4. For $A \neq \emptyset$ and $B = \{0, 1\}$, the function $F: {}^{A}B \to \mathcal{P}(A)$ defined by $F(f) = \{x \in A \mid f(x) = 1\}$ is always a bijection.

To see that F is injective, let $f, g \in {}^A B$ with $f \neq g$. Since f and g are different, there is some $a \in A$ such that either $f(a) = 0, g(a) = 1$ or $f(a) = 1, g(a) = 0$. Without loss of generality, assume that $f(a) = 0$ and $g(a) = 1$. Since $f(a) = 0$, $a \notin F(f)$. Since $g(a) = 1$, $a \in F(g)$. So, $F(f) \neq F(g)$. Since $f \neq g$ implies $F(f) \neq F(g)$, F is injective.

To see that F is surjective, let $C \in \mathcal{P}(A)$, so that $C \subseteq A$. Define $f \in {}^A B$ by $f(x) = \begin{cases} 0 & \text{if } x \notin C. \\ 1 & \text{if } x \in C. \end{cases}$ Then $x \in F(f)$ if and only if $f(x) = 1$ if and only if $x \in C$. So, $F(f) = C$. Since $C \in \mathcal{P}(A)$ was arbitrary, F is surjective.

As in 3, the inverse of F is the function $F^{-1} : \mathcal{P}(A) \to {}^A B$ defined by $F^{-1}(C)(x) = \begin{cases} 0 & \text{if } x \notin C. \\ 1 & \text{if } x \in C. \end{cases}$

Notes: (1) In part 4 of Example 6.8, we used the expression "Without loss of generality." This expression can be used when an argument can be split up into 2 or more cases, and the proof of each of the cases is nearly identical.

In the example above, the two cases are (i) $f(a) = 0, g(a) = 1$ and (ii) $f(a) = 1, g(a) = 0$. The argument for case (ii) is the same as the argument for case (i), essentially word for word—only the roles of f and g are interchanged.

(2) Using the definition $n = \{0, 1, 2, \ldots, n - 1\}$, we have just shown that for any nonempty set A, there is a bijection $f : {}^A 2 \to \mathcal{P}(A)$.

Composite Functions

Given functions $f : A \to B$ and $g : B \to C$, the **composite** (or **composition**) of f and g, written $g \circ f : A \to C$, is defined by $(g \circ f)(a) = g(f(a))$ for all $a \in A$. Symbolically, we have

$$g \circ f = \{(a, c) \in A \times C \mid \text{There is a } b \in B \text{ such that } (a, b) \in f \text{ and } (b, c) \in g\}.$$

We can visualize the composition of two functions f and g as follows.

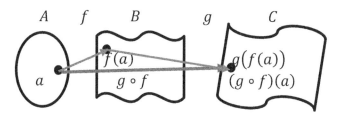

In the picture above, sets A, B, and C are drawn as different shapes simply to emphasize that they can all be different sets. Starting with an arbitrary element $a \in A$, we have an arrow showing a being mapped by f to $f(a) \in B$ and another arrow showing $f(a)$ being mapped by g to $g(f(a)) \in C$. There is also an arrow going directly from $a \in A$ to $(g \circ f)(a) = g(f(a))$ in C. However, note that the only way we know how to get from a to $(g \circ f)(a)$ is to first travel from a to $f(a)$, and then to travel from $f(a)$ to $g(f(a))$.

Example 6.9: Define $f: \mathbb{Z} \to \mathbb{Q}$ by $f(n) = \frac{n}{2}$ and define $g: \mathbb{Q} \to \{0, 1\}$ by $g(n) = \begin{cases} 0 & \text{if } n \in \mathbb{Z}. \\ 1 & \text{if } n \in \mathbb{Q} \setminus \mathbb{Z}. \end{cases}$ Then $g \circ f: \mathbb{Z} \to \{0, 1\}$ is defined by $(g \circ f)(n) = \begin{cases} 0 & \text{if } n \text{ is even.} \\ 1 & \text{if } n \text{ is odd.} \end{cases}$

To see this, observe that if $n \in \mathbb{Z}$ is even, then there is an integer k such that $n = 2k$. It follows that $(g \circ f)(n) = g(f(n)) = g\left(\frac{n}{2}\right) = g\left(\frac{2k}{2}\right) = g(k) = 0$ because $k \in \mathbb{Z}$. If n is odd, then there is an integer k such that $n = 2k + 1$. So, $(g \circ f)(n) = g(f(n)) = g\left(\frac{n}{2}\right) = g\left(\frac{2k+1}{2}\right) = 1$ because $\frac{2k+1}{2} \in \mathbb{Q} \setminus \mathbb{Z}$. To see that $\frac{2k+1}{2} \in \mathbb{Q}$, simply observe that $2k + 1 \in \mathbb{Z}$, $2 \in \mathbb{Z}$, and $2 \neq 0$. To see that $\frac{2k+1}{2} \notin \mathbb{Z}$, first note that, $\frac{2k+1}{2} = \frac{2k}{2} + \frac{1}{2} = k + \frac{1}{2}$ (Check this!). Now, let $m = k + \frac{1}{2}$. If $m \in \mathbb{Z}$, then we would have $m - k \in \mathbb{Z}$ because when we subtract one integer from another, we always get an integer (Check this!). It would then follow that $\frac{1}{2} \in \mathbb{Z}$, which we know it is not. Since assuming that $\frac{2k+1}{2} \in \mathbb{Z}$ would lead to the false statement $\frac{1}{2} \in \mathbb{Z}$, we know that the statement $\frac{2k+1}{2} \in \mathbb{Z}$ must be false.

Note: In Example 6.9 above, to show that $\frac{2k+1}{2} \notin \mathbb{Z}$, we began with the assumption that $\frac{2k+1}{2} \in \mathbb{Z}$, and then used a logically valid argument to derive a false statement. This is known as a proof by contradiction. See the proof of Theorem 7.1 in Lesson 7 for a formal proof by contradiction and a detailed explanation as to how it works. Theorem 8.1 in Lesson 8 provides another example.

It will be important to know that when we take the composition of bijective functions, we always get a bijective function. We will prove this in two steps. We will first show that the composition of injective functions is injective. We will then show that the composition of surjective functions is surjective.

Theorem 6.1: If $f: A \hookrightarrow B$ and $g: B \hookrightarrow C$, then $g \circ f: A \hookrightarrow C$.

Note: We are given that f and g are injections, and we want to show that $g \circ f$ is an injection. We can show this directly using the definition of injectivity, or we can use the contrapositive of the definition of injectivity. Let's do it both ways.

Direct proof of Theorem 6.1: Suppose that $f: A \hookrightarrow B$ and $g: B \hookrightarrow C$, and let $x, y \in A$ with $x \neq y$. Since f is injective, $f(x) \neq f(y)$. Since g is injective, $g(f(x)) \neq g(f(y))$. So, $(g \circ f)(x) \neq (g \circ f)(y)$. Since $x, y \in A$ were arbitrary, $g \circ f: A \hookrightarrow C$. □

Contrapositive proof of Theorem 6.1: Suppose that $f: A \hookrightarrow B$ and $g: B \hookrightarrow C$, let $x, y \in A$ and suppose that $(g \circ f)(x) = (g \circ f)(y)$. Then $g(f(x)) = g(f(y))$. Since g is injective, $f(x) = f(y)$. Since f is injective, $x = y$. Since $x, y \in A$ were arbitrary, $g \circ f: A \hookrightarrow C$. □

Theorem 6.2: If $f: A \mapsto B$ and $g: B \mapsto C$, then $g \circ f: A \mapsto C$.

Proof: Suppose that $f: A \mapsto B$ and $g: B \mapsto C$, and let $c \in C$. Since g surjective, there is $b \in B$ with $g(b) = c$. Since f is surjective, there is $a \in A$ with $f(a) = b$. So, $(g \circ f)(a) = g(f(a)) = g(b) = c$. Since $c \in C$ was arbitrary, $g \circ f$ is surjective. □

Corollary 6.3: If $f: A \cong B$ and $g: B \cong C$, then $g \circ f: A \cong C$.

Proof: Suppose that $f: A \cong B$ and $g: B \cong C$. Then f and g are injective. By Theorem 6.1, $g \circ f$ is injective. Also, f and g are surjective. By Theorem 6.2, $g \circ f$ is surjective. Since $g \circ f$ is both injective and surjective, $g \circ f$ is bijective. $\qquad\qquad\square$

Note: A **corollary** is a theorem that follows easily from a theorem or theorems that have already been proved.

Identity Functions

If A is any set, then we define the **identity function** on A, written $i_A: A \to A$ by $i_A(a) = a$ for all $a \in A$. Note that the identity function on A is a bijection from A to itself.

Theorem 6.4: If $f: A \cong B$, then $f^{-1} \circ f = i_A$ and $f \circ f^{-1} = i_B$.

Proof: Let $a \in A$ with $f(a) = b$. Then $f^{-1}(b) = a$, and so, $(f^{-1} \circ f)(a) = f^{-1}(f(a)) = f^{-1}(b) = a$. Since $i_A(a) = a$, we see that $(f^{-1} \circ f)(a) = i_A(a)$. Since $a \in A$ was arbitrary, $f^{-1} \circ f = i_A$.

Now, let $b \in B$. Since $f: A \cong B$, there is a unique $a \in A$ with $f(a) = b$. Equivalently, $f^{-1}(b) = a$. We have $(f \circ f^{-1})(b) = f(f^{-1}(b)) = f(a) = b$ Since $i_B(b) = b$, we see that $(f \circ f^{-1})(b) = i_B(b)$. Since $b \in B$ was arbitrary, $f \circ f^{-1} = i_B$. $\qquad\qquad\square$

Images and and Inverse Images

If $f: X \to Y$ and $A \subseteq X$, then the **image of A under f** is the set $f[A] = \{f(x) \mid x \in A\}$. Similarly, if $B \subseteq Y$, then the **inverse image of B under f** is the set $f^{-1}[B] = \{x \in X \mid f(x) \in B\}$.

Example 6.10:

1. Let $f: \{a, b, c, d\} \to \{0, 1, 2\}$ be defined by $f = \{(a, 0), (b, 0), (c, 1), (d, 2)\}$. Let $A = \{a\}$, $B = \{a, b\}$, $C = \{a, c\}$, and $D = \{b, c, d\}$. Then $f[A] = \{0\}$, $f[B] = \{0\}$, $f[C] = \{0, 1\}$, and $f[D] = \{0, 1, 2\}$. Now, let $X = \{0\}$, $Y = \{0, 1\}$, $Z = \{0, 2\}$, and $W = \{0, 1, 2\}$. Then we have $f^{-1}[X] = \{a, b\}$, $f^{-1}[Y] = \{a, b, c\}$, $f^{-1}[Z] = \{a, b, d\}$, and $f^{-1}[W] = \{a, b, c, d\}$.

2. Define $f: \mathbb{R} \to \mathbb{R}$ by $f(x) = x^4$. Then we have $f[\mathbb{R}] = [0, \infty)$, $f(\{-2, 0, 3\}) = \{0, 16, 81\}$, $f[(-3, 2]] = [0, 81)$, $f^{-1}[\mathbb{R}] = \mathbb{R}$, $f^{-1}[\{16\}] = \{-2, 2\}$, $f^{-1}[[0, \infty)] = \mathbb{R}$, $f^{-1}[(-\infty, 0)] = \emptyset$, and $f^{-1}[(0, \infty)] = (-\infty, 0) \cup (0, \infty) = \mathbb{R} \setminus \{0\}$.

Problem Set 6

Full solutions to these problems are available for free download here:
www.SATPrepGet800.com/STFBYKG

LEVEL 1

1. Determine if each of the following relations are functions. For each such function, determine if it is injective. State the domain and range of each function.

   (i) $R = \{(a, b), (b, b), (c, d), (e, a)\}$

   (ii) $S = \{(a, a), (a, b), (b, a)\}$

   (iii) $T = \{(a, b) \mid a, b \in \mathbb{R} \wedge b < 0 \wedge a^2 + b^2 = 9\}$

2. Define $f: \mathbb{Z} \to \mathbb{Z}$ by $f(n) = n^2$. Let $A = \{0, 1, 2, 3, 4\}$, $B = \mathbb{N}$, and $C = \{-2n \mid n \in \mathbb{N}\}$. Evaluate each of the following:

   (i) $f[A]$

   (ii) $f^{-1}[A]$

   (iii) $f^{-1}[B]$

   (iv) $f^{-1}[B \cup C]$

LEVEL 2

3. Find sets A and B and a function f such that $f[A \cap B] \neq f[A] \cap f[B]$.

4. Determine if each of the following sequences are Cauchy sequences. Are any of the Cauchy sequences equivalent?

   (i) $(x_n) = \left(1 + \frac{1}{n+1}\right)$

   (ii) $(y_n) = (2^n)$

   (iii) $(z_n) = \left(1 - \frac{1}{2n+1}\right)$

LEVEL 3

5. For $f, g \in {}^{\mathbb{R}}\mathbb{R}$, define $f \preccurlyeq g$ if and only if for all $x \in \mathbb{R}$, $f(x) \leq g(x)$. Is $({}^{\mathbb{R}}\mathbb{R}, \preccurlyeq)$ a poset? Is it a linearly ordered set? What if we replace $\preccurlyeq$ by $\preccurlyeq^*$, where $f \preccurlyeq^* g$ if and only if there is an $x \in \mathbb{R}$ such that $f(x) \leq g(x)$?

6. Prove that the function $f: \mathbb{N} \to \mathbb{Z}$ defined by $f(n) = \begin{cases} \dfrac{n}{2} & \text{if } n \text{ is even} \\ -\dfrac{n+1}{2} & \text{if } n \text{ is odd} \end{cases}$ is a bijection.

LEVEL 4

7. For $f, g \in {}^{\mathbb{N}}\mathbb{N}$, define $f <^* g$ if and only if there is $n \in \mathbb{N}$ such that for all $m > n$, $f(m) < g(m)$.

    (i)   Is $({}^{\mathbb{N}}\mathbb{N}, <^*)$ a strict poset?

    (ii)   Is $({}^{\mathbb{N}}\mathbb{N}, <^*)$ a strict linearly ordered set?

    (iii) Let $\mathcal{F} = \{f_n : \mathbb{N} \to \mathbb{N} \mid n \in \mathbb{N}\}$ be a set of functions. Must there be a function $g \in {}^{\mathbb{N}}\mathbb{N}$ such that for all $n \in \mathbb{N}$, $f_n <^* g$?

8. Let $A = \{(x_n) \mid (x_n) \text{ is a Cauchy sequence of rational numbers}\}$ and define the relation R on A by $(x_n)R(y_n)$ if and only if for every $k \in \mathbb{N}^+$, there is $K \in \mathbb{N}$ such that $n > K$ implies $|x_n - y_n| < \frac{1}{k}$. Prove that R is an equivalence relation on A.

LEVEL 5

9. Let X be a nonempty set of sets and let f be a function such that $\cup X \subseteq \operatorname{dom} f$. Prove each of the following:

    (i) $f[\cup X] = \cup\{f[A] \mid A \in X\}$

    (ii) $f[\cap X] \subseteq \cap\{f[A] \mid A \in X\}$

    (iii) $f^{-1}[\cup X] = \cup\{f^{-1}[A] \mid A \in X\}$

    (iv) $f^{-1}[\cap X] = \cap\{f^{-1}[A] \mid A \in X\}$

10. Prove that addition of real numbers is well-defined and that the sum of two real numbers is a real number.

CHALLENGE PROBLEMS

11. Prove that multiplication of real numbers is well-defined and that the product of two real numbers is a real number.

12. Prove that $<_{\mathbb{R}}$ is a well-defined strict linear ordering on $\mathbb{R}$.

LESSON 7
EQUINUMEROSITY

Basic Definitions and Examples

We say that two sets A and B are **equinumerous**, written $A \sim B$ if there is a bijection $f: A \cong B$.

It is easy to see that $\sim$ **is an equivalence relation**. For any set A, the identity function $i_A: A \to A$ is a bijection, showing that $\sim$ is reflexive. For sets A and B, if $f: A \cong B$, then $f^{-1}: B \cong A$, showing that $\sim$ is symmetric. For sets A, B, and C, if $f: A \cong B$ and $g: B \cong C$, then $g \circ f: A \cong C$ by Corollary 6.3 from Lesson 6, showing that $\sim$ is transitive.

Example 7.1:

1. Let $A = \{\text{anteater}, \text{elephant}, \text{giraffe}\}$ and $B = \{\text{apple}, \text{banana}, \text{orange}\}$. Then $A \sim B$. We can define a bijection $f: A \cong B$ by $f(\text{anteater}) = \text{apple}$, $f(\text{elephant}) = \text{banana}$, and $f(\text{giraffe}) = \text{orange}$. This is not the only bijection from A to B, but we need only find one (or prove one exists) to show that the sets are equinumerous.

2. At this point it should be easy to see that two finite sets are equinumerous if and only if they have the same number of elements. It should also be easy to see that a finite set can never be equinumerous with an infinite set.

3. Let $\mathbb{N} = \{0, 1, 2, 3, 4 \dots\}$ be the set of natural numbers and $\mathbb{E} = \{0, 2, 4, 6, 8 \dots\}$ the set of even natural numbers. Then $\mathbb{N} \sim \mathbb{E}$. We can actually see a bijection between these two sets just by looking at the sets themselves.

$$0 \quad 1 \quad 2 \quad 3 \quad 4 \quad 5 \quad 6 \dots$$
$$0 \quad 2 \quad 4 \quad 6 \quad 8 \quad 10 \quad 12 \dots$$

The function $f: \mathbb{N} \to \mathbb{E}$ defined by $f(n) = 2n$ is an explicit bijection. To see that f maps $\mathbb{N}$ into $\mathbb{E}$, just observe that if $n \in \mathbb{N}$, then $2n \in \mathbb{E}$ by the definition of an even integer ($a \in \mathbb{N}$ is even if there is $b \in \mathbb{N}$ with $a = 2b$). f is injective because if $f(n) = f(m)$, then $2n = 2m$, and so, $n = m$ (see part (viii) of Problem 3 from Problem Set 8). Finally, f is surjective because if $n \in \mathbb{E}$, then there is $k \in \mathbb{N}$ such that $n = 2k$. So, $f(k) = 2k = n$.

4. $\mathbb{N} \sim \mathbb{Z}$ via the bijection $f: \mathbb{N} \cong \mathbb{Z}$ defined by $f(n) = \begin{cases} \dfrac{n}{2} & \text{if } n \text{ is even.} \\ -\dfrac{n+1}{2} & \text{if } n \text{ is odd.} \end{cases}$

   You were asked to show that f is a bijection in Problem 6 from Problem Set 6. Let's look at this correspondence visually:

$$0 \quad 1 \quad 2 \quad 3 \quad 4 \quad 5 \quad 6 \dots$$
$$0 \quad -1 \quad 1 \quad -2 \quad 2 \quad -3 \quad 3 \dots$$

   Many students get confused here because they are under the misconception that the integers should be written "in order." However, when checking to see if two sets are equinumerous, we **do not** include any other structure. In other words, we are just trying to "pair up" elements—it does not matter how we do so.

5. For A any nonempty set, $^A2 \sim \mathcal{P}(A)$. We showed this in part 4 of Example 6.8 from Lesson 6.

Countable and Uncountable Sets

We say that a set is **countable** if it is equinumerous with a subset of $\mathbb{N}$. It's easy to visualize a countable set because a bijection from a subset of $\mathbb{N}$ to a set A generates a list. For example, the set $\mathbb{E}$ can be listed as 0, 2, 4, 6, ... and the set $\mathbb{Z}$ can be listed as 0, – 1, 1, – 2, 2, ... (see Example 7.1 above).

There are two kinds of countable sets: **finite** sets and **denumerable** (or **countably infinite**) sets. A **finite** set is a countable set that is equinumerous with $n = \{0, 1, 2, ..., n-1\}$ for some $n \in \mathbb{N}$. An **infinite** set is a set that is not finite and a denumerable set is a countable set that is not finite. The dedicated reader may want to prove that a countable set is denumerable if and only if it is equinumerous with $\mathbb{N}$.

At this point, you may be asking yourself if all infinite sets are denumerable. If this were the case, then we would simply have finite sets and infinite sets, and that would be the end of it. However, there are in fact infinite sets that are **not** denumerable. An infinite set that is not denumerable is **uncountable**.

Theorem 7.1 (Cantor's Theorem): If A is any set, then A is **not** equinumerous with $\mathcal{P}(A)$.

Analysis: How can we prove that A is not equinumerous with $\mathcal{P}(A)$? Well, we need to show that there **does not** exist a bijection from A to $\mathcal{P}(A)$. Recall that a bijection is a function which is both an injection and a surjection. So, we will attempt to show that there do not exist any surjections from A to $\mathcal{P}(A)$. To do this, we will take an arbitrary function $f: A \rightarrow \mathcal{P}(A)$, and then argue that f is not surjective. We will show that $\operatorname{ran} f \neq \mathcal{P}(A)$ by finding a set $B \in \mathcal{P}(A) \setminus \operatorname{ran} f$. In words, we will find a subset of A that is **not** in the range of f.

Let's begin by looking at $\mathbb{N}$, the set of natural numbers. Given a specific function $f: \mathbb{N} \rightarrow \mathcal{P}(\mathbb{N})$, it's not too hard to come up with a set $B \in \mathcal{P}(\mathbb{N}) \setminus \operatorname{ran} f$. Let's choose a specific such f and use this example to try to come up with a procedure for describing the set B.

$$f(0) = \{\mathbf{0}, 1, 2, 3, 4, 5, 6, 7, 8, 9, 10, ...\}$$
$$f(1) = \{0, \mathbf{1}, 3, 4, 5, 6, 7, 8, 9, 10, ...\}$$
$$f(2) = \{0, 1, 4, 5, 6, 7, 8, 9, 10, ...\}$$
$$f(3) = \{0, 1, 4, 6, 7, 8, 9, 10, ...\}$$
$$f(4) = \{0, 1, \mathbf{4}, 6, 8, 9, 10, ...\}$$
$$...$$

Technical note: Recall that a **prime number** is a natural number with **exactly** two factors, 1 and itself. The set of prime numbers looks like this: $\{2, 3, 5, 7, 11, 13, 17, ...\}$. The function $f: \mathbb{N} \rightarrow \mathcal{P}(\mathbb{N})$ that we chose to use here is defined by $f(n) = \{k \in \mathbb{N} \mid k$ is not equal to one of the first n prime numbers$\}$. Notice how $f(0)$ is just the set $\mathbb{N}$ of all natural numbers, $f(1)$ is the set of all natural numbers except 2 (we left out the first prime), $f(2)$ is the set of all natural numbers except 2 and 3 (we left out the first two primes), and so on.

Observe that the "inputs" of our function are natural numbers, and the "outputs" are sets of natural numbers. So, it's perfectly natural to ask the question "Is n in $f(n)$?"

For example, we see that $0 \in f(0)$, $1 \in f(1)$, and $4 \in f(4)$ (indicated in bold in the definition of the function above). However, we also see that $2 \notin f(2)$ and $3 \notin f(3)$.

Let's let B be the set of natural numbers n that are **not** inside their images. Symbolically, we have

$$B = \{n \in \mathbb{N} \mid n \notin f(n)\}.$$

Which natural numbers are in the set B? Well, we already said that $0 \in f(0)$. It follows that $0 \notin B$. Similarly, $1 \notin B$ and $4 \notin B$, but $2 \in B$ and $3 \in B$.

Why did we choose to define B this way? The reason is because we are trying to make sure that B cannot be equal to $f(n)$ for every n. Since $0 \in f(0)$, but $0 \notin B$, it follows that $f(0)$ and B are different sets because they differ by at least one element, namely 0. Similarly, since $1 \in f(1)$, but $1 \notin B$, B cannot be equal to $f(1)$. What about 2? Well $2 \notin f(2)$, but $2 \in B$. Therefore, $B \neq f(2)$ as well... and so on down the line. We intentionally chose to make B disagree with $f(n)$ for every natural number n, ensuring that B will not be in the range of f.

I think we are now ready to prove the theorem.

Proof of Theorem 7.1: Let $f: A \to \mathcal{P}(A)$, and let $B = \{a \in A \mid a \notin f(a)\}$. Suppose toward contradiction that $B \in \operatorname{ran} f$. Then there is $a \in A$ with $f(a) = B$. But then we have $a \in B$ if and only if $a \notin f(A)$ if and only if $a \notin B$. This contradiction tells us that $B \notin \operatorname{ran} f$, and so, f is not surjective. Since $f: A \to \mathcal{P}(A)$ was arbitrary, there does not exist a surjection from A to $\mathcal{P}(A)$, and therefore, there is no bijection from A to $\mathcal{P}(A)$. So, A is not equinumerous with $\mathcal{P}(A)$. □

Notes: (1) The proof given here is a **proof by contradiction**. A proof by contradiction works as follows:

1. We assume the negation of what we are trying to prove.

2. We use a logically valid argument to derive a statement which is false.

3. Since the argument was logically valid, the only possible error is our original assumption. Therefore, the negation of our original assumption must be true.

(2) In this problem we are trying to prove that A is **not** equinumerous with $\mathcal{P}(A)$. The negation of this statement is that A **is** equinumerous with $\mathcal{P}(A)$, and so that is what we assume. Since $A \sim \mathcal{P}(A)$, there is a bijection $f: A \to \mathcal{P}(A)$. So, f is a surjection, which means that every subset of $\mathcal{P}(A)$ is in the range of f. In particular, the set B described in the proof is a subset of $\mathcal{P}(A)$, and therefore it is in the range of f. We then use a logically valid argument to derive the obviously false statement "$a \in B$ if and only if $a \notin B$."

By Theorem 7.1, $\mathbb{N}$ is not equinumerous with $\mathcal{P}(\mathbb{N})$. Which of these two sets is the "bigger" one? Let's consider the function $f: \mathbb{N} \to \mathcal{P}(\mathbb{N})$ defined by $f(n) = \{n\}$. This function looks like this:

$$\begin{array}{ccccc} 0 & 1 & 2 & 3 & 4 \ldots \\ \{0\} & \{1\} & \{2\} & \{3\} & \{4\} \ldots \end{array}$$

Observe that we are matching up each natural number with a subset of natural numbers (a very simple subset consisting of just one natural number) in a way so that different natural numbers get matched with different subsets. In other words, we defined an injective function from $\mathbb{N}$ to $\mathcal{P}(\mathbb{N})$. It seems like there are lots of subsets of $\mathbb{N}$ that didn't get mapped to (for example, all infinite subsets of $\mathbb{N}$). So, it seems that $\mathbb{N}$ is a "smaller" set than $\mathcal{P}(\mathbb{N})$.

We use the notation $A \preccurlyeq B$ if there is an injective function from A to B.

$$A \preccurlyeq B \text{ if and only if } \exists f\, (f : A \hookrightarrow B)$$

Recall: The symbol $\exists$ is called an **existential quantifier**, and it is pronounced "There exists" or "There is." The expression $\exists f\, (f : A \hookrightarrow B)$ can be translated into English as "There exists an f such that f is an injective function from A to B."

We write $A \prec B$ if $A \preccurlyeq B$ and $A \nsim B$.

So, for example, $\mathbb{N} \prec \mathcal{P}(\mathbb{N})$.

Theorem 7.2: If A is any set, then $A \prec \mathcal{P}(A)$.

Proof: The function $f : A \to \mathcal{P}(A)$ defined by $f(a) = \{a\}$ is injective. So, $A \preccurlyeq \mathcal{P}(A)$. By Theorem 7.1, $A \nsim \mathcal{P}(A)$. It follows that $A \prec \mathcal{P}(A)$. $\qquad \square$

Example 7.2: If we let $A = \mathcal{P}(\mathbb{N})$, we can apply Theorem 7.2 to this set A to see that $\mathcal{P}(\mathbb{N}) \prec \mathcal{P}\big(\mathcal{P}(\mathbb{N})\big)$. Continuing in this fashion, we get a sequence of increasingly larger sets.

$$\mathbb{N} \prec \mathcal{P}(\mathbb{N}) \prec \mathcal{P}\big(\mathcal{P}(\mathbb{N})\big) \prec \mathcal{P}\left(\mathcal{P}\big(\mathcal{P}(\mathbb{N})\big)\right) \prec \cdots$$

If A and B are arbitrary sets, in general it can be difficult to determine if A and B are equinumerous by producing a bijection. Luckily, the next theorem provides an easier way.

Theorem 7.3 (The Cantor-Schroeder-Bernstein Theorem): If A and B are sets such that $A \preccurlyeq B$ and $B \preccurlyeq A$, then $A \sim B$.

Note: At first glance, many students think that Theorem 7.3 is obvious and that the proof must be trivial. This is not true. The theorem says that if there is an injective function from A to B and another injective function from B to A, then there is a bijective function from A to B. This is a deep result, which is far from obvious. Constructing a bijection from two arbitrary injections is not an easy thing to do. I suggest that the reader takes a few minutes to try to do it, if for no other reason than to convince themselves that the proof is difficult. I leave the proof itself as an exercise (see Problem 11 below).

Example 7.3: Let's use Theorem 7.3 to prove that the open interval of real numbers $(0, 1)$ is equinumerous to the closed interval of real numbers $[0, 1]$.

Analysis: Since $(0, 1) \subseteq [0, 1]$, there is an obvious injective function $f : (0, 1) \to [0, 1]$ (just send each element to itself).

The harder direction is finding an injective function g from $[0, 1]$ into $(0, 1)$. We will do this by drawing a line segment with endpoints $\left(0, \frac{1}{4}\right)$ and $\left(1, \frac{3}{4}\right)$. This will give us a bijection from $[0, 1]$ to $\left[\frac{1}{4}, \frac{3}{4}\right]$. We can visualize this bijection using the graph to the right. We will write an equation for this line segment in the slope-intercept form $y = mx + b$. Here m is the slope of the line and b is the y-intercept of the line. We can use the graph to see that $b = \frac{1}{4}$ and $m = \frac{\text{rise}}{\text{run}} = \frac{\frac{3}{4} - \frac{1}{4}}{1 - 0} = \frac{2}{4} = \frac{1}{2}$. So, we define $g \colon [0, 1] \to (0, 1)$ by $g(x) = \frac{1}{2}x + \frac{1}{4}$.

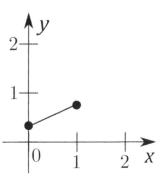

Let's write out the details of the proof.

Proof: Let $f \colon (0, 1) \to [0, 1]$ be defined by $f(x) = x$. Clearly, f is injective, so that $(0, 1) \preccurlyeq [0, 1]$.

Next, we define $g \colon [0, 1] \to \mathbb{R}$ by $g(x) = \frac{1}{2}x + \frac{1}{4}$. If $0 \leq x \leq 1$, then $0 \leq \frac{1}{2}x \leq \frac{1}{2}$, and therefore, $\frac{1}{4} \leq \frac{1}{2}x + \frac{1}{4} \leq \frac{3}{4}$. Since $0 < \frac{1}{4}$ and $\frac{3}{4} < 1$, we have $0 < g(x) < 1$. Therefore, $g \colon [0, 1] \to (0, 1)$. If $x \neq x'$, then $\frac{1}{2}x \neq \frac{1}{2}x'$, and so, $g(x) = \frac{1}{2}x + \frac{1}{4} \neq \frac{1}{2}x' + \frac{1}{4} = g(x')$. This shows that g is injective. It follows that $[0, 1] \preccurlyeq (0, 1)$.

Since $(0, 1) \preccurlyeq [0, 1]$ and $[0, 1] \preccurlyeq (0, 1)$, it follows from the Cantor-Schroeder-Bernstein Theorem that $(0, 1) \sim [0, 1]$. □

Notes: (1) If $A \subseteq B$, then the function $f \colon A \to B$ defined by $f(a) = a$ for all $a \in A$ is always injective. It is called the **inclusion map**.

(2) It is unfortunate that the same notation is used for points (ordered pairs of real numbers) and open intervals. Normally this isn't an issue, but in this particular example both usages of this notation appear. Take another look at the analysis above and make sure you can see when the notation (a, b) is being used for a point and when it is being used for an open interval.

(3) We could have used any closed interval $[a, b]$ with $0 < a < b < 1$ in place of $\left[\frac{1}{4}, \frac{3}{4}\right]$.

Problem Set 7

LEVEL 1

1. Let A and B be sets such that $A \subseteq B$. Prove that $\mathcal{P}(A) \preccurlyeq \mathcal{P}(B)$.

2. Let A, B, and C be sets. Prove the following:
   (i) $\preccurlyeq$ is transitive.
   (ii) $\prec$ is transitive.
   (iii) If $A \preccurlyeq B$ and $B \prec C$, then $A \prec C$.
   (iv) If $A \prec B$ and $B \preccurlyeq C$, then $A \prec C$.

LEVEL 2

3. Define $\mathcal{P}_k(\mathbb{N})$ for each $k \in \mathbb{N}$ by $\mathcal{P}_0(\mathbb{N}) = \mathbb{N}$ and $\mathcal{P}_{k+1}(\mathbb{N}) = \mathcal{P}\big(\mathcal{P}_k(\mathbb{N})\big)$ for $k > 0$. Find a set B such that for all $k \in \mathbb{N}$, $\mathcal{P}_k(\mathbb{N}) \prec B$.

4. Prove that if $A \sim B$ and $C \sim D$, then $A \times C \sim B \times D$.

LEVEL 3

5. Prove the following:
   (i) There is a partition $\boldsymbol{P}$ of $\mathbb{N}$ such that $\boldsymbol{P} \sim \mathbb{N}$ and for each $X \in \boldsymbol{P}$, $X \sim \mathbb{N}$
   (ii) A countable union of countable sets is countable.

6. Let A and B be sets such that $A \sim B$. Prove that $\mathcal{P}(A) \sim \mathcal{P}(B)$.

LEVEL 4

7. Prove the following:
   (i) $\mathbb{N} \times \mathbb{N} \sim \mathbb{N}$.
   (ii) $\mathbb{Q} \sim \mathbb{N}$.
   (iii) Any two intervals of real numbers are equinumerous (including $\mathbb{R}$ itself).
   (iv) $^{\mathbb{N}}\mathbb{N} \sim \mathcal{P}(\mathbb{N})$.

8. Prove that if $A \sim B$ and $C \sim D$, then $^A C \sim {}^B D$.

9. Prove that for any sets A, B, and C, ${}^{B \times C}A \sim {}^{C}({}^{B}A)$.

10. Prove the following:

  (i) $\mathcal{P}(\mathbb{N}) \sim \{f \in {}^{\mathbb{N}}\mathbb{N} \mid f \text{ is a bijection}\}$.

  (ii) $\mathbb{R} \sim \mathcal{P}(\mathbb{N})$.

  (iii) ${}^{\mathbb{N}}\mathbb{R} \not\sim {}^{\mathbb{R}}\mathbb{N}$.

CHALLENGE PROBLEM

11. Prove the Cantor-Schroeder-Bernstein Theorem.

Lesson 8
Induction and Recursion on $\mathbb{N}$

The Natural Numbers Revisited

Recall that we define the **natural numbers** as follows:

$$0 = \emptyset$$
$$1 = \{\emptyset\} = \{0\}$$
$$2 = \{\emptyset, \{\emptyset\}\} = \{0, 1\}$$
$$3 = \{\emptyset, \{\emptyset\}, \{\emptyset, \{\emptyset\}\}\} = \{0, 1, 2\}$$

In general, we let $n = \{0, 1, 2, \ldots, n - 1\}$ and we define the **natural numbers** to be the set

$$\mathbb{N} = \{0, 1, 2, 3, 4, \ldots\}$$

If n is a natural number, we define the **successor** of n, written n^+, to be the natural number $n^+ = n \cup \{n\}$. Note that $n^+ = \{0, 1, 2, \ldots, n - 1, n\}$.

Example 8.1:

1. $0^+ = 0 \cup \{0\} = \{0\} = 1$.

2. $1^+ = 1 \cup \{1\} = \{0\} \cup \{1\} = \{0, 1\} = 2$.

3. $2^+ = 2 \cup \{2\} = \{0, 1\} \cup \{2\} = \{0, 1, 2\} = 3$.

If n is a natural number such that $n \neq 0$, we define the **predecessor** of n, written n^-, to be the natural number k such that $n = k^+$ (by Problem 3, part (vii) below, k is unique). Thus, $n = n^- \cup \{n^-\}$.

Note that for all $n \in \mathbb{N}$, $(n^+)^- = n$ and for $n \in \mathbb{N}$ with $n \neq 0$, $(n^-)^+ = n$.

Example 8.2:

1. Since $1 = 0^+$, $1^- = 0$.

2. Since $2 = 1^+$, $2^- = 1$.

3. Since $3 = 2^+$, $3^- = 2$.

We define the ordering $<_\mathbb{N}$ on $\mathbb{N}$ by $n <_\mathbb{N} m$ if and only if $n \in m$. We will usually abbreviate $<_\mathbb{N}$ simply by $<$, especially if it is already clear that we are working with the natural numbers.

Example 8.3:

1. $0 \in \{0\}$. Therefore, $0 \in 0 \cup \{0\} = 1$. So, $0 < 1$.

2. $1 = \{0\} \notin \emptyset = 0$. So, $1 \not< 0$.

3. $1 = \{0\} \notin 0$ and $1 = \{0\} \notin \{0\}$. Therefore, $1 = \{0\} \notin 0 \cup \{0\} = 1$. So, $1 \not< 1$.

4. If $n \neq 0$, then $n^- \in \{n^-\}$. Therefore, $n^- \in n^- \cup \{n^-\} = n$. So, $n^- < n$.

Well Ordering and the Principle of Mathematical Induction

If A is a subset of natural numbers, then we say that a is the **least** element of A if a is less than every other element of A. Symbolically, $\forall b \in A(b \neq a \rightarrow a < b)$.

Example 8.4: The least element of $\mathbb{N}$ itself is 0.

We now describe two important principles that are equivalent to each other.

The **Well Ordering Principle** (abbreviated **WOP**) is the following statement: Every nonempty subset of natural numbers has a least element.

The **Principle of Mathematical Induction** (abbreviated **POMI**) is the following statement: Let S be a set of natural numbers such that (i) $0 \in S$ and (ii) for all $k \in \mathbb{N}$, $k \in S \rightarrow k^+ \in S$. Then $S = \mathbb{N}$.

Notes: (1) The Principle of Mathematical Induction works like a chain reaction. We know that $0 \in S$ (this is condition (i)). Substituting 0 in for k in the expression "$k \in S \rightarrow k^+ \in S$" (condition (ii)) gives us $0 \in S \rightarrow 1 \in S$. So, we have that 0 is in the set S, and "if 0 is in the set S, then 1 is in the set S." So, $1 \in S$ must also be true.

(2) In terms of logic, if we let p be the statement $0 \in S$ and q the statement $1 \in S$, then we are given that $p \wedge (p \rightarrow q)$ is true. Observe that the only way that this statement can be true is if q is also true. Indeed, we must have both $p \equiv \mathrm{T}$ and $p \rightarrow q \equiv \mathrm{T}$. If q were false, then we would have $p \rightarrow q \equiv \mathrm{T} \rightarrow \mathrm{F} \equiv \mathrm{F}$. So, we must have $q \equiv \mathrm{T}$.

(3) Now that we showed $1 \in S$ is true (from Note 1 above), we can substitute 1 for k in the expression "$k \in S \rightarrow k^+ \in S$" (condition (ii)) to get $1 \in S \rightarrow 2 \in S$. So, we have $1 \in S \wedge (1 \in S \rightarrow 2 \in S)$ is true. So, $2 \in S$ must also be true.

(4) In general, we get the following chain reaction:

$$0 \in S \rightarrow 1 \in S \rightarrow 2 \in S \rightarrow 3 \in S \rightarrow \cdots$$

I hope that the "argument" presented in Notes 1 through 4 above convinces you that the Principle of Mathematical Induction is a reasonable one.

Now let's show that the Principle of Mathematical Induction follows from the Well Ordering Principle (In Problem 6 below, you will be asked to show that the Well Ordering Principle follows from the Principle of Mathematical Induction, thus showing that the two statements are equivalent). Proofs involving the Well Ordering Principle are generally done by contradiction.

Theorem 8.1: WOP $\rightarrow$ POMI.

Proof: Assume WOP and let S be a set of natural numbers such that $0 \in S$ (condition (i)), and such that whenever $k \in S$, $k^+ \in S$ (condition (ii)). Assume toward contradiction that $S \neq \mathbb{N}$. Let $A = \{k \in \mathbb{N} \mid k \notin S\}$ (so, A is the set of natural numbers **not** in S). Since $S \neq \mathbb{N}$, A is nonempty. So, by the Well Ordering Principle, A has a least element, let's call it a. $a \neq 0$ because $0 \in S$ and $a \notin S$. So, $a^- \in \mathbb{N}$. Letting $k = a^-$, we have $a^- \in S \rightarrow k \in S \rightarrow k^+ \in S \rightarrow (a^-)^+ \in S \rightarrow a \in S$. But $a \in A$, which means that $a \notin S$. This is a contradiction, and so, $S = \mathbb{N}$. $\qquad\square$

Recall: A proof by contradiction works as follows:

1. We assume the negation of what we are trying to prove.

2. We use a logically valid argument to derive a statement which is false.

3. Since the argument was logically valid, the only possible error is our original assumption. Therefore, the negation of our original assumption must be true.

In this problem we are trying to prove that $S = \mathbb{N}$. The negation of this statement is that $S \neq \mathbb{N}$, and so that is what we assume.

We then define a set A which contains elements of $\mathbb{N}$ that are not in S. In reality, this set is empty (because the conclusion of the theorem is $S = \mathbb{N}$). However, our (wrong!) assumption that $S \neq \mathbb{N}$ tells us that this set A actually has something in it. Saying that A has something in it is an example of a false statement that was derived from a logically valid argument. This false statement occurred not because of an error in our logic, but because we started with an incorrect assumption ($S \neq \mathbb{N}$).

The Well Ordering Principle then allows us to pick out the least element of this set A. Note that we can do this because A is a subset of $\mathbb{N}$. This wouldn't work if we knew only that A was a subset of $\mathbb{Z}$, as $\mathbb{Z}$ does **not** satisfy the Well Ordering Principle (for example, $\mathbb{Z}$ itself has no least element).

Again, although the argument that A has a least element is logically valid, A does not actually have any elements at all. We are working from the (wrong!) assumption that $S \neq \mathbb{N}$.

Once we have our hands on this least element a, we can get our contradiction. What can this least element a be? Well a was chosen to not be in S, so a cannot be 0 (because 0 **is** in S). Also, we know that $a^- \in S$ (because a is the **least** element not in S and $a^- < a$). But condition (ii) then forces a to be in S (because $a = (a^-)^+$).

So, we wind up with $a \in S$, contradicting the fact that a is the least element **not** in S.

The Principle of Mathematical Induction is often written in the following way:

($\star$) Let $P(n)$ be a statement and suppose that (i) $P(0)$ is true and (ii) for all $k \in \mathbb{N}$, $P(k) \rightarrow P(k^+)$. Then $P(n)$ is true for all $n \in \mathbb{N}$.

In Problem 8 below, you will be asked to show that statement ($\star$) is equivalent to POMI.

There are essentially two steps involved in a proof by mathematical induction. The first step is to prove that $P(0)$ is true (this is called the **base case**), and the second step is to assume that $P(k)$ is true, and use this to show that $P(k^+)$ is true (this is called the **inductive step**). While doing the inductive step, the statement "$P(k)$ is true" is often referred to as the **inductive hypothesis**.

The **sum** of the natural numbers m and n is defined as follows:

(i) If $n = 0$, then $m + n = m$.
(ii) If $n = k^+$, then $m + n = (m + k)^+$.

Notes: (1) This is an example of a **recursive definition**. See Example 8.6 below for its justification.

(2) With this definition, we see that for all natural numbers m, we have $m + 1 = (m + 0)^+ = m^+$. So, from now on, we can write $m + 1$ instead of m^+. In particular, clause (ii) in the definition of the sum of two natural numbers can be written as follows:

(ii) If $n = k + 1$, then $m + n = (m + k) + 1$.

Theorem 8.2: The sum of two natural numbers is a natural number.

Note: Consider the sum $m + n$ of the natural numbers m and n. We will prove this theorem by induction on n (and **not** by induction on m). We will start by letting m be an arbitrary natural number.

The base case will be to show that $m + 0$ is a natural number.

The inductive step will be to assume that $m + k$ is a natural number and then to prove that $m + k^+$ (or equivalently, $m + (k + 1)$) is a natural number.

Let's begin:

Proof: Assume that m is a natural number.

Base Case ($k = 0$): $m + 0 = m$ (by clause (i) in the definition of the sum of two natural numbers), which we assumed was a natural number. Thus, we have shown that $m + 0$ is a natural number.

Inductive Step: Let k be a natural number and assume that $m + k$ is also a natural number. Then $m + k^+ = (m + k)^+$ (or equivalently, $m + (k + 1) = (m + k) + 1$), which is also a natural number.

Here we used the fact that the successor of a natural number is a natural number.

By the Principle of Mathematical Induction, $m + n$ is a natural number for all natural numbers n.

Since m was an arbitrary natural number, we have shown that the sum of any two natural numbers is a natural number. □

Note: Since the sum of two natural numbers is always a natural number (by Theorem 8.2), we say that $\mathbb{N}$ is **closed** under addition. We may also say that $+$ is a **binary operation** on $\mathbb{N}$.

Theorem 8.3: For all natural numbers n, $0 + n = n$.

Proof: Base Case ($k = 0$): $0 + 0 = 0$ by definition of addition of natural numbers.

Inductive Step: Let $k \in \mathbb{N}$ and assume that $0 + k = k$. Then $0 + (k + 1) = (0 + k) + 1 = k + 1$, as desired.

For the first equality, we used the definition of addition of natural numbers. For the second equality, we used the inductive hypothesis.

By the Principle of Mathematical Induction, for all natural numbers n, $0 + n = n$. □

Notes: (1) It's also true that for all natural numbers n, $n + 0 = n$. This follows right from the definition of addition of natural numbers.

(2) Since for all natural numbers n, we have $0 + n = n + 0 = 0$, we say that 0 is an **identity** with respect to addition, or that 0 is an **additive identity**.

Theorem 8.4: For all natural numbers m, n, and t, $(m + n) + t = m + (n + t)$.

Proof: Let m and n be natural numbers.

Base Case $(k = 0)$: $(m + n) + 0 = m + n = m + (n + 0)$ by definition of addition in $\mathbb{N}$.

Inductive Step: Let $k \in \mathbb{N}$ and assume that $(m + n) + k = m + (n + k)$. Then we have

$$(m + n) + (k + 1) = \big((m + n) + k\big) + 1 = \big(m + (n + k)\big) + 1$$
$$= m + \big((n + k) + 1\big) = m + \big(n + (k + 1)\big).$$

For the first, third, and fourth equalities, we used the definition of addition of natural numbers. For the second equality, we used the inductive hypothesis.

By the Principle of Mathematical Induction, for all natural numbers t, $(m + n) + t = m + (n + t)$.

Since m and n were arbitrary natural numbers, we have shown that for all natural numbers m, n, and t, $(m + n) + t = m + (n + t)$. $\square$

Notes: (i) Since for all natural numbers m, n, and t, we have $(m + n) + t = m + (n + t)$, we say that addition is **associative** in $\mathbb{N}$.

(ii) A **monoid** is a pair $(S, \star)$, where S is a set, $\star$ is an associative binary operation on S, and there is an identity $e \in S$ with respect to the operation $*$. Theorems 8.2, 8.3, and 8.4 prove that $(\mathbb{N}, +)$ is a monoid.

(iii) Addition is also **commutative** in $\mathbb{N}$. That is, for all natural numbers m and n, $m + n = n + m$. You will be asked to prove this in part (i) of Problem 3 below. We say that $(\mathbb{N}, +)$ is a **commutative monoid**.

The **product** of the natural numbers m and n is defined as follows:

   (i) If $n = 0$, then $mn = 0$.
   (ii) If $n = k + 1$, then $mn = mk + m$.

Notes: (1) Technically, the expression $mk + m$ has no meaning because it is unclear which operation we should be performing first (addition or multiplication). However, from now on we will always give precedence to multiplication as we were taught to do in elementary school. So, the expression $mk + m$ will always mean $(mk) + n$ and **not** $m(k + n)$.

(2) This is another example of a **recursive definition**. See Example 8.7 below for its justification.

Just like the sum operation, the product operation on the set of natural numbers has many nice algebraic properties such as

1. **Closure:** For all natural numbers m and n, mn is a natural number.
2. **Identity:** For all natural numbers n, $1 \cdot n = n \cdot 1 = n$.
3. **Associativity:** For all natural numbers m, n, and t, $(mn)t = m(nt)$.
4. **Commutativity:** For all natural numbers m and n, $mn = nm$.
5. **Distributivity:** For all natural numbers m, n, and t, $m(n + t) = mn + mt$.

The proofs that these properties hold are very similar to the proofs already given for addition. You will be asked to provide detailed proofs in Problem 3 below.

If $n \in \mathbb{N}$, we define n^2 to be the product of n with itself. So, $n^2 = n \cdot n$.

We define the **difference** between two natural numbers as follows: we say that $m - n = t$ if and only if $m = t + n$. For example, $7 - 2 = 5$ because $7 = 5 + 2$.

A natural number n is called **even** if there is another natural number b such that $n = 2b$.

Example 8.5:

1. 6 is even because $6 = 2 \cdot 3$.

2. 14 is even because $14 = 2 \cdot 7$.

3. We can write $1 = 2 \cdot \frac{1}{2}$, but this does **not** show that 1 is even (and as we all know, it is not). In the definition of even, it is very important that b is a natural number. The problem here is that $\frac{1}{2}$ is not a natural number, and so, it cannot be used as a value for b in the definition of even.

Let's use the Principle of Mathematical Induction to prove a theorem about natural numbers using these definitions.

Theorem 8.5: For all natural numbers n, $n^2 - n$ is an even natural number.

The proof of this result will require two very simple technical theorems about differences between natural numbers. A **lemma** is a theorem whose primary purpose is to prove a more important theorem. Let's prove these two preliminary lemmas first before we prove the main theorem.

Lemma 8.6: For all natural numbers m, n, and t, if $n - t \in \mathbb{N}$, then $m(n - t) = mn - mt$.

Proof: Suppose that $n - t \in \mathbb{N}$, say $n - t = a$. Then $n = a + t$. So, $mn = m(a + t) = ma + mt$ (using the distributivity of multiplication over addition in $\mathbb{N}$). Therefore, $mn - mt = ma = m(n - t)$. $\qquad \square$

Lemma 8.7: For all natural numbers m, n, and t, $(m + n) - n = m$.

Proof: The equation $m + n = m + n$ is equivalent to $(m + n) - n = m$. $\qquad \square$

Proof of Theorem 8.5: We will prove this theorem by induction on n.

Base Case ($k = 0$): $0^2 - 0 = 2 \cdot 0$ because $0^2 = 2 \cdot 0 + 0$. So, $0^2 - 0$ is even.

Inductive Step: Let $k \in \mathbb{N}$ and assume that $k^2 - k$ is an even natural number. Then $k^2 - k = 2b$ for some natural number b. Now,

$$(k+1)^2 - (k+1) = (k+1)(k+1) - (k+1) \cdot 1 = (k+1)[(k+1) - 1] = (k+1) \cdot k$$
$$= k(k+1) = k \cdot k + k \cdot 1 = k^2 + k = (k^2 - k) + 2k = 2b + 2k = 2(b+k).$$

Since $\mathbb{N}$ is closed under addition, $b + k \in \mathbb{N}$. Therefore, $(k+1)^2 - (k+1)$ is an even natural number. By the Principle of Mathematical Induction, $n^2 - n$ is an even natural number for all $n \in \mathbb{N}$. ☐

Notes: (1) For the first equality, we used the definition of $(k+1)^2$ and the multiplicative identity property in $\mathbb{N}$.

(2) For the second equality, we used Lemma 8.6.

(3) For the third equality, we used Lemma 8.7.

(4) For the fourth equality, we used the commutativity of multiplication in $\mathbb{N}$.

(5) For the fifth and ninth equalities, we used the distributivity of multiplication over addition in $\mathbb{N}$.

(6) For the sixth equality, we used the definition of k^2 and the multiplicative identity property in $\mathbb{N}$.

(7) For the seventh equality, we used what I call the "**Standard Advanced Calculus Trick.**" I sometimes abbreviate this as **SACT**. The trick is simple. If you need something to appear, just put it in. Then correct it by performing the opposite of what you just did.

In this case, in order to use the inductive hypothesis, we need $k^2 - k$ to appear, but unfortunately, we have $k^2 + k$ instead. Using SACT, I do the following:

- I simply put in what I need (and exactly where I need it): $k^2 - \boldsymbol{k} + k$.
- Now, I undo the damage by performing the reverse operation: $k^2 - k + \boldsymbol{k} + k$.
- Finally, I leave the part I need as is, and simplify the rest: $(k^2 - k) + 2k$

(8) For the eighth equality, we simply replaced $k^2 - k$ by $2b$. We established that these two quantities were equal in the second sentence of the inductive step.

Sometimes a statement involving the natural numbers may be false for 0, but true from some natural number on. In this case, we can still use induction. We just need to adjust the base case.

Theorem 8.8: $n^2 > 2n + 1$ for all natural numbers $n \geq 3$.

Proof: Base Case ($k = 3$): $3^2 = 9$ and $2 \cdot 3 + 1 = 6 + 1 = 7$. So, $3^2 > 2 \cdot 3 + 1$.

Inductive Step: Let $k \in \mathbb{N}$ with $k \geq 3$ and assume that $k^2 > 2k + 1$. Then we have

$$(k+1)^2 = (k+1)(k+1) = (k+1)k + (k+1)(1) = k^2 + k + k + 1 > (2k+1) + k + k + 1$$
$$= 2k + 2 + k + k = 2(k+1) + k + k \geq 2(k+1) + 1 \text{ (because } k + k \geq 3 + 3 = 6 \geq 1).$$

By the Principle of Mathematical Induction, $n^2 > 2n + 1$ for all $n \in \mathbb{N}$ with $n \geq 3$. $\quad\quad\square$

Notes: (1) If we have a sequence of equations and inequalities of the form $=$, $\geq$, and $>$ (with at least one inequality symbol appearing), beginning with a and ending with b, then the final result is $a > b$ if $>$ appears at least once and $a \geq b$ otherwise.

For example, if $a = j = h = m > n = p = q \geq b$, then $a > b$. The sequence that appears in the solution above has this form.

(2) By definition, $x^2 = x \cdot x$. We used this in the first equality in the inductive step to write $(k + 1)^2$ as $(k + 1)(k + 1)$.

(3) For the second equality in the inductive step, we used distributivity to write $(k + 1)(k + 1)$ as $(k + 1)k + (k + 1)(1)$.

(4) For the third equality in the inductive step, we used commutativity, distributivity, and the multiplicative identity property to write $(k + 1)k$ as $k(k + 1) = k \cdot k + k \cdot 1 = k^2 + k$. We also used the multiplicative identity property to write $(k + 1)(1) = k + 1$.

(5) Associativity of addition is being used when we write the expression $k^2 + k + k + 1$. Notice the lack of parentheses. Technically speaking, we should have written $(k^2 + k) + (k + 1)$ and then taken another step to rewrite this as $k^2 + \big(k + (k + 1)\big)$. However, since we have associativity, we can simply drop all those parentheses.

(6) The inequality "$k^2 + k + k + 1 > (2k + 1) + k + k + 1$" was attained by using the inductive hypothesis "$k^2 > 2k + 1$" together with part (x) from Problem 3 below.

(7) The dedicated reader should verify that the remaining equalities and inequalities in the proof are valid by determining which properties were used at each step.

Theorem 8.9: For every natural number n, there is a natural number j such that $n = 2j$ or $n = 2j + 1$.

Proof: Base Case ($k = 0$): $0 = 2 \cdot 0$ by definition of mutiplication in $\mathbb{N}$.

Inductive Step: Suppose that $k \in \mathbb{N}$ and there is $j \in \mathbb{N}$ such that $k = 2j$ or $k = 2j + 1$. If $k = 2j$, then $k + 1 = 2j + 1$. If $k = 2j + 1$, then $k + 1 = (2j + 1) + 1 = 2j + (1 + 1) = 2j + 2 = 2(j + 1)$. Here we used associativity of addition in $\mathbb{N}$ and distributivity of multiplication over addition in $\mathbb{N}$. Since $\mathbb{N}$ is closed under addition, $j + 1 \in \mathbb{N}$.

By the Principle of Mathematical Induction, for every natural number n, there is a natural number j such that $n = 2j$ or $n = 2j + 1$. $\quad\quad\square$

Recursion on $\mathbb{N}$

The definitions of the sum and product given above are examples of **recursive definitions**. These two particular functions are 2-valued. The following theorem gives us permission to define 2-valued functions in this way.

Theorem 8.10 ($\mathbb{N}$-Recursion Theorem): Let A, M be sets, let $a\colon M \to A$, and let $g\colon M \times A \times \mathbb{N} \to A$. Then there is a unique function $f\colon M \times \mathbb{N} \to A$ such that

   (i) $\forall m \in M\big(f(m, 0) = a(m)\big)$.

   (ii) $\forall n \in \mathbb{N} \forall m \in M\big(f(m, n+1) = g(m, f(m, n), n)\big)$.

I call this theorem the $\mathbb{N}$-Recursion Theorem (instead of simply the Recursion Theorem) to differentiate it from the transfinite version that we will see later in Lesson 12.

Before we prove Theorem 8.10, let's look at some examples to help us understand how it works.

Example 8.6: If we let $A = M = \mathbb{N}$, we let $a\colon \mathbb{N} \to \mathbb{N}$ be the identity function $a(m) = m$, and we let $g\colon \mathbb{N} \times \mathbb{N} \times \mathbb{N} \to \mathbb{N}$ be defined by $g(m, k, n) = k + 1$, then the $\mathbb{N}$-Recursion Theorem gives us a unique function $f\colon \mathbb{N} \times \mathbb{N} \to \mathbb{N}$ such that

   (i) $f(m, 0) = a(m) = m$.
   (ii) $f(m, n+1) = g(m, f(m, n), n) = f(m, n) + 1$.

This is precisely the definition of the sum of two natural numbers. Indeed, if we abbreviate $f(x, y)$ as $x + y$, then (i) and (ii) above are equivalent to

   (i) $m + 0 = m$.
   (ii) $m + (n+1) = (m+n) + 1$.

Example 8.7: If we let $A = M = \mathbb{N}$, we let $a\colon \mathbb{N} \to \mathbb{N}$ be the constant zero function $a(m) = 0$, and we let $g\colon \mathbb{N} \times \mathbb{N} \times \mathbb{N} \to \mathbb{N}$ be defined by $g(m, k, n) = k + m$, then the $\mathbb{N}$-Recursion Theorem gives us a unique function $f\colon \mathbb{N} \times \mathbb{N} \to \mathbb{N}$ such that

   (i) $f(m, 0) = a(m) = 0$.
   (ii) $f(m, n+1) = g(m, f(m, n), n) = f(m, n) + m$.

This is precisely the definition of the product of two natural numbers. Indeed, if we abbreviate $f(x, y)$ as xy, then (i) and (ii) above are equivalent to

   (i) $m \cdot 0 = 0$.
   (ii) $m(n+1) = mn + m$.

Example 8.8: If we let $A = M = \mathbb{N}$, we let $a\colon \mathbb{N} \to \mathbb{N}$ be the constant function $a(m) = 1$, and we let $g\colon \mathbb{N} \times \mathbb{N} \times \mathbb{N} \to \mathbb{N}$ be defined by $g(m, k, n) = km$, then the $\mathbb{N}$-Recursion Theorem gives us a unique function $f\colon \mathbb{N} \times \mathbb{N} \to \mathbb{N}$ such that

   (i) $f(m, 0) = a(m) = 1$.
   (ii) $f(m, n+1) = g(m, f(m, n), n) = f(m, n) \cdot m$.

This is the definition of the **power** of two natural numbers. If we abbreviate $f(x, y)$ as x^y, then (i) and (ii) above are equivalent to

   (i) $m^0 = 1$.
   (ii) $m^{n+1} = m^n \cdot m$.

Let's get back to the proof of the $\mathbb{N}$-Recursion Theorem. This proof is a bit tedious, but it is also quite straightforward. Let's start with a brief analysis to help you better understand the proof.

Analysis: Note that there are two parts to this theorem: we need to show that the function f exists, and then we need to show that the function f is unique.

The proof of uniqueness is straightforward. The harder part of the argument is showing that f exists.

We start by approximating the desired function f with "mini functions."

We define $s_0: M \times 1 \to A$ by $s_0(m, 0) = a(m)$.

We then define $s_1: M \times 2 \to A$ by $s_1(m, 0) = a(m)$ and $s_1(m, 1) = g(m, s_1(m, 0), 0)$. So, we have $s_1(m, 1) = g(m, a(m), 0)$. Observe that s_1 is a function that agrees with s_0 on $M \times 1$.

Next, we define $s_2: M \times 3 \to A$ by $s_2(m, 0) = a(m)$, $s_2(m, 1) = g(m, s_2(m, 0), 0)$ and $s_2(m, 2) = g(m, s_2(m, 1), 1)$. So, $s_2(m, 1) = g(m, a(m), 0)$ and $s_2(m, 2) = g(m, g(m, a(m), 0), 1)$. Observe that s_2 is a function that agrees with both s_0 on $M \times 1$ and s_1 on $M \times 2$.

We continue in this way defining $s_0, s_1, s_2, s_3, \ldots$ We then let f be the union of all these "mini functions."

We finish the proof of existence by showing that $f: M \times \mathbb{N} \to A$ and that f satisfies conditions (i) and (ii) in the statement of the theorem. Let's write out the details.

Proof of Theorem 8.10: Let A, M be sets, let $a: M \to A$, and let $g: M \times A \times \mathbb{N} \to A$ be given. For each $n \in \mathbb{N}$, let $s_n: M \times (n + 1) \to A$ be defined by

$$s_n(m, 0) = a(m), \qquad s_n(m, k + 1) = g(m, s_n(m, k), k) \text{ for } 0 \le k < n. \quad (\star)$$

For each $n \in \mathbb{N}$, s_n is the only function satisfying $(\star)$ above. To see this, suppose that t_n also satisfies $t_n: M \times (n + 1) \to A$, $t_n(m, 0) = a(m)$, and $t_n(m, k + 1) = g(m, t_n(m, k), k)$ for $0 \le k < n$. Let $m \in M$. We show by induction that for each $k < n + 1$, $t_n(m, k) = s_n(m, k)$. For the base case, $t_n(m, 0) = a(m) = s_n(m, 0)$. For the inductive step, assume that $k < n$ and $t_n(m, k) = s_n(m, k)$. Then we have $t_n(m, k + 1) = g(m, t_n(m, k), k) = g(m, s_n(m, k), k) = s_n(m, k + 1)$.

By the Principle of Mathematical Induction, for all $k < n + 1$, $t_n(m, k) = s_n(m, k)$. Since $m \in \mathbb{N}$ was arbitrary, we have that for all $m \in M$ and all $k < n + 1$, $t_n(m, k) = s_n(m, k)$. So, $t_n = s_n$.

Next, we show that if $n \le j$, then $m \in M$ and $0 \le k < n + 1$ implies that $s_n(m, k) = s_j(m, k)$. We prove this by induction on $k < n + 1$. For the base case, $s_n(m, 0) = a(m) = s_j(m, 0)$. For the inductive step, assume that $k < n + 1$ and $s_n(m, k) = s_j(m, k)$. Then we have

$$s_n(m, k + 1) = g(m, s_n(m, k), k) = g(m, s_j(m, k), k) = s_j(m, k + 1).$$

Now, let $F = \{s_n \mid n \in \mathbb{N}\}$ and let $f = \bigcup F$. We first show that $f: M \times \mathbb{N} \to A$.

To see that f is a function, let $(m, x, y), (m, x, z) \in f$. Then there are $n, j \in \mathbb{N}$ with $(m, x, y) \in s_n$ and $(m, x, z) \in s_j$. Without loss of generality, assume that $n \le j$. Then $s_j(m, x) = s_n(m, x) = y$. Since s_j is a function, $y = z$. Since $(m, x, y), (m, x, z) \in f$ were arbitrary, f is a function.

We now show that $\text{dom } f = M \times \mathbb{N}$. If $x \in \text{dom } f$, then $x \in \text{dom } s_n$ for some $n \in \mathbb{N}$. Therefore, we have $x \in M \times (n + 1) \subseteq M \times \mathbb{N}$. So, $\text{dom } f \subseteq M \times \mathbb{N}$. For the reverse inclusion, let $m, n \in M \times \mathbb{N}$. Then $(m, n) \in \text{dom } s_n$. Since $s_n \subseteq f$, $(m, n) \in \text{dom } f$. So, $M \times \mathbb{N} \subseteq \text{dom } f$, and therefore, we have $\text{dom } f = M \times \mathbb{N}$.

Next, we show that $\text{ran } f \subseteq A$. To see this, let $z \in \text{ran } f$, and let $f(x) = z$. Then $(x, z) \in f$, and so, there is $n \in \mathbb{N}$ with $(x, z) \in s_n$. Since $s_n : M \times (n + 1) \to A$, $z \in A$. Since $z \in \text{ran } f$ was arbitrary, $\text{ran } f \subseteq A$.

Next, let $m \in M$. Then $f(m, 0) = s_0(m, 0) = a(m)$, so that (i) holds.

Also, $f(m, n + 1) = s_{n+1}(m, n + 1) = g(m, s_{n+1}(m, n), n) = g(m, f(m, n), n)$, so that (ii) holds.

Finally, we prove the uniqueness of f. Suppose that $h : M \times \mathbb{N} \to A$ also satisfies

(i) $\forall m \in M\big(h(m, 0) = a(m)\big)$.
(ii) $\forall n \in \mathbb{N} \forall m \in M\big(h(m, n + 1) = g(m, h(m, n), n)\big)$.

Let $m \in M$. We show by induction on $n \in \mathbb{N}$ that $\forall n \in \mathbb{N}\big(h(m, n) = f(m, n)\big)$.

For the base case, we have $h(m, 0) = a(m) = f(m, 0)$. For the inductive step, assuming that $h(m, k) = f(m, k)$, we have $h(m, k + 1) = g(m, h(m, k), k) = g(m, f(m, k), k) = f(m, k + 1)$. By the Principle of Mathematical Induction, $h = f$. $\qquad \square$

There are many different versions of the $\mathbb{N}$-Recursion Theorem. Theorem 8.10 is a version that allows us to define the types of functions we are most interested in (2-valued functions such as addition and multiplication of natural numbers). If we wish to define single-valued functions, then we can use the following simpler version of the $\mathbb{N}$-Recursion Theorem:

Corollary 8.11: Let A be a set, let $a \in A$, and let $g : A \times \mathbb{N} \to A$. Then there is a unique function $f : \mathbb{N} \to A$ such that

(i) $f(0) = a$.
(ii) $\forall n \in \mathbb{N}\big(f(n + 1) = g(f(n), n)\big)$.

Corollary 8.11 follows easily from Theorem 8.10 by letting $M = \{0\}$, $a = a(0)$, and identifying $\{0\} \times \mathbb{N}$ with $\mathbb{N}$ and identifying $\{0\} \times A \times \mathbb{N}$ with $A \times \mathbb{N}$. I leave the details of the proof to the reader.

Example 8.9: If we let $A = \mathbb{N}$, we let $a = 1$, and we let $g : \mathbb{N} \times \mathbb{N} \to \mathbb{N}$ be defined by $g(x, n) = x \cdot (n + 1)$, then Corollary 8.11 gives us a unique function $f : \mathbb{N} \to \mathbb{N}$ such that

(i) $f(0) = 1$.
(ii) $f(n + 1) = g(f(n), n) = f(n) \cdot (n + 1)$.

This function is known as the **factorial** function. We generally denote the factorial of n by $n!$. So, we see that we have $0! = 1$, $1! = 1 \cdot (0 + 1) = 1 \cdot 1 = 1$, $2! = 1 \cdot (1 + 1) = 1 \cdot 2$, $3! = 1 \cdot 2 \cdot 3$, and in general, $(n + 1)! = n! \cdot (n + 1)$.

Problem Set 8

LEVEL 1

1. Use the Principle of Mathematical Induction to prove each of the following:

   (i) $2^n > n$ for all natural numbers $n \geq 1$.

   (ii) $0 + 1 + 2 + \cdots + n = \frac{n(n+1)}{2}$ for all natural numbers.

   (iii) $n! > 2^n$ for all natural numbers $n \geq 4$ (where $n! = 1 \cdot 2 \cdots n$ for all natural numbers $n \geq 1$).

   (iv) $2^n \geq n^2$ for all natural numbers $n \geq 4$.

2. A natural number n is **divisible** by a natural number k, written $k|n$, if there is another natural number b such that $n = kb$. Prove that $n^3 - n$ is divisible by 3 for all natural numbers n.

LEVEL 2

3. Prove each of the following. (You may assume that $<$ is a strict linear ordering of $\mathbb{N}$.)

   (i) Addition is commutative in $\mathbb{N}$.

   (ii) The set of natural numbers is closed under multiplication.

   (iii) 1 is a multiplicative identity in $\mathbb{N}$.

   (iv) Multiplication is distributive over addition in $\mathbb{N}$.

   (v) Multiplication is associative in $\mathbb{N}$.

   (vi) Multiplication is commutative in $\mathbb{N}$.

   (vii) For all natural numbers m, n, and k, if $m + k = n + k$, then $m = n$.

   (viii) For all natural numbers m, n, and k with $k \neq 0$, if $mk = nk$, then $m = n$.

   (ix) For all natural numbers m and n, $m < n$ if and only if there is a natural number $k > 0$ such that $n = m + k$.

   (x) For all natural numbers m, n, and k, $m < n$ if and only if $m + k < n + k$.

   (xi) For all natural numbers m and n, if $m > 0$ and $n > 0$, then $mn > 0$.

4. A set A is **transitive** if $\forall x(x \in A \to x \subseteq A)$ (in words, every element of A is also a subset of A). Prove that every natural number is transitive.

LEVEL 3

5. Prove that if $n \in \mathbb{N}$ and A is a nonempty subset of n, then A has a least element.

6. Prove POMI $\rightarrow$ WOP.

LEVEL 4

7. Prove that $3^n - 1$ is even for all natural numbers n.

8. Show that the Principle of Mathematical Induction is equivalent to the following statement:

   ($\star$) Let $P(n)$ be a statement and suppose that (i) $P(0)$ is true and (ii) for all $k \in \mathbb{N}$, $P(k) \rightarrow P(k + 1)$. Then $P(n)$ is true for all $n \in \mathbb{N}$.

LEVEL 5

9. The Principle of Strong Induction is the following statement:

   ($\star\star$) Let $P(n)$ be a statement and suppose that (i) $P(0)$ is true and (ii) for all $k \in \mathbb{N}$, $\forall j \leq k \left(P(j) \right) \rightarrow P(k + 1)$. Then $P(n)$ is true for all $n \in \mathbb{N}$.

   Use the Principle of Mathematical Induction to prove the Principle of Strong Induction.

10. Use the Principle of Mathematical Induction to prove that for every $n \in \mathbb{N}$, if S is a set with $|S| = n$, then S has 2^n subsets. (Hint: Use Problem 10 from Problem Set 2.)

CHALLENGE PROBLEMS

11. Prove that $\{A \in \mathcal{P}(\mathbb{N}) \mid A$ is finite$\}$ is countable and $\{A \in \mathcal{P}(\mathbb{N}) \mid A$ is infinite$\}$ is uncountable.

12. Define a set to be **selfish** if the number of elements it has is in the set. For example, the set $K_5 = \{1, 2, 3, 4, 5\}$ is selfish because it has 5 elements and 5 is in the set. A selfish set is **minimal** if none of its proper subsets is also selfish. For example, the set K_5 is not a minimal selfish set because $\{1\}$ is a selfish subset. Let $K_n = \{1, 2, 3, \ldots n\}$. Determine with proof how many minimal selfish subsets K_n has in terms of n.

LESSON 9
PROPOSITIONAL LOGIC

The Basics

We use **propositional variables** such as p, q, and r to represent the building blocks of **statements** (or **propositions**) and we use the **logical connectives** ∧, ∨, →, ↔, and ¬ to form **compound statements**.

A **truth assignment** of a list of propositional variables is a choice of T or F for each propositional variable in the list. The truth value of a compound statement is determined by the truth values of the propositional variables together with applying the following rules for the connectives.

- $p ∧ q$ is called the **conjunction** of p and q. It is pronounced "p and q." $p ∧ q$ is true when both p and q are true, and it is false otherwise.

- $p ∨ q$ is called the **disjunction** of p and q. It is pronounced "p or q." $p ∨ q$ is true when p or q (or both) are true, and it is false when p and q are both false.

- $p → q$ is called a **conditional** or **implication**. It is pronounced "if p, then q" or "p implies q." $p → q$ is true when p is false or q is true (or both), and it is false when p is true and q is false.

- $p ↔ q$ is called a **biconditional**. It is pronounced "p if and only if q." $p ↔ q$ is true when p and q have the same truth value (both true or both false), and it is false when p and q have opposite truth values (one true and the other false).

- $¬p$ is called the **negation** of p. It is pronounced "not p." $¬p$ is true when p is false, and it is false when p is true (p and $¬p$ have opposite truth values.)

A **truth table** can be used to display the possible truth values of a compound statement. We start by labelling the columns of the table with the propositional variables that appear in the statement, followed by the statement itself. We then use the rows to run through every possible combination of truth values for the propositional variables followed by the resulting truth values for the compound statement. Here are the truth tables for the five most common logical connectives.

p	q	$p ∧ q$
T	T	T
T	F	F
F	T	F
F	F	F

p	q	$p ∨ q$
T	T	T
T	F	T
F	T	T
F	F	F

p	q	$p → q$
T	T	T
T	F	F
F	T	T
F	F	T

p	q	$p ↔ q$
T	T	T
T	F	F
F	T	F
F	F	T

p	$¬p$
T	F
F	T

We can use these five truth tables to compute the truth values of compound statements involving the five basic logical connectives.

Note: For statements involving just 1 propositional variable (such as $\neg p$), the truth table requires 2 rows, 1 for each truth assignment of p (T or F).

For statements involving 2 propositional variables (such as $p \wedge q$), the truth table requires $2 \cdot 2 = 4$ (or $2^2 = 4$) rows, as there are 4 possible combinations for truth assignments of p and q (TT, TF, FT, FF).

In general, for a statement involving n propositional variables, the truth table will require 2^n rows. For example, if we want to build an entire truth table for $\neg p \vee (\neg q \rightarrow r)$, we will need $2^3 = 2 \cdot 2 \cdot 2 = 8$ rows in the truth table. We will create the truth table for this statement in Example 9.2 below (see the third solution).

Example 9.1: If p is true and q is false, then we can compute the truth value of $p \wedge q$ by looking at the second row of the truth table for the conjunction.

p	q	$p \wedge q$
T	T	T
T	F	F
F	T	F
F	F	F

We see from the highlighted row that $p \wedge q \equiv \text{T} \wedge \text{F} \equiv \textbf{F}$.

Note: Here the symbol $\equiv$ can be read "is logically equivalent to." So, we see that if p is true and q is false, then $p \wedge q$ is logically equivalent to F, or more simply, $p \wedge q$ is false.

We can use statements in place of propositional variables to form compound statements. For example, given the statements $p \leftrightarrow q$ and $\neg r$, we can form the compound statement $(p \leftrightarrow q) \wedge \neg r$. If A and B are arbitrary statements and we know the truth values of A and B, then we can find the truth value of A $\wedge$ B in the same way as if A and B were propositional variables. The same holds true when applying other logical connectives to compound statements. The next example will illustrate how this is done.

Example 9.2: Let p, q, and r be propositional variables with p and q true, and r false. Let's compute the truth value of $\neg p \vee (\neg q \rightarrow r)$.

Solution: We have $\neg p \vee (\neg q \rightarrow r) \equiv \neg \text{T} \vee (\neg \text{T} \rightarrow \text{F}) \equiv \text{F} \vee (\text{F} \rightarrow \text{F}) \equiv \text{F} \vee \text{T} \equiv \textbf{T}$.

Notes: (1) For the first equivalence, we simply replaced the propositional variables by their given truth values. We replaced p and q by T, and we replaced r by F.

(2) For the second equivalence, we used the first row of the truth table for the negation (drawn to the right for your convenience).

p	$\neg p$
T	F
F	T

We see from the highlighted row that $\neg \text{T} \equiv \text{F}$. We applied this result twice.

(3) For the third equivalence, we used the fourth row of the truth table for the conditional.

p	q	$p \rightarrow q$
T	T	T
T	F	F
F	T	T
F	**F**	**T**

We see from the highlighted row that $F \rightarrow F \equiv T$.

(4) For the last equivalence, we used the third row of the truth table for the disjunction.

p	q	$p \vee q$
T	T	T
T	F	T
F	**T**	**T**
F	F	F

We see from the highlighted row that $F \vee T \equiv T$.

(5) We can save a little time by immediately replacing the negation of a propositional variable by its truth value (which will be the opposite truth value of the propositional variable's). For example, since p has truth value T, we can replace $\neg p$ by F. The faster solution would look like this:

$$\neg p \vee (\neg q \rightarrow r) \equiv F \vee (F \rightarrow F) \equiv F \vee T \equiv \mathbf{T}.$$

Quicker solution: Since q has truth value T, it follows that $\neg q$ has truth value F. So, $\neg q \rightarrow r$ has truth value T. Finally, $\neg p \vee (\neg q \rightarrow r)$ must then have truth value T.

Notes: (1) Symbolically, we can write the following:

$$\neg p \vee (\neg q \rightarrow r) \equiv \neg p \vee (\neg T \rightarrow r) \equiv \neg p \vee (F \rightarrow r) \equiv \neg p \vee T \equiv \mathbf{T}$$

(2) We can display this reasoning visually as follows:

$$\neg p \vee (\neg q \rightarrow r)$$

The vertical lines have just been included to make sure you see which connective each truth value is written below.

We began by placing a T under the propositional variable q to indicate that q is true. Since $\neg T \equiv F$, we then place an F under the negation symbol. Next, since $F \rightarrow r \equiv T$ regardless of the truth value of r, we place a T under the conditional symbol. Finally, since $\neg p \vee T \equiv T$ regardless of the truth value of p, we place a T under the disjunction symbol. We made this last T bold to indicate that we are finished.

(3) Knowing that q has truth value T is enough to determine the truth value of $\neg p \lor (\neg q \rightarrow r)$, as we saw in Note 1 above. It's okay if you didn't notice that right away. This kind of reasoning takes a bit of practice and experience.

Truth table solution: An alternative solution is to build the whole truth table of $\neg p \lor (\neg q \rightarrow r)$ one column at a time. Since there are 3 propositional variables (p, q, and r), we will need $2^3 = 8$ rows to get all the possible truth values. We then create a column for each compound statement that appears within the given statement starting with the statements of smallest length and working our way up to the given statement (we will define these "substatements" more formally in the next section). We will need columns for p, q, r (the propositional variables), $\neg p$, $\neg q$, $\neg q \rightarrow r$, and finally, the statement itself, $\neg p \lor (\neg q \rightarrow r)$. Below is the final truth table with the relevant row highlighted and the final answer circled.

p	q	r	$\neg p$	$\neg q$	$\neg q \rightarrow r$	$\neg p \lor (\neg q \rightarrow r)$
T	T	T	F	F	T	(T)
T	T	F	F	F	T	T
T	F	T	F	T	T	T
T	F	F	F	T	F	F
F	T	T	T	F	T	T
F	T	F	T	F	T	T
F	F	T	T	T	T	T
F	F	F	T	T	F	T

Notes: (1) We fill out the first three columns of the truth table by listing all possible combinations of truth assignments for the propositional variables p, q, and r. Notice how down the first column we have 4 T's followed by 4 F's, down the second column we alternate sequences of 2 T's with 2 F's, and down the third column we alternate T's with F's one at a time. This is a nice systematic way to make sure we get all possible combinations of truth assignments.

If you're having trouble seeing the pattern of T's and F's, here is another way to think about it: In the first column, the first half of the rows have a T and the remainder have an F. This gives 4 T's followed by 4 F's.

For the second column, we take half the number of consecutive T's in the first column (half of 4 is 2) and then we alternate between 2 T's and 2 F's until we fill out the column.

For the third column, we take half the number of consecutive T's in the second column (half of 2 is 1) and then we alternate between 1 T and 1 F until we fill out the column.

(2) Since the connective $\neg$ has the effect of taking the opposite truth value, we generate the entries in the fourth column by taking the opposite of each truth value in the first column. Similarly, we generate the entries in the fifth column by taking the opposite of each truth value in the second column.

(3) For the sixth column, we apply the connective $\to$ to the fifth and third columns, respectively, and finally, for the last column, we apply the connective $\lor$ to the fourth and sixth columns, respectively.

(4) The original question is asking us to compute the truth value of $\neg p \lor (\neg q \to r)$ when p and q are true, and r is false. In terms of the truth table, we are being asked for the entry in the second row and last (seventh) column. Therefore, the answer is **T**.

(5) This is certainly not the most efficient way to answer the given question. However, building truth tables is not too difficult, and it's a foolproof way to determine truth values of compound statements.

Statements and Substatements

We now define the set of **statements** formally as follows:

1.   We have a list of symbols $p, q, r, \ldots$ called propositional variables, each of which is a statement (these are called **atomic statements**).

2.   Whenever ϕ is a statement, $(\neg \phi)$ is a statement.

3.   Whenever ϕ and ψ are statements, $(\phi \land \psi)$, $(\phi \lor \psi)$, $(\phi \to \psi)$, and $(\phi \leftrightarrow \psi)$ are statements.

Notes: (1) We will generally use greek letters such as ϕ (phi), ψ (psi), and τ (tau) to represent statements and capital Greek letters such as Φ (phi), Γ (gamma), and Σ (sigma) for sets of statements.

(2) For easier readability, we will always drop the outermost pair of parentheses. For example, we will write $(p \land q)$ as $p \land q$, and we will write $\left(p \to (q \lor r)\right)$ as $p \to (q \lor r)$.

(3) Also, for easier readability, we will often drop the parentheses around $(\neg \phi)$ to get $\neg \phi$. For example, we will write $\left(p \land (\neg q)\right)$ as $p \land \neg q$. Notice that we dropped the outermost pair of parentheses to get $p \land (\neg q)$, and then we dropped the parentheses around $\neg q$.

(4) When we apply the negation symbol two or more times in a row, we will **not** drop parentheses. For example, $\left(\neg(\neg p)\right)$ will be written as $\neg(\neg p)$ and not as $\neg\neg p$.

(5) ϕ is called a **substatement** of $(\neg \phi)$. For example, p is a substatement of $\neg p$ ($\neg p$ is the abbreviated version of $(\neg p)$). Similarly, ϕ and ψ are substatements of $(\phi \land \psi)$, $(\phi \lor \psi)$, $(\phi \to \psi)$, and $(\phi \leftrightarrow \psi)$. For example, p and q are both substatements of $p \leftrightarrow q$. Also, if ϕ is a substatement of ψ and ψ is a substatement of τ, then we will consider ϕ to be a substatement of τ. For example, p is a substatement of $\neg(\neg p)$ because p is a substatement of $\neg p$ and $\neg p$ is a substatement of $\neg(\neg p)$.

(6) Although we are abbreviating statements by eliminating parentheses, it is important to realize that those parentheses are there. If we were to use $\land$ to form a new statement from $p \to q$ and r, it would be incorrect to write $p \to q \land r$. This expression is meaningless, as we do not know whether to apply $p \to q$ or $q \land r$ first. The correct expression is $(p \to q) \land r$. This is now an acceptable abbreviation for the statement $\left((p \to q) \land r\right)$.

Notice that p, q, r, and $p \to q$ are all substatements of $(p \to q) \land r$, whereas $q \land r$ is **not** a substatement of $(p \to q) \land r$.

Example 9.3: Let p, q, and r be propositional variables. Then we have the following:

1. p, q, and r are statements.

2. $(p \to q)$ is a statement (by 3 above). Using Note 2, we will abbreviate this statement as $p \to q$. p and q are both substatements of $p \to q$.

Example 9.4: Let's find the substatements of $\big((p \to q) \vee \neg r\big) \leftrightarrow \neg(q \wedge r)$.

Solution: The substatements are $p, q, r, \neg r, p \to q, (p \to q) \vee \neg r, q \wedge r$, and $\neg(q \wedge r)$.

Note: The given statement is an abbreviation for $\Big(\big((p \to q) \vee (\neg r)\big) \leftrightarrow \big(\neg(q \wedge r)\big)\Big)$. This is much harder to read and shows why we like to use abbreviations.

Logical Equivalence

Let ϕ and ψ be statements. We say that ϕ and ψ are **logically equivalent**, written $\phi \equiv \psi$, if every truth assignment of the propositional variables appearing in either ϕ or ψ (or both) leads to the same truth value for both statements.

Example 9.5: Let p be a propositional variable, let $\phi = p$, and let $\psi = \neg(\neg p)$. If $p \equiv T$, then $\phi \equiv T$ and $\psi \equiv \neg(\neg T) \equiv \neg F \equiv T$. If $p \equiv F$, then $\phi \equiv F$ and $\psi \equiv \neg(\neg F) \equiv \neg T \equiv F$. So, both possible truth assignments of p lead to the same truth value for ϕ and ψ. It follows that $\phi \equiv \psi$ (ϕ and ψ are logically equivalent).

Notes: (1) One way to determine if two statements ϕ and ψ are logically equivalent is to draw the truth table for each statement. We would generally put all the information into a single table. If the columns corresponding to ϕ and ψ are a perfect match, then $\phi \equiv \psi$.

Here is a truth table with columns for $\phi = p$ and $\psi = \neg(\neg p)$.

p	$\neg p$	$\neg(\neg p)$
T	F	T
F	T	F

Observe that the first column gives the truth values for ϕ, the third column gives the truth values for ψ, and both these columns are identical. It follows that $\phi \equiv \psi$.

(2) The logical equivalence $p \equiv \neg(\neg p)$ is called the **law of double negation**.

Example 9.6: Let p and q be propositional variables, let $\phi = \neg(p \wedge q)$, and let $\psi = \neg p \vee \neg q$. If $p \equiv F$ or $q \equiv F$, then $\phi \equiv \neg F \equiv T$ and $\psi \equiv T$ (because $\neg p \equiv T$ or $\neg q \equiv T$). If $p \equiv T$ and $q \equiv T$, then $\phi \equiv \neg T \equiv F$ and $\psi \equiv F \vee F \equiv F$. So, all four possible truth assignments of p and q lead to the same truth value for ϕ and ψ. It follows that $\phi \equiv \psi$.

Notes: (1) Here is a truth table with columns for $\phi = \neg(p \wedge q)$ and $\psi = \neg p \vee \neg q$.

p	q	$\neg p$	$\neg q$	$p \wedge q$	$\neg(p \wedge q)$	$\neg p \vee \neg q$
T	T	F	F	T	F	F
T	F	F	T	F	T	T
F	T	T	F	F	T	T
F	F	T	T	F	T	T

Observe that the sixth column gives the truth values for ϕ, the seventh column gives the truth values for ψ, and both these columns are identical. It follows that $\phi \equiv \psi$.

(2) The logical equivalence $\neg(\boldsymbol{p} \wedge \boldsymbol{q}) \equiv \neg\boldsymbol{p} \vee \neg\boldsymbol{q}$ is one of **De Morgan's laws**.

(3) There are two De Morgan's laws. The second one is $\neg(\boldsymbol{p} \vee \boldsymbol{q}) \equiv \neg\boldsymbol{p} \wedge \neg\boldsymbol{q}$. I leave it to the reader to verify this equivalence.

List 9.1: Here is a list of some useful logical equivalences. The reader should verify each of these by drawing a truth table or by using arguments similar to those used in Examples 9.5 and 9.6 (see Problem 4 below).

1. **Law of double negation:** $p \equiv \neg(\neg p)$

2. **De Morgan's laws:** $\quad \neg(p \wedge q) \equiv \neg p \vee \neg q \qquad\qquad \neg(p \vee q) \equiv \neg p \wedge \neg q$

3. **Commutative laws:** $\quad p \wedge q \equiv q \wedge p \qquad\qquad\qquad p \vee q \equiv q \vee p$

4. **Associative laws:** $\quad (p \wedge q) \wedge r \equiv p \wedge (q \wedge r) \qquad (p \vee q) \vee r \equiv p \vee (q \vee r)$

5. **Distributive laws:** $\quad p \wedge (q \vee r) \equiv (p \wedge q) \vee (p \wedge r) \quad p \vee (q \wedge r) \equiv (p \vee q) \wedge (p \vee r)$

6. **Identity laws:** $\quad p \wedge \mathrm{T} \equiv p \qquad p \wedge \mathrm{F} \equiv \mathrm{F} \qquad p \vee \mathrm{T} \equiv \mathrm{T} \qquad p \vee \mathrm{F} \equiv p$

7. **Negation laws:** $\quad p \wedge \neg p \equiv \mathrm{F} \qquad\qquad\qquad p \vee \neg p \equiv \mathrm{T}$

8. **Redundancy laws:** $\quad p \wedge p \equiv p \qquad\qquad\qquad p \vee p \equiv p$

9. **Absorption laws:** $\quad (p \vee q) \wedge p \equiv p \qquad\qquad (p \wedge q) \vee p \equiv p$

10. **Law of the conditional:** $\quad p \rightarrow q \equiv \neg p \vee q$

11. **Law of the contrapositive:** $p \rightarrow q \equiv \neg q \rightarrow \neg p$

12. **Law of the biconditional:** $\quad p \leftrightarrow q \equiv (p \rightarrow q) \wedge (q \rightarrow p)$

Notes: (1) Although this is a fairly long list of laws, a lot of it is quite intuitive. For example, in English the word "and" is commutative. If the statement "I have a cat and I have a dog" is true, then the statement "I have a dog and I have a cat" is also true. So, it's easy to see that $p \wedge q \equiv q \wedge p$ (the first law in 3 above). As another example, the statement "I have a cat and I do not have a cat" could never be true. So, it's easy to see that $p \wedge \neg p \equiv \mathrm{F}$ (the first law in 7 above).

(2) The law of the conditional allows us to replace the conditional statement $p \rightarrow q$ by the more intuitive statement $\neg p \lor q$. We can think of the conditional statement $p \rightarrow q$ as having the **hypothesis** (or **premise** or **assumption**) p and the **conclusion** q. The disjunctive form $\neg p \lor q$ tells us quite explicitly that a conditional statement is true if and only if the hypothesis p is false or the conclusion q is true.

(3) A statement that has truth value T for all truth assignments of the propositional variables is called a **tautology**. A statement that has truth value F for all truth assignments of the propositional variables is called a **contradiction**.

In laws 6 and 7 above, we can replace T by any tautology and F by any contradiction, and the law still holds. For example, since $q \leftrightarrow \neg q$ is a contradiction, by the fourth identity law, $p \lor (q \leftrightarrow \neg q) \equiv p$.

(4) It's worth observing that if ϕ and ψ are statements, then $\phi \equiv \psi$ if and only if $\phi \leftrightarrow \psi$ is a tautology. This follows from the fact that $\phi \leftrightarrow \psi \equiv$ T if and only if ϕ and ψ have the same truth value.

For example, $(p \rightarrow q) \leftrightarrow (\neg q \rightarrow \neg p)$ is a tautology. This follows from the law of the contrapositive and the remark in the last paragraph. Let's look at the complete truth table for this example.

p	q	$\neg p$	$\neg q$	$p \rightarrow q$	$\neg q \rightarrow \neg p$	$(p \rightarrow q) \leftrightarrow (\neg p \rightarrow \neg q)$
T	T	F	F	T	T	T
T	F	F	T	F	F	T
F	T	T	F	T	T	T
F	F	T	T	T	T	T

Notice how the columns for $(p \rightarrow q)$ and $(\neg q \rightarrow \neg p)$ have the same truth values. So, it should be obvious that the column for $(p \rightarrow q) \leftrightarrow (\neg q \rightarrow \neg p)$ will have only T's.

The following three additional laws of logical equivalence will be used freely (often without mention):

1. **Law of transitivity of logical equivalence:** Let ϕ, ψ, and τ be statements such that $\phi \equiv \psi$ and $\psi \equiv \tau$. Then $\phi \equiv \tau$.

2. **Law of substitution of logical equivalents:** Let ϕ, ψ, and τ be statements such that $\phi \equiv \psi$ and ϕ is a substatement of τ. Let τ^* be the statement formed by replacing ϕ by ψ inside of τ. Then $\tau^* \equiv \tau$.

3. **Law of substitution of statements:** Let ϕ and ψ be statements such that $\phi \equiv \psi$, let p be a propositional variable, and let τ be a statement. Let ϕ^* and ψ^* be the statements formed by replacing every instance of p with τ in ϕ and ψ, respectively. Then $\phi^* \equiv \psi^*$.

Example 9.7:

1. Since $q \equiv \neg(\neg q)$ (by the law of double negation), we have $p \land q \equiv p \land \neg(\neg q)$. Here we have used the law of substitution of logical equivalents with $\phi = q$, $\psi = \neg(\neg q)$, $\tau = p \land q$, and $\tau^* = p \land \neg(\neg q)$.

87

2. Let's show that the negation of the conditional statement $p \to q$ is logically equivalent to the statement $p \land \neg q$.

   We have $\neg(p \to q) \equiv \neg(\neg p \lor q) \equiv \neg(\neg p) \land \neg q \equiv p \land \neg q$. Here we have used the law of substitution of logical equivalents together with the law of the conditional, the second De Morgan's law, the law of double negation, and the law of transitivity of logical equivalence.

3. Since $p \to q \equiv \neg p \lor q$ (by the law of the conditional), $(p \land q) \to (p \lor q) \equiv \neg(p \land q) \lor (p \lor q)$. Here we have used the law of substitution of statements twice. We replaced the propositional variable p by the statement $p \land q$, and then we replaced the propositional variable q by the statement $p \lor q$.

Notes: (1) If you think about the equivalence $\neg(p \to q) \equiv p \land \neg q$ from part 2 of Example 9.7 for a moment, you will realize that it makes perfect sense. Again, we can think of the conditional statement $p \to q$ as having the **hypothesis** p and the **conclusion** q. We know the only way to make a conditional statement **false** is to make the hypothesis true and the conclusion false.

So, to make the negation of the conditional statement **true**, we would do the same thing. In other words, the negation of the conditional is true if p is true and q is false, or equivalently, if $p \land \neg q$ is true.

In summary, the logical equivalence $\neg(p \to q) \equiv p \land \neg q$ says that a conditional statement is false if and only if the hypothesis is true and the conclusion is false.

(2) By the second associative law, $(p \lor q) \lor r \equiv p \lor (q \lor r)$. So, we can write $p \lor q \lor r$ because whichever way we choose to think about it ($p \lor q$ first or $q \lor r$ first), we get the same truth values.

In part 3 of Example 9.7, we saw that $(p \land q) \to (p \lor q) \equiv \neg(p \land q) \lor (p \lor q)$. By our remarks in the last paragraph, we can write $\neg(p \land q) \lor (p \lor q)$ as $\neg(p \land q) \lor p \lor q$ without causing any confusion.

Example 9.8: Let's show that the statement $p \land [(p \land \neg q) \lor q]$ is logically equivalent to the atomic statement p.

Solution:
$$p \land [(p \land \neg q) \lor q] \equiv p \land [q \lor (p \land \neg q)] \equiv p \land [(q \lor p) \land (q \lor \neg q)] \equiv p \land [(q \lor p) \land \text{T}]$$
$$\equiv p \land (q \lor p) \equiv (q \lor p) \land p \equiv (p \lor q) \land p \equiv p$$

So, we see that $p \land [(p \land \neg q) \lor q]$ is logically equivalent to the atomic statement p.

Notes: (1) For the first equivalence, we used the second commutative law.

(2) For the second equivalence, we used the second distributive law.

(3) For the third equivalence, we used the second negation law.

(4) For the fourth equivalence, we used the first identity law.

(5) For the fifth equivalence, we used the first commutative law.

(6) For the sixth equivalence, we used the second commutative law.

(7) For the last equivalence, we used the first absorption law.

(8) We also used the law of transitivity of logical equivalence and the law of substitution of logical equivalents several times.

Validity in Propositional Logic

A **logical argument** or **proof** consists of **premises** (statements that we are given) and **conclusions** (statements we are not given).

One way to write an argument is to list the premises and conclusions vertically with a horizontal line separating the premises from the conclusions. If there are two premises ϕ and ψ, and one conclusion τ, then the argument would look like this:

$$\frac{\begin{array}{c} \phi \\ \psi \end{array}}{\tau}$$

Example 9.9: Let's take $p \to q$ and p to be premises and q to be a conclusion. Here is the argument.

$$\frac{\begin{array}{c} p \to q \\ p \end{array}}{q}$$

A logical argument is **valid** if every truth assignment that makes all premises true also makes all the conclusions true. A logical argument that is not valid is called **invalid** or a **fallacy**.

There are several ways to determine if a logical argument is valid. We will give three methods in the next example.

Example 9.10: Let's show that the logical argument given in Example 9.9 is valid. The premises are $p \to q$ and p, and the conclusion is q.

$$\frac{\begin{array}{c} p \to q \\ p \end{array}}{q}$$

Solution: Let's use a truth table to illustrate the three methods.

p	q	$p \to q$	$(p \to q) \wedge p$	$[(p \to q) \wedge p] \to q$
T	T	T	T	T
T	F	F	F	T
F	T	T	F	T
F	F	T	F	T

There are several ways to use this truth table to see that the logical argument is valid.

<u>Method 1:</u> We use only the first three columns. We look at each row where both premises (columns 1 and 3) are true. Only the first row satisfies this. Since the conclusion (column 2) is also true in the first row, the logical argument is valid. Symbolically, we write $p \to q, p \vdash q$, and we say that $\{p \to q, p\}$

tautologically implies q.

Method 2: We can take the conjunction of the premises, as we did in column 4. We look at each row where this conjunction is true. Again, only the first row satisfies this. Since the conclusion (column 2) is also true in the first row, the logical argument is valid. Symbolically, we write $(p \to q) \wedge p \vdash q$, and we say that $(p \to q) \wedge p$ **tautologically implies** q.

Method 3: We can use the conjunction of the premises as the hypothesis of the conditional with the appropriate conclusion, as we did in column 5. We now check that this statement is a tautology. Symbolically, we can write $\vdash [(p \to q) \wedge p] \to q$ (this can be read "$[(p \to q) \wedge p] \to q$ is a tautology").

Notes: (1) A valid argument is called a **rule of inference**. The rule of inference in this example is called **modus ponens**.

(2) We didn't need to draw a whole truth table to verify that the argument presented here was valid. For example, for Method 1, we could argue as follows: If $p \equiv T$ and $p \to q \equiv T$, then we must have $q \equiv T$ because if q were false, we would have $p \to q \equiv T \to F \equiv F$.

(3) p and q could be any statements here. For example, suppose p is the statement "Pigs have wings," and q is the statement "pigs can fly." Then the argument looks like this:

> If pigs have wings, then they can fly
> Pigs have wings
> Pigs can fly

This seems like a good time to point out that just because a logical argument is valid, it does **not** mean that the conclusion is true. We have shown in the solution above that this argument is valid. However, I think we can all agree that pigs cannot fly!

(4) We say that a logical argument is **sound** if it is valid **and** all the premises are true. Note 3 above gives an example of an argument that is valid, but not sound.

Every tautology gives us at least one rule of inference.

Example 9.11: Recall the first De Morgan's law: $\neg(p \wedge q) \equiv \neg p \vee \neg q$. This law gives us the following two rules of inference.

$$\frac{\neg(p \wedge q)}{\neg p \vee \neg q} \qquad \qquad \frac{\neg p \vee \neg q}{\neg(p \wedge q)}$$

To show that an argument is invalid, we need only produce a single truth assignment that makes all the premises true and the conclusion (or one of the conclusions) false. Such a truth assignment is called a **counterexample**.

Example 9.12: The following invalid argument is called the **fallacy of the converse**.

$$\frac{p \to q}{q \to p}$$

To see that this argument is invalid, we will find a counterexample. Here we can use the truth assignment $p \equiv F$, $q \equiv T$. We then have that $p \to q \equiv F \to T \equiv T$ and $q \to p \equiv T \to F \equiv F$.

Notes: (1) Consider the conditional statement $p \to q$. The statement $q \to p$ is called the **converse** of the original conditional statement. The argument in this example shows that the converse of a conditional statement is **not** logically equivalent to the original conditional statement.

(2) The statement $\neg p \to \neg q$ is called the **inverse** of the original conditional statement. This statement is also **not** logically equivalent to the original conditional statement. The reader should write down the fallacy of the inverse and give a counterexample to show that it is invalid (as we did above for the converse).

(3) The statement $\neg q \to \neg p$ is called the **contrapositive** of the original conditional statement. By the law of the contrapositive, this statement **is** logically equivalent to the original conditional statement. The reader should write down the law of the contrapositive as a rule of inference, as was done for the first De Morgan's law in Example 9.11.

List 9.2: Here is a list of some useful rules of inference that **do not** come from tautologies. The reader should verify that each of the logical arguments given here is valid (see Problem 4 below).

Modus Ponens	Modus Tollens	Disjunctive Syllogism	Hypothetical Syllogism
$p \to q$	$p \to q$	$p \lor q$	$p \to q$
p	$\neg q$	$\neg p$	$q \to r$
q	$\neg p$	q	$p \to r$

Conjunctive Introduction	Disjunctive Introduction	Biconditional Introduction	Constructive Dilemma
p	p	$p \to q$	$p \to q$
q	$p \lor q$	$q \to p$	$r \to s$
$p \land q$		$p \leftrightarrow q$	$p \lor r$
			$q \lor s$

Conjunctive Elimination	Disjunctive Resolution	Biconditional Elimination	Destructive Dilemma
$p \land q$	$p \lor q$	$p \leftrightarrow q$	$p \to q$
p	$\neg p \lor r$	$p \to q$	$r \to s$
	$q \lor r$		$\neg q \lor \neg s$
			$\neg p \lor \neg r$

A **derivation** is a valid logical argument such that each conclusion follows from the premises and conclusions above it using a rule of inference.

When creating a derivation, we will label each premise and conclusion with a number and state the rule of inference and numbers that are used to derive each conclusion.

Example 9.13: Let's give a derivation of the following logical argument.

$$\frac{\begin{array}{c} \neg p \\ \neg p \to \neg q \end{array}}{\neg q \lor p}$$

Solution:

$$
\begin{array}{ll}
1 \quad \neg p & \text{Premise} \\
2 \quad \neg p \to \neg q & \text{Premise} \\
\hline
3 \quad \neg q & \text{Modus ponens (2, 1)} \\
4 \quad \neg q \lor p & \text{Disjunctive introduction (3)}
\end{array}
$$

Notes: (1) We started by listing the premises above the line.

(2) If we let $\phi = \neg p$ and $\psi = \neg q$, then by modus ponens, we have $\phi \to \psi, \phi \vdash \psi$. So, we can write $\psi \equiv \neg q$ as the third line of the derivation. We applied modus ponens to the statements in lines 2 and 1 to derive $\neg q$.

(3) If we let $\phi = \neg q$, then by disjunctive introduction, $\phi \vdash \phi \lor p$, or equivalently, $\neg q \vdash \neg q \lor p$. So, we can write $\neg q \lor p$ as the fourth line of the derivation. We applied disjunctive introduction to the statement in line 3 to derive $\neg q \lor p$.

Example 9.14: Let's determine if the following logical argument is valid.

> If cats hiss and purr, then dogs can talk.
> Cats hiss.
> Dogs cannot talk.
> Therefore, cats do not purr.

Solution: Let h represent "Cats hiss," let p represent "Cats purr," and let t represent "Dogs can talk." We now give a derivation showing that the argument is valid.

$$
\begin{array}{ll}
1 \quad (h \land p) \to t & \text{Premise} \\
2 \quad h & \text{Premise} \\
3 \quad \neg t & \text{Premise} \\
\hline
4 \quad \neg(h \land p) & \text{Modus tollens (1, 3)} \\
5 \quad \neg h \lor \neg p & \text{De Morgan's law (4)} \\
6 \quad \neg(\neg h) & \text{Law of double negation (2)} \\
7 \quad \neg p & \text{Disjunctive syllogism (5, 6)}
\end{array}
$$

Note: The derivation in the solution above shows us that the logical argument is valid. However, notice that the statement we derived is **false**. After all, cats **do** purr. So, although the logical argument is valid, it is **not** sound (see Note 4 following Example 9.10). This means that one of the premises must be false. Which one is it? Well cats do hiss and dogs cannot talk. So, the false statement must be "If cats hiss and purr, then dogs can talk." If it's not clear to you that this statement is false, use the law of the conditional to rewrite it as "Neither cats hiss nor purr, or dogs can talk." Since cats do hiss and purr, the statement "Neither cats hiss nor purr" is false. Since dogs cannot talk, the statement "Dogs can talk" is also false. Therefore, the disjunction of those two statements is false.

Problem Set 9

Full solutions to these problems are available for free download here:

www.SATPrepGet800.com/STFBYKG

LEVEL 1

1. Let p, q, and r represent true statements. Compute the truth value of each of the following compound statements:

   (i) $(p \lor q) \lor r$

   (ii) $(p \lor q) \land \neg r$

   (iii) $\neg p \to (q \lor r)$

   (iv) $\neg (p \leftrightarrow \neg q) \land r$

   (v) $\neg [p \land (\neg q \to r)]$

   (vi) $\neg [(\neg p \lor \neg q) \leftrightarrow \neg r]$

   (vii) $p \to (q \to \neg r)$

   (viii) $\neg [\neg p \to (q \to \neg r)]$

2. Let ϕ be the following statement: $(p \land \neg q) \leftrightarrow \neg [p \lor (\neg r \to q)]$.

   (i)   The statement ϕ is abbreviated. Write ϕ in its unabbreviated form.

   (ii)   Write down all the substatements of ϕ in both abbreviated and unabbreviated form.

LEVEL 2

3. Consider the compound statement "You can have a cookie or ice cream." In English this would most likely mean that you can have one or the other but not both. The word "or" used here is generally called an "exclusive or" because it excludes the possibility of both. The disjunction is an "inclusive or." Using the symbol $\oplus$ for exclusive or, draw the truth table for this connective. Then using only the logical connectives $\neg$, $\land$, and $\lor$, produce a statement using the propositional variables p and q that has the same truth table as $p \oplus q$.

4. Verify all the logical equivalences in List 9.1 and all the rules of inference in List 9.2.

LEVEL 3

5. Let ϕ, ψ, and τ be statements. Prove each of the following:

   (i) $\phi \vdash \psi$ and $\psi \vdash \tau$ implies $\phi \vdash \tau$.

(ii) $\phi \vdash \psi$ if and only if $\phi \to \psi$ is a tautology.

6. Let p represent a true statement. Decide if this is enough information to determine the truth value of each of the following statements. If so, state that truth value.

   (i) $p \lor q$

   (ii) $p \to q$

   (iii) $\neg p \to \neg(q \lor \neg r)$

   (iv) $\neg(\neg p \land q) \leftrightarrow p$

   (v) $(p \leftrightarrow q) \leftrightarrow \neg p$

   (vi) $\neg[(\neg p \land \neg q) \leftrightarrow \neg r]$

   (vii) $[(p \land \neg p) \to p] \land (p \lor \neg p)$

   (viii) $r \to [\neg q \to (\neg p \to \neg r)]$

LEVEL 4

7. Determine if each of the following statements is a tautology, a contradiction, or neither.

   (i) $p \land p$

   (ii) $p \land \neg p$

   (iii) $(p \lor \neg p) \to (p \land \neg p)$

   (iv) $\neg(p \lor q) \leftrightarrow (\neg p \land \neg q)$

   (v) $p \to (\neg q \land r)$

   (vi) $(p \leftrightarrow q) \to (p \to q)$

8. Assume that the given compound statement is true. Determine the truth value of each propositional variable.

   (i) $p \land q$

   (ii) $\neg(p \to q)$

   (iii) $p \leftrightarrow [\neg(p \land q)]$

   (iv) $[p \land (q \lor r)] \land \neg r$

LEVEL 5

9. Simplify each statement.

   (i) $p \lor (p \land \neg p)$

(ii) $(p \land q) \lor \neg p$

(iii) $\neg p \rightarrow (\neg q \rightarrow p)$

(iv) $(p \land \neg q) \lor p$

(v) $[(q \land p) \lor q] \land [(q \lor p) \land p]$

10. Determine whether each of the following logical arguments is valid or invalid. If the argument is valid, provide a deduction. If the argument is invalid, provide a counterexample.

(i)
$$\frac{\begin{array}{c} p \lor q \\ q \end{array}}{p}$$

(ii)
$$\frac{\begin{array}{c} \neg(p \land q) \\ q \end{array}}{\neg p}$$

(iii)
$$\frac{\begin{array}{c} \neg p \\ p \lor r \\ q \rightarrow \neg r \end{array}}{\neg q}$$

(iv)
$$\frac{\begin{array}{c} p \rightarrow q \\ r \rightarrow \neg q \end{array}}{p \rightarrow r}$$

(v)   If a piano has 88 keys, then the box is empty.
       If a piano does not have 88 keys, then paintings are white.
       If we are in immediate danger, then the box is not empty.
       Therefore, paintings are white or we are not in immediate danger.

(vi)   Tangs have fangs or tings have wings.
       It is not the case that tangs have fangs and tings do not have wings.
       It is not the case that tangs do not have fangs and tings have wings.
       Therefore, tangs have fangs and either tings have wings or tangs do not have fangs.

CHALLENGE PROBLEMS

11. Without drawing a truth table, show that $[p \land (q \lor r)] \leftrightarrow [(p \land q) \lor (p \land r)]$ is always true.

12. Without drawing a truth table, show that $\big[[(p \land q) \rightarrow r] \rightarrow s\big] \rightarrow [(p \rightarrow r) \rightarrow s]$ is always true.

13. Let Σ be a set of statements and let ϕ be a statement such that Σ tautologically implies ϕ. Prove that there is a finite subset Σ' of Σ such that Σ' tautologically implies ϕ.

LESSON 10
FIRST-ORDER LOGIC

Quantifiers

There are two "quantifiers" that appear repeatedly in both informal and formal mathematics. The **universal quantifier**, written $\forall$, is pronounced "For all," "For every," or "For each." The **existential quantifier**, written $\exists$, is pronounced "For some," "For at least one," or "There exists."

Without adding any restrictions, the statements "For all" and "There exists" may seem way too general. When we say "For all," what exactly do we mean? Do we mean "For all people?" Do we mean "For all complex numbers?" To make this clear, we should always start off with a specific **universe** (or **domain of discourse**), U, that we have decided to work within.

Example 10.1:

1. Let $U = \{x \mid x \text{ is an animal}\}$ be the universe consisting of all animals. Let $C(x)$ represent the statement "x is a cat." Let a represent "Achilles" and let o represent "Odin." Then $C(a)$ represents "Achilles is a cat" and $C(o)$ represents "Odin is a cat." Assuming that Achilles and Odin are both cats, the statements $C(a)$ and $C(o)$ are both true.

   The statement $\forall x\big(C(x)\big)$ can be read "For all x, x is a cat." Since our universe consists of all animals, this reduces to "All animals are cats." Therefore, $\forall x\big(C(x)\big)$ is a false statement.

   Similarly, the statement $\exists x\big(C(x)\big)$ can be read "For some x, x is a cat," or "Some animals are cats." Therefore, $\exists x\big(C(x)\big)$ is a true statement.

2. Define U and $C(x)$ as in part 1 above, and also let $B(x)$ represent the statement "x has black fur." The statement $\forall x\big(C(x) \to B(x)\big)$ can be read "For all x, if x is a cat, then x has black fur." This can be said more simply as "All cats have black fur." Therefore, $\forall x\big(C(x) \to B(x)\big)$ is a false statement.

   The statement $\exists x\big(C(x) \land B(x)\big)$ can be read "There is an x such that x is a cat and x has black fur. This can be said more simply as "Some cats have black fur." Therefore, $\exists x\big(C(x) \land B(x)\big)$ is a true statement.

   Notice how our usage of the unary relation symbol C in the statements $\forall x\big(C(x) \to B(x)\big)$ and $\exists x\big(C(x) \land B(x)\big)$ allows us to simulate quantifying over "cats" instead of "animals." In other words, these statements would just be written $\forall x\big(B(x)\big)$ and $\exists x\big(B(x)\big)$, respectively, if the universe was "cats" instead of "animals." This is a neat little trick that allows us to "chop up" a universe in a way that we can quantify over pieces of the universe as needed.

3. Let $U = \mathbb{Z}$, the set of integers, and define $+$ and $<$ in the usual way. The statement $x + y < 0$ is neither true nor false. There are two ways we can modify this statement to give it a truth value. The first way is to substitute values from the universe in for x and y. For example, if we let $x = 3$ and $y = 7$, then we get the false statement $3 + 7 < 0$.

Another way to modify the statement is to turn the "free variables" x and y into "bound variables" by introducing quantifiers. For example, the statement $\forall x \forall y(x + y < 0)$ is false. Indeed, we just provided a counterexample a moment ago by setting $x = 3$ and $y = 7$. As another example, the statement $\forall x \exists y(x + y < 0)$ is true. Indeed, given x, let $y = -x - 1$. Then $x + y = x + (-x - 1) = -1$ and $-1 < 0$. What about the statement $\exists y \forall x(x + y < 0)$? Given y, the value $x = -y$ provides a counterexample, showing that this statement is false.

The statements $\forall x \exists y(x + y < 0)$ and $\exists y \forall x(x + y < 0)$ prove that universal quantifiers **do not** commute with existential quantifiers. In other words, in general, the statements $\forall x \exists y\big(P(x, y)\big)$ and $\exists y \forall x\big(P(x, y)\big)$ are **not** logically equivalent.

4. Let $U = \{0, 1\}$ and define $\cdot$ (multiplication) in the usual way. The statement $\forall x(x \cdot x = x)$ is true in this universe. After all, $0 \cdot 0 = 0$ and $1 \cdot 1 = 1$. In this case, the statement $\forall x(x \cdot x = x)$ is logically equivalent to $0 \cdot 0 = 0 \wedge 1 \cdot 1 = 1$.

    More generally, if $U = \{a_1, a_2, \ldots, a_n\}$ is a finite set, then the statement $\forall x\big(P(x)\big)$ is logically equivalent to $P(a_1) \wedge P(a_2) \wedge \cdots \wedge P(a_n)$. Similarly, the statement $\exists x\big(P(x)\big)$ is logically equivalent to $P(a_1) \vee P(a_2) \vee \cdots \vee P(a_n)$.

    In the case where U is an infinite set, a universal quantifier can be thought of as an infinitary conjunction and an existential quantifier can be thought of as an infinitary disjunction. These quantifiers give us a neat little way to talk about all elements of a structure simultaneously even if that structure is infinite.

$\neg \forall x\big(P(x)\big)$ is logically equivalent to $\exists x\big(\neg P(x)\big)$. In other words, when we pass a negation symbol through a universal quantifier, the quantifier changes to an existential quantifier. Symbolically, we can write $\neg \forall x\big(P(x)\big) \equiv \exists x\big(\neg P(x)\big)$, where as usual $\equiv$ is pronounced "is logically equivalent to."

Similarly, $\neg \exists x\big(P(x)\big) \equiv \forall x\big(\neg P(x)\big)$.

Example 10.2:

1. As in part 1 of Example 10.1, let $U = \{x \mid x \text{ is an animal}\}$ and let $C(x)$ represent the statement "x is a cat." Recall that the false statement $\forall x\big(C(x)\big)$ can be read as "All animals are cats." The negation of this statement is the true statement $\neg \forall x\big(C(x)\big)$, which can be read "It is not the case that all animals are cats." By the above remarks, if we simultaneously pass the negation symbol through the universal quantifier and change the universal quantifier to an existential quantifier, we get the logically equivalent statement $\exists x\big(\neg C(x)\big)$, which can be read "Some animals are not cats."

    To summarize the above paragraph, $\neg \forall x\big(C(x)\big) \equiv \exists x\big(\neg C(x)\big)$. In words, "It is not the case that all animals are cats" is logically equivalent to "Some animals are not cats."

    Similarly, the negation of the statement $\exists x\big(C(x)\big)$ is $\neg \exists x\big(C(x)\big)$, which is logically equivalent to $\forall x\big(\neg C(x)\big)$. In words, "It is not the case that there is a cat" is logically equivalent to "Every animal is not a cat." This can be stated a little nicer in English as "No animal is a cat."

2. As in part 2 of Example 10.1, let $B(x)$ represent the statement "x has black fur." Recall that the statement $\forall x\big(C(x) \to B(x)\big)$ can be read "All cats have black fur." The negation of this statement is $\neg\forall x\big(C(x) \to B(x)\big)$, which is logically equivalent to $\exists x\left(\neg\big(C(x) \to B(x)\big)\right)$. Now, by part 2 of Example 9.7 from Lesson 9, $\neg\big(C(x) \to B(x)\big) \equiv C(x) \wedge \neg B(x)$. It follows that $\neg\forall x\big(C(x) \to B(x)\big) \equiv \exists x\big(C(x) \wedge \neg B(x)\big)$.

    Let's translate these last two statements into English. $\neg\forall x\big(C(x) \to B(x)\big)$ can be read "It is not the case that all cats have black fur." $\exists x\big(C(x) \wedge \neg B(x)\big)$ can be read "There is a cat that does not have black fur." Notice that both these statements are true and in fact, they have the same meaning in English.

    Similarly, the negation of the statement $\exists x\big(C(x) \wedge B(x)\big)$ is $\neg\exists x\big(C(x) \wedge B(x)\big)$, which is logically equivalent to $\forall x\left(\neg\big(C(x) \wedge B(x)\big)\right)$. Now, by De Morgan's law from List 9.1 in Lesson 9, we have $\neg\big(C(x) \wedge B(x)\big) \equiv \neg C(x) \vee \neg B(x)$. By the law of the conditional from the same list (and the law of double negation), we have $\neg C(x) \vee \neg B(x) \equiv C(x) \to \neg B(x)$. It follows that $\neg\exists x\big(C(x) \wedge B(x)\big) \equiv \forall x\big(C(x) \to \neg B(x)\big)$.

    Let's translate these last two statements into English. $\neg\exists x\big(C(x) \wedge B(x)\big)$ can be read "It is not the case that some cats have black fur." $\forall x\big(C(x) \to \neg B(x)\big)$ can be read "Every cat does not have black fur." Notice that both these statements are false and in fact, they have the same meaning in English. Also note that "Every cat does not have black fur" can be stated a little nicer in English as "No cat has black fur."

3. As in part 3 of Example 10.1, let $U = \mathbb{Z}$ and define $+$ and $<$ in the usual way. We have the following sequence of logical equivalences:

    $$\neg\forall x\forall y(x + y < 0) \equiv \exists x\big(\neg\forall y(x + y < 0)\big) \equiv \exists x\exists y\big(\neg(x + y < 0)\big) \equiv \exists x\exists y(x + y \geq 0).$$

    So, the negation of the statement "For all integers x and y, $x + y$ is negative" is logically equivalent to the statement "There exist integers x and y such that $x + y$ is nonnegative." Notice that the first statement is false, while the second statement is true.

    Similarly, $\neg\forall x\exists y(x + y < 0) \equiv \exists x\forall y(x + y \geq 0)$. So, the negation of the statement "For every integer x, there is an integer y such that $x + y$ is negative" is logically equivalent to the statement "There is an integer x such that for every integer y, $x + y$ is nonnegative." Notice that the first statement is true, while the second statement is false.

Languages and Formulas

A **language** is a collection of symbols. There are up to three different kinds of symbols in any language: **relation symbols**, **function symbols**, and **constant symbols**. Each relation and function symbol is n-ary for some $n \in \mathbb{Z}^+$. Note that there are no 0-ary relation or function symbols, although we could choose to consider constant symbols as 0-ary function symbols.

Example 10.3:

1. The language of set theory, $\mathcal{L} = \{\in\}$, consists of a single binary (or 2-ary) relation symbol $\in$.

2. The language of partial orders, $\mathcal{L} = \{\leq\}$, also consists of a single binary relation symbol.

3. The language of groups, $\mathcal{L} = \{\star, e\}$ consists of a binary function symbol $\star$ and a constant symbol e. We will see the definition of a group in Example 10.22 below.

4. The language of rings, $\mathcal{L} = \{+, \cdot, 0, 1\}$ consists of two binary function symbols $+$ and $\cdot$ and two constant symbols 0 and 1. We will see the definition of a ring in Example 10.22 below.

5. The language of ordered rings, $\mathcal{L} = \{+, \cdot, <, 0, 1\}$ consists of two binary function symbols $+$ and $\cdot$, a binary relation symbol $<$, and two constant symbols 0 and 1.

6. The language of number theory, $\mathcal{L} = \{+, \cdot, S, <, 0\}$ consists of two binary function symbols $+$ and $\cdot$, a unary function symbol S, a binary relation symbol $<$, and a constant symbol 0.

To define a formula, we will need some additional symbols. Specifically, we will need left and right parentheses, symbols for the logical connectives "and," "or," "if...then," "if and only if," and "not," symbols for the quantifiers "for all" and "there exists," an equality symbol, and infinitely many variable symbols. We let $\mathcal{S} = \{(,), \wedge, \vee, \rightarrow, \leftrightarrow, \neg, \forall, \exists, =, v_0, v_1, v_2, \dots\}$.

Note: Given a language $\mathcal{L}$, we will always assume that all the symbols in $\mathcal{L} \cup \mathcal{S}$ are distinct. Note that $\mathcal{L}$ has only relation, function, and constant symbols, whereas $\mathcal{S}$ has all the other symbols that may appear in formulas: parentheses, connectives, quantifiers, equality, and variables. Some authors leave the symbols $\vee, \rightarrow, \leftrightarrow$, and $\exists$ out of the set $\mathcal{S}$. This doesn't change much because any formula that uses these symbols is logically equivalent to a formula without these symbols. For example, by De Morgan's law, $p \vee q \equiv \neg p \wedge \neg q$ and by our discussion on quantifiers above, $\exists x(P(x)) \equiv \neg \forall x(\neg P(x))$.

An **expression** in the language $\mathcal{L}$ is a finite string of symbols from $\mathcal{L} \cup \mathcal{S}$. In other words, we form an expression by writing down symbols from $\mathcal{L} \cup \mathcal{S}$ one after the other.

The **length** of the expression is the number of symbols in the expression.

If an expression E has length $n \in \mathbb{Z}^+$, then an **initial segment** of the expression E is an expression D consisting of the first k symbols of E for some positive integer $k \leq n$. If $k < n$, then D is a **proper initial segment** of E.

Example 10.4:

1. $\wedge \neg (\leftrightarrow v_3 \in \in \exists == $ is an expression in the language of set theory of length 10. This particular expression is meaningless.

   There are 9 proper initial segments of this expression. For example, $\wedge$ is a proper initial segment of length 1, while $\wedge \neg (\leftrightarrow v_3$ is a proper initial segment of length 5.

   A more meaningful expression in the language of set theory is $\left(\forall v_0(v_0 \in v_1) \wedge \left(\neg(v_1 = v_5)\right)\right)$. However, it should be noted that this expression is an abbreviation for the expression $\left(\forall v_0(\in (v_0 v_1)) \wedge \left(\neg(= (v_1 v_5))\right)\right)$. This expression has length 22. Therefore, there are 21 proper initial segments of this expression. Write down a few of the proper initial segments and see if you notice that they are all meaningless.

2. $00 + 1 + \cdot = +11 + (v_0 v_1 \forall$ is an expression in the language of rings of length 15. This expression is also meaningless.

A more meaningful expression in the language of rings is $\left(\forall v_0\left((v_0 \cdot 1 = v_0) \wedge (1 \cdot v_0 = v_0)\right)\right)$. See if you can write down the unabbreviated form of this expression (see Example 10.5 below).

Notice that if we randomly write down a string of symbols, we will probably wind up with a meaningless expression. Our first goal is to isolate the expressions that are meaningful.

The set of **terms**, $\mathcal{T}$, is the smallest set of expressions (strings of symbols) such that (i) for each $n \in \mathbb{N}$, each variable symbol v_n is a term, (ii) each constant symbol $c \in \mathcal{L}$ is a term, and (iii) for each $n \in \mathbb{Z}^+$, if $f \in \mathcal{L}$ is an n-ary function symbol and $t_1, t_2, \ldots, t_n$ are terms, then $\left(f(t_1 t_2 \cdots t_n)\right)$ is a term.

Example 10.5:

1. Since the language of set theory has no constant or function symbols, the only terms are the variables $v_0, v_1, v_2, \ldots$ Note that all the variables are terms no matter what language we use.

2. In addition to the variables, some terms from the language of groups are e, $(\star (ee))$, $(\star (\star (ee)e))$, $\left(\star \left(e \star (ee)\right)\right)$, and $\left(\star \left(\star \left(v_0 \star (v_1 e)\right)v_5\right)\right)$

    Some of these terms are a bit hard to read. We may want to use some standard abbreviations for easier readability. We will always remove the outermost pair of parentheses. For example, we can abbreviate $(\star (ee))$ as $\star (ee)$. Furthermore, we abbreviate $\star (ee)$ as $e \star e$. We abbreviate $\star (\star (ee)e)$ as $(e \star e) \star e$. We abbreviate $\star \left(e \star (ee)\right)$ as $e \star (e \star e)$. Finally, we abbreviate $\star \left(\star \left(v_0 \star (v_1 e)\right)v_5\right)$ as $\left(v_0 \star (v_1 \star e)\right) \star v_5$.

3. Some terms from the language of number theory (with outermost parentheses removed) are
    $$0, S(0), S\big(S(0)\big), +\big(0\ S(0)\big), \cdot (v_0\ 0), \text{ and } +\left(\cdot \left(S\big(S(S(0))\big) + \big(v_3\ S(0)\big)\right) + (S(0)\ 0)\right).$$

    Thinking of S as the "successor" function, we may want to abbreviate $S(0)$ as 1, $S\big(S(0)\big)$ as 2, and so on. So, an abbreviation for $+\big(0\ S(0)\big)$ is $0 + 1$. An abbreviation for $\cdot (v_0\ 0)$ is $v_0 \cdot 0$. An abbreviation for $+\left(\cdot \left(S\big(S(S(0))\big) + \big(v_3\ S(0)\big)\right) + (S(0)\ 0)\right)$ is $\big(3 \cdot (v_3 + 1)\big) + (1 + 0)$.

    Using the standard order of operations that says multiplication is performed before addition, we can abbreviate this last term further as $3 \cdot (v_3 + 1) + (1 + 0)$.

Note: When we write terms, we will generally write the abbreviated versions for easier readability. However, it is important to understand that when we are proving theorems about terms, we are thinking of them in their unabbreviated form. For example, $e \star e$ is **not** a term, as the function symbol $\star$ requires two symbols to appear to the right of it in parentheses. $e \star e$ is merely an abbreviation for the term $\star (ee)$, which in turn is an abbreviation for $(\star (ee))$.

We can prove that all terms have a certain property by using "induction on terms." We first prove that all variable symbols and constant symbols have the desired property. Then, for each n-ary function symbol f, assuming that the terms $t_1, t_2, \ldots, t_n$ have the desired property, we show that $\left(f(t_1 t_2 \cdots t_n)\right)$ has the desired property.

As an example of this principle, let's prove a simple theorem.

Theorem 10.1: Every term has the same number of left and right parentheses.

Proof: Each variable and constant symbol has 0 left parentheses and 0 right parentheses. Let f be an n-ary function symbol and assume that the terms t_1, t_2,...,t_n each have the same number of left and right parentheses, say for each $k = 1, 2, ..., n$, t_k has x_k left parentheses and x_k right parentheses. Then $\left(f(t_1 t_2 \cdots t_n) \right)$ has $x_1 + x_2 + \cdots + x_n + 2$ left parentheses and $x_1 + x_2 + \cdots + x_n + 2$ right parentheses. By the principle of induction on terms, every term has the same number of left and right parentheses. □

Example 10.6: Remember that a term is just a string of symbols. For example, in the language of number theory, the expression $\left(3 \cdot (v_3 + 1) \right) + (1 + 0)$ is an abbreviation for the term $\left(+ \left(\cdot \left(S \left(S(S(0)) \right) + (v_3 \, S(0)) \right) + (S(0) \, 0) \right) \right)$. Observe that this term has 10 left parentheses and 10 right parentheses. By Theorem 10.1, no matter what language we are in and no matter what term we write down using symbols from that language, there will always be the same number of left and right parentheses in that term. Also, notice that every proper initial segment of this term has more left parentheses than right parentheses. This is a general fact about proper initial segments of terms, as we now prove.

Theorem 10.2: Every proper initial segment of a term has more left parentheses than right parentheses.

Proof: Variable and constant symbols have no proper initial segments and so for them, the statement is vacuously true. Let f be an n-ary function symbol and assume that the given statement is true for the terms t_1, t_2,...,t_n. A proper initial segment of $\left(f(t_1 t_2 \cdots t_n) \right)$ has one of the following forms:

$$($$
$$(f$$
$$(f($$
$$(f(s_1, \text{ where } s_1 \text{ is a proper initial segment of } t_1$$
$$(f(t_1$$
$$(f(t_1 t_2 \cdots s_k, \text{ where } s_k \text{ is a proper initial segment of } t_k$$
$$(f(t_1 t_2 \cdots t_k$$
$$(f(t_1 t_2 \cdots t_n)$$

It is easy to check that each of these expressions has more left than right parentheses. For example, (has 1 left parenthesis and 0 right parentheses. As another example, if s_1 has i left parentheses and j right parentheses, then by the inductive assumption, $i > j$. It follows that $(f(s_1$ has $i + 2$ left parentheses and j right parentheses, and $i + 2 > i > j$. I leave it to the reader to check the other six cases. By the principle of induction on terms, every proper initial segment of a term has more left parentheses than right parentheses. □

We now show that each term can be created in exactly one way.

Theorem 10.3 (Unique Readability for Terms): For each term t, exactly one of the following holds: (i) $t = v_n$ for some $n \in \mathbb{N}$; (ii) $t = c$ for some constant symbol $c \in \mathcal{L}$; (iii) there is exactly one $n \in \mathbb{Z}^+$ and one sequence $f, t_1, t_2, \dots t_n$, where $f \in \mathcal{L}$ and $t_1, t_2, \dots t_n \in \mathcal{T}$ such that $t = \big(f(t_1 t_2 \cdots t_n)\big)$.

Proof: The expressions v_n, c, and $\big(f(t_1 t_2 \cdots t_n)\big)$ are all distinct because they disagree in the first symbol. Suppose t can be written as both $\big(f(t_1 t_2 \cdots t_n)\big)$ and $\big(g(u_1 u_2 \cdots u_n)\big)$. Since the second symbols must agree, we have $f = g$ (as symbols). Deleting the first three symbols from each expression, we now have $t_1 t_2 \cdots t_n)) = u_1 u_2 \cdots u_n))$. Suppose toward contradiction that there is a positive integer k such that $t_k \neq u_k$. Let j be the least such positive integer. Then, as sequences of symbols, t_j is a proper initial segment of u_j or u_j is a proper initial segment of t_j. Without loss of generality, assume that t_j is a proper initial segment of u_j. Since u_j is a term, by Theorem 10.2 t_j has more left parentheses than right parentheses, contradicting Theorem 10.1 (because t_j is a term). It follows that for each $k \leq n$, we have $t_k = u_k$. Therefore, $\big(f(t_1 t_2 \cdots t_n)\big)$ and $\big(g(u_1 u_2 \cdots u_n)\big)$ are the same string of symbols. $\qquad\square$

An **atomic formula** is an expression of the form $\big(R(t_1 t_2 \cdots t_n)\big)$, where R is an n-ary relation symbol and $t_1, t_2, \dots, t_n$ are terms.

Notes: (1) We will often abbreviate an atomic formula of the form $\big(R(t_1 t_2)\big)$ as $t_1 R t_2$. In particular, for the equality relation, we abbreviate $\big(= (t_1 t_2)\big)$ as $t_1 = t_2$.

(2) We will abbreviate an arbitrary atomic formula by removing the outermost parentheses. So, we abbreviate $\big(R(t_1 t_2 \cdots t_n)\big)$ as $R(t_1 t_2 \cdots t_n)$.

Example 10.7:

1. In the language of set theory, there are just two kinds of atomic formulas: $x = y$ and $x \in y$, where x and y are arbitrary variable symbols (each of x and y are one of the variables $v_0, v_1, \dots$). As usual, it is important to realize that these are abbreviations for $\big(= (xy)\big)$ and $\big(\in (xy)\big)$.

2. In the language of groups, the only relation symbol is $=$. So, all atomic formulas have the form $t_1 = t_2$, or in unabbreviated form, $\big(= (t_1 t_2)\big)$. For example, the following are (abbreviated) atomic formulas: $e = e$, $e = v_0$, $e \star v_1 = (v_0 \star e) \star v_1$, and $\big(v_0 \star (v_1 \star e)\big) \star v_5 = e \star (e \star e)$. The unabbreviated version of the atomic formula $e = e$ is $\big(= (ee)\big)$. The unabbreviated version of the atomic formula $e \star v_1 = (v_0 \star e) \star v_1$ is $\Big(= \big((\star (ev_1))(\star (\star (v_0 e)v_1))\big)\Big)$. I leave it as an exercise for the reader to write the unabbreviated version of $\big(v_0 \star (v_1 \star e)\big) \star v_5 = e \star (e \star e)$.

3. In the language of number theory, there are two kinds of atomic formulas: $t_1 = t_2$ and $t_1 < t_2$, where t_1 and t_2 are arbitrary terms. For example, $0 \cdot v_2 < v_2 \cdot v_2$ is the abbreviated version of $\Big(< \big((\cdot (0 \, v_2)) (\cdot (v_2 \, v_2))\big)\Big)$.

The set of **formulas**, $\mathcal{F}$, is the smallest set of expressions such that (i) every atomic formula is a formula, (ii) if ϕ is a formula, then $(\neg\phi)$ is a formula, (iii) if ϕ and ψ are formulas, then $(\phi \wedge \psi)$, $(\phi \vee \psi)$, $(\phi \rightarrow \psi)$, and $(\phi \leftrightarrow \psi)$ are formulas, and (iv) if ϕ is a formula and x is a variable, then $(\forall x \phi)$ and $(\exists x \phi)$ are formulas.

Notes: (1) We will abbreviate an arbitrary formula by removing the outermost parentheses. For example, we abbreviate $(\phi \wedge \psi)$ as $\phi \wedge \psi$. As another example, we abbreviate $(\forall x\phi)$ as $\forall x\phi$.

(2) Recall that we can abbreviate $\big(= (v_0v_1)\big)$ as $(v_0 = v_1)$ or $v_0 = v_1$. Therefore, we can abbreviate $\Big(\neg\big(= (v_0v_1)\big)\Big)$ as $\neg(v_0 = v_1)$ or $\neg v_0 = v_1$. We abbreviate this further as $v_0 \neq v_1$. We will also follow this convention for other binary relation symbols. For example, $v_1 \notin v_2$ is an abbreviation for $\Big(\neg\big(\in (v_1v_2)\big)\Big)$.

(3) We will usually abbreviate $(\forall x\phi)$ as $\forall x\phi$ and $(\exists x\phi)$ as $\exists x\phi$ regardless of where they appear in a formula. For example, we abbreviate $x = y \wedge \big(\forall z(x = z)\big)$ as $x = y \wedge \forall z(x = z)$. As another example, we abbreviate $\forall x\Big(\exists y\big(\forall z(x = z \wedge y \neq x)\big)\Big)$ as $\forall x \exists y \forall z(x = z \wedge y \neq x)$.

(4) We may use letters such as $x, y, z, w, \ldots$ to represent variables. It is understood that each of these letters represents one of the variables $v_0, v_1, v_2, \ldots$ Also, in this lesson, the letters s, t, and u will always represent general terms (these terms may or may not be variables).

Example 10.8: In the language of set theory, we have the following abbreviated formula:

$$\forall x \left(\exists z(\mathbf{z \in x}) \wedge \left(\neg \forall y \big(\mathbf{y \in x} \wedge \neg \forall w(\mathbf{w \in y} \wedge \mathbf{w \notin x}) \big) \right) \right)$$

The atomic formulas and negations of atomic formulas are in boldface to make the formula easier to read.

Theorem 10.4 (Unique Readability for Formulas): For each formula ϕ, exactly one of the following holds: (i) ϕ is an atomic formula; (ii) there is a unique formula ψ such that $\phi = (\neg\psi)$; (iii) there is a unique string $s = \psi C\theta$, where ψ and θ are formulas, C is one of the connectives $\wedge$, $\vee$, $\rightarrow$, or $\leftrightarrow$, and $\phi = (s)$; (iv) there is a unique string $s = Qx\psi$, where ψ is a formula, x is a variable, Q is one of the quantifiers $\forall$ or $\exists$, and $\phi = (s)$.

The proof of this theorem uses "induction on formulas" and is similar to the proof of Theorem 10.3, and so, we leave it as an exercise for the reader (see Problem 11 below).

Each occurrence of a variable in a formula can be **free** or **bound**. Bound variables are in the **scope** of a quantifier. So, if a formula has no quantifiers, then all occurrences of variables in the formula are free. If a formula has quantifiers, then we will need to check carefully if each occurrence of each variable is free or bound. We will give a more rigorous definition of free and bound variables in a moment. Let's look at an example first.

Example 10.9: The following formulas are in the language of set theory.

1. In the formula $\forall v_5(v_5 \in v_0)$, v_0 is free and v_5 is bound (because v_5 is in the scope of $\forall v_5$).

2. In the formula $\exists v_0 \forall v_5(v_5 \in v_0)$, both v_0 and v_5 are bound (because v_0 is in the scope of $\exists v_0$ and v_5 is in the scope of $\forall v_5$). There are no free variables.

3. In the formula $\forall v_5(v_5 \in v_0) \wedge \exists v_0(v_0 \in v_5)$, the first occurrence of v_0 is free and the second occurrence of v_0 is bound. Also, the first occurrence of v_5 is bound and the second occurrence of v_5 is free.

We now **formally** define what it means for a variable x to occur **free** in a formula ϕ.

(1) If ϕ is an atomic formula, then x occurs free in ϕ if and only if x is a symbol of ϕ.

(2) If $\phi = \neg\psi$, then x occurs free in ϕ if and only if x occurs free in ψ.

(3) If ϕ is $\psi \wedge \tau$, $\psi \vee \tau$, $\psi \rightarrow \tau$, or $\psi \leftrightarrow \tau$, then x occurs free in ϕ if and only if x occurs free in either ψ or τ (or both).

(4) x occurs free in $\forall y\phi$ if and only if x occurs free in ϕ and $x \neq y$.

(5) x occurs free in $\exists y\phi$ if and only if x occurs free in ϕ and $x \neq y$.

A formula ϕ is a **sentence** if no variable occurs free in ϕ.

Example 10.10: The following formulas are in the language of ordered rings.

1. The formula $x \cdot 1 = x$ is atomic. Therefore, each occurrence of x is free.

2. The formula $x + (y \cdot z) = x \rightarrow y \cdot y = y$ has no quantifiers. Therefore, each occurrence of x, y, and z is free.

3. In the formula $\exists v_0(v_0 \cdot 1 < v_0)$, each occurrence of v_0 is **bound** by $\exists v_0$. This formula is a sentence.

4. In the formula $\exists y(x \cdot 1 < y)$, x is free. The variable y is bound by $\exists y$.

5. The formula $\forall v_3(v_3 < v_3 \leftrightarrow v_3 = v_3)$ is a sentence.

6. The formula $\forall v_1 \exists v_2\big(v_2 < v_1 \wedge \exists v_4(v_4 \not< v_2 \vee v_4 < v_1)\big)$ is a sentence.

7. The formula $\exists x(\forall y(x < y) \rightarrow x = y)$ is **not** a sentence. Although the first occurrence of y is bound by $\forall y$, the second occurrence of y is not. However, both occurrences of x are bound by $\exists x$.

Logical Equivalence and Tautologies

We would now like to extend the ideas of propositional logic (Lesson 9) to first-order logic. Recall List 9.1, where we provided a collection of logical equivalences. Each of the laws given in this list can also be expressed as a statement that is always true. For example, the logical equivalence $p \equiv \neg(\neg p)$ can be expressed by saying that $p \leftrightarrow \neg(\neg p)$ is always true. As another example, the logical equivalence $p \vee \neg p \equiv T$ can be expressed by saying that $p \vee \neg p$ is always true. We can therefore consider $p \leftrightarrow \neg(\neg p)$ and $p \vee \neg p$ to be **logical axioms**. Using the terminology from Lesson 9, we can consider every **tautology** to be a logical axiom.

In propositional logic, we can determine if statements are logical axioms (or tautologies) simply by looking at their truth tables. In first-order logic, we will not always have this luxury due to the existence of quantifiers.

However, we can find **some** logical axioms in a similar way. For example, by replacing p by the formula $\forall x\forall y(x = y)$ in the statement $p \vee \neg p$, we get $\forall x\forall y(x = y) \vee \neg\forall x\forall y(x = y)$. Therefore, we will consider the statement $\forall x\forall y(x = y) \vee \neg\forall x\forall y(x = y)$ to be a logical axiom. In fact, we will say the same about $\phi \vee \neg\phi$ for any formula ϕ.

We will also want to add two new laws to our list of logical equivalences. These are the **generalized De Morgan's laws**, which tell us how to pass a negation symbol through a quantifier.

Let's make all this precise.

The **prime formulas** are the atomic formulas and the formulas of the form $\forall x \phi$ and $\exists x \phi$. All other formulas are **not prime**. A formula that is not prime has one of the forms $\neg \phi$, $\phi \wedge \psi$, $\phi \vee \psi$, $\phi \to \psi$, or $\phi \leftrightarrow \psi$.

Example 10.11:

1. In the language of set theory, the following formulas are prime: $x \in y$, $z = z$, $\forall y(y = z)$, $\exists v_5(v_5 \notin v_2)$, $\forall v_3(v_3 = v_2 \wedge (\exists v_1(v_1 \notin v_3) \to v_7 = v_7))$.

   The following formulas are **not** prime: $x \notin y$, $z \neq z$, $\neg \forall y(y = z)$, $y = y \leftrightarrow y \in y$.

   Remember that $x \notin y$ is an abbreviation for $\neg x \in y$, and similarly, $z \neq z$ is an abbreviation for $\neg z = z$.

2. In the language of number theory, the following formulas are prime: $y + 0 < 2$, $S(x) = 0$, $\exists v_3(1 \not< v_3 \wedge (v_2 = v_2 \cdot v_2 \to v_5 + v_2 \cdot v_0 < 2))$.

   Remember that 1 is an abbreviation for $S(0)$ and 2 is an abbreviation for $S(S(0))$.

3. If ϕ and ψ are formulas and x is a variable, then $\forall x(\phi \wedge \psi)$ is prime and $\forall x \phi \wedge \psi$ is not prime.

Recall that in propositional logic (see Lesson 9), statements are built up from the propositional variables $p, q, r, \ldots$ by applying the connectives $\neg$, $\wedge$, $\vee$, $\to$, and $\leftrightarrow$. Also recall (as mentioned above) that a tautology is a statement that is true for every possible truth assignment of the propositional variables.

In first-order logic, we define a **tautology** to be a tautology of propositional logic where the propositional variables are replaced by the prime formulas.

Example 10.12:

1. In propositional logic, the statement $(p \to q) \leftrightarrow (\neg q \to \neg p)$ is a tautology. Let's use the language of groups. If we replace p by the prime formula $\forall x(x \star y = e)$ and q by the prime formula $\exists x(x = x)$, we get the following tautology:

$$\big(\forall x(x \star y = e) \to \exists x(x = x)\big) \leftrightarrow \big(\neg \exists x(x = x) \to \neg \forall x(x \star y = e)\big)$$

   The tautology $(p \to q) \leftrightarrow (\neg q \to \neg p)$ is known as the **law of the contrapositive**. We can also write this law in the form of the logical equivalence $(p \to q) \equiv (\neg q \to \neg p)$. For this example, this gives us the following:

$$\big(\forall x(x \star y = e) \to \exists x(x = x)\big) \equiv \big(\neg \exists x(x = x) \to \neg \forall x(x \star y = e)\big)$$

2. $\forall x(x = x)$ is **not** a tautology, as a prime formula can **never** be considered a tautology. Similarly, in the language of number theory, the formula $\forall z(0 < z \to 0 < z)$ is **not** a tautology because it is prime. We can *assign* the truth value F to a prime formula.

We will see shortly that both these formulas **are** always valid, as they should be (clearly, they should always be considered true). They just **cannot** be considered tautologies.

3. $\forall x(x + y = y) \rightarrow (x + y = y)$ is **not** a tautology. Assigning truth values of T to the prime formula $\forall x(x + y = y)$ and F to the prime formula $x + y = y$ results in a truth value of F.

    Once again, we will see shortly that this formula is always valid. It is just **not** a tautology.

4. By the **law of substitution of logical equivalents** from Lesson 9, if we replace the propositional variables in a tautology from propositional logic by **any** first-order formula, we get a tautology.

    For example, since $p \vee \neg p$ is a tautology in propositional logic, the following formula in the language of number theory is a tautology:

$$(\exists x \forall y(x < y) \rightarrow x = y) \vee \neg(\exists x \forall y(x < y) \rightarrow x = y)$$

Every tautology gives us at least one **rule of inference**.

Example 10.13: Recall from Example 9.11 in Lesson 9 that in propositional logic the first De Morgan's law gives us the following two rules of inference.

$$\frac{\neg(p \wedge q)}{\neg p \vee \neg q} \qquad\qquad \frac{\neg p \vee \neg q}{\neg(p \wedge q)}$$

If we replace p by the formula $\forall x \exists y(x \neq y)$ and q by the formula $\exists y(y \in y)$, we get the following two rules of inference in first-order logic.

$$\frac{\neg\big(\forall x \exists y(x \neq y) \wedge \exists y(y \in y)\big)}{\neg \forall x \exists y(x \neq y) \vee \neg \exists y(y \in y)} \qquad\qquad \frac{\neg \forall x \exists y(x \neq y) \vee \neg \exists y(y \in y)}{\neg\big(\forall x \exists y(x \neq y) \wedge \exists y(y \in y)\big)}$$

Notes: (1) Each rule of inference can also be expressed as a tautology (in both propositional logic and first-order logic). For example, the first two rules of inference in propositional logic above can be expressed as the tautologies $\neg(p \wedge q) \rightarrow (\neg p \vee \neg q)$ and $(\neg p \vee \neg q) \rightarrow \neg(p \wedge q)$. So, each of these statements would be considered a logical axiom.

(2) We can combine the two tautologies from Note 1 into the single tautology $\neg(p \wedge q) \leftrightarrow (\neg p \vee \neg q)$. The tautologies in Note 1 can easily be derived from this one, and so, there is really no need to include all these as logical axioms. However, since decreasing the number of logical axioms only makes it more tedious to prove theorems, we will not try to reduce the number of logical axioms in this book.

(3) Similar to what was discussed in Notes 1 and 2, the second pair of rules of inference above (expressed using first-order logic) leads to several tautologies. For example, the following tautology would be considered a logical axiom:

$$\neg\big(\forall x \exists y(x \neq y) \wedge \exists y(y \in y)\big) \leftrightarrow \big(\neg \forall x \exists y(x \neq y) \vee \neg \exists y(y \in y)\big)$$

(4) Some authors begin with a collection of logical axioms, other authors begin with a collection of rules of inference, and most authors begin with some mixture of the two. All these methods lead to the same set of **theorems**. Theorems are the formulas that are derivable from the logical axioms using the rules of inference. Therefore, as stated in Note 2, we will take the approach of taking as many logical axioms as we like (for example, **all** tautologies) and as many rules of inference as we like.

(5) As an example of Note 4, suppose we choose the statement $\neg(p \wedge q) \leftrightarrow (\neg p \vee \neg q)$ to be a logical axiom and we choose Biconditional Elimination to be a rule of inference (see List 9.2 in Lesson 9). Assuming that $(\neg p \wedge \neg q) \rightarrow \neg(p \vee q)$ is **not** being considered a logical axiom, then it will still be a theorem. In fact, here is a derivation:

$$
\begin{array}{r|ll}
1 & \neg(p \wedge q) \leftrightarrow (\neg p \vee \neg q) & \text{Logical Axiom} \\
2 & \neg(p \wedge q) \rightarrow (\neg p \vee \neg q) & \text{Biconditional Elimination (1)}
\end{array}
$$

Observe how in the derivation above that there are no formulas above the line. In other words, there are no premises being given here. Logical axioms can be used freely and will generally be written below the line.

The derivation above shows that although $\neg(p \wedge q) \rightarrow (\neg p \vee \neg q)$ is not being considered a logical axiom, it is still a theorem, and therefore, it can always be used in any derivation. The only difference is the length of the derivation. Here I prefer to take the approach of allowing lots of logical axioms and lots of rules of inference.

We now add one additional entry to list 9.1.

13. **Generalized De Morgan's laws:** $\neg\forall x\phi \equiv \exists x(\neg\phi)$ $\qquad\qquad$ $\neg\exists x\phi \equiv \forall x(\neg\phi)$

Equivalently, we consider the formulas $\neg\forall x\phi \leftrightarrow \exists x(\neg\phi)$ and $\neg\exists x\phi \leftrightarrow \forall x(\neg\phi)$ to be logical axioms.

Here is the complete list (renamed as List 10.1) with propositional variables replaced by prime (or arbitrary) formulas.

List 10.1:

1. **Law of double negation:** $\phi \equiv \neg(\neg\phi)$

2. **De Morgan's laws:** $\quad\neg(\phi \wedge \psi) \equiv \neg\phi \vee \neg\psi$ $\qquad\qquad$ $\neg(\phi \vee \psi) \equiv \neg\phi \wedge \neg\psi$

3. **Commutative laws:** $\quad\phi \wedge \psi \equiv \psi \wedge \phi$ $\qquad\qquad$ $\phi \vee \psi \equiv \psi \vee \phi$

4. **Associative laws:** $\quad(\phi \wedge \psi) \wedge \tau \equiv \phi \wedge (\psi \wedge \tau)$ $\qquad$ $(\phi \vee \psi) \vee \tau \equiv \phi \vee (\psi \vee \tau)$

5. **Distributive laws:** $\quad\phi \wedge (\psi \vee \tau) \equiv (\phi \wedge \psi) \vee (\phi \wedge \tau)$ $\quad$ $\phi \vee (\psi \wedge \tau) \equiv (\phi \vee \psi) \wedge (\phi \vee \tau)$

6. **Identity laws:** $\quad\phi \wedge T \equiv \phi$ $\qquad$ $\phi \wedge F \equiv F$ $\qquad$ $\phi \vee T \equiv T$ $\qquad$ $\phi \vee F \equiv \phi$

7. **Negation laws:** $\quad\phi \wedge \neg\phi \equiv F$ $\qquad\qquad$ $\phi \vee \neg\phi \equiv T$

8. **Redundancy laws:** $\quad\phi \wedge \phi \equiv \phi$ $\qquad\qquad$ $\phi \vee \phi \equiv \phi$

9. **Absorption laws:** $\quad(\phi \vee \psi) \wedge \phi \equiv \phi$ $\qquad\qquad$ $(\phi \wedge \psi) \vee \phi \equiv \phi$

10. **Law of the conditional:** $\qquad\phi \rightarrow \psi \equiv \neg\phi \vee \psi$

11. **Law of the contrapositive:** $\qquad\phi \rightarrow \psi \equiv \neg\psi \rightarrow \neg\phi$

12. **Law of the biconditional:** $\qquad\phi \leftrightarrow \psi \equiv (\phi \rightarrow \psi) \wedge (\psi \rightarrow \phi)$

13. **Generalized De Morgan's laws:** $\neg\forall x\phi \equiv \exists x(\neg\phi)$ $\qquad\qquad$ $\neg\exists x\phi \equiv \forall x(\neg\phi)$

Substitution

List 9.2 in Lesson 9 gave us a collection of rules of inference for propositional logic. By using prime formulas as sentence symbols, each of those rules is a rule of inference in first-order logic as well.

With the introduction of quantifiers, we will need to introduce some additional rules. For example, if ϕ is any formula and c is a constant symbol, then the following should be a rule of inference:

$$\frac{\forall x \phi(x)}{\phi(c)}$$

More generally, given a formula ϕ, suppose we take **any** structure (as defined below) of the language under consideration and we substitute any elements from that structure for the free variables of the formula. If the result is **always** true, then there should be a derivation of ϕ even if no premises are given.

Given a formula ϕ, a variable x, and a term t, we define ϕ_t^x by replacing each free occurrence of x in ϕ by the term t. We will make this definition more precise shortly.

It might seem like a good idea to make each instance of the following a rule of inference.

$$\frac{\forall x \phi}{\phi_t^x}$$

After all, if the formula ϕ is true for all x, then shouldn't it also be true if we replace x by an arbitrary term t? We will see in Example 10.15 below (part 4) that we will need to be a bit careful about how we answer this question.

Let s and t be terms and let x be a variable. Then s_t^x is defined as follows:

1. If s is a variable, then $s_t^x = \begin{cases} s & \text{if } s \neq x. \\ t & \text{if } s = x. \end{cases}$

2. If s is a constant symbol, then $s_t^x = s$.

3. If s is $F(s_1 s_2 \cdots s_n)$, then $s_t^x = F((s_1)_t^x (s_2)_t^x \ldots (s_n)_t^x)$ (here F is a function symbol and $s_1, s_2, \ldots, s_n$ are terms).

In other words, we get s_t^x by replacing each occurrence of the variable x in s with the term t.

Example 10.14: The following are in the language of number theory. Let x, y, and z be distinct variable symbols.

1. $x_y^x = y$, $x_0^x = 0$, $x_0^y = x$, and $x_{2 \cdot y}^x = 2 \cdot y$ (recall that 2 is an abbreviation for $S(S(0))$).

2. $0_y^x = 0$. In fact, $0_t^x = 0$ for any term t.

3. $x \cdot (y + z)_0^x = 0 \cdot (y + z)$, $x \cdot (y + z)_1^y = x \cdot (1 + z)$, and $x \cdot (y + z)_{x+y}^z = x \cdot (y + (x + y))$.

Let ϕ be a formula, x a variable, and t a term. Then ϕ_t^x is defined as follows:

1. If ϕ is $R(s_1 s_2 \cdots s_n)$, where $s_1, s_2, \ldots, s_n$ are terms, then $\phi_t^x = R((s_1)_t^x (s_2)_t^x \ldots (s_n)_t^x)$.

2. $(\neg \phi)_t^x = \neg \phi_t^x$.

3. $(\phi \wedge \psi)_t^x = \phi_t^x \wedge \psi_t^x, (\phi \vee \psi)_t^x = \phi_t^x \vee \psi_t^x, (\phi \to \psi)_t^x = \phi_t^x \to \psi_t^x, (\phi \leftrightarrow \psi)_t^x = \phi_t^x \leftrightarrow \psi_t^x$.

4. $(\forall y \phi)_t^x = \begin{cases} \forall y\, \phi & \text{if } x = y \\ \forall y \phi_t^x & \text{if } x \neq y \end{cases}$ and $(\exists y \phi)_t^x = \begin{cases} \exists y \phi & \text{if } x = y. \\ \exists y \phi_t^x & \text{if } x \neq y. \end{cases}$

In other words, we get ϕ_t^x by replacing each occurrence of the variable x in ϕ with the term t unless x is in the scope of $\forall x$ or $\exists x$.

Example 10.15: The following are in the language of number theory. Let x, y, and z be distinct variable symbols.

1. $\phi_x^x = \phi$ for all formulas ϕ.

2. $\left(x \cdot 0 = 0 \to \forall x (x \cdot 0 = 0) \right)_y^x = \left(y \cdot 0 = 0 \to \forall x\, (x \cdot 0 = 0) \right)$. Note how we substituted y for the first occurrence of x, but not the second. The first occurrence of x is free, whereas the second occurrence is bound.

3. $\left(x \cdot y = z \to \forall x (x \cdot y = z) \right)_y^x = \left(y \cdot y = z \to \forall x\, (x \cdot y = z) \right)$. Once again, observe how we substituted y for the first occurrence of x, but not the second.

4. If ϕ is $\exists y(x \neq y)$, then $\forall x \phi$ is $\forall x \exists y(x \neq y)$ and ϕ_z^x is $\exists y(z \neq y)$. It seems reasonable that the following should be a rule of inference:

$$\frac{\forall x \exists y(x \neq y)}{\exists y(z \neq y)}$$

In other words, in this case, ϕ_z^x should be derivable from $\forall x \phi$.

What about ϕ_y^x? Should $\exists y(y \neq y)$ be derivable from $\forall x \exists y(x \neq y)$?

This does **not** seem like a reasonable derivation. The sentence $\forall x \exists y(x \neq y)$ can be interpreted as "there are at least two elements," while the sentence $\exists y(y \neq y)$ can be interpreted as "there is an element not equal to itself." In this case, we should **not** get a rule of inference.

The problem is that when we replaced x by y in $\exists y(x \neq y)$, the new y was "captured" by $\exists y$. It seems that if there is a variable y in a term t that is "captured" by $\forall y$ or $\exists y$ in ϕ_t^x, then the formula ϕ_t^x should **not** be derivable from $\forall x \phi$.

Let x be a variable and let t be a term. Then "t is **substitutable** for x in ϕ" is defined as follows:

1. If ϕ is an atomic formula, then t is substitutable for x in ϕ.

2. t is substitutable for x in $\neg \phi$ if and only if t is substitutable for x in ϕ.

3. t is substitutable for x in $\phi \wedge \psi$ (as well as $\phi \vee \psi$, $\phi \to \psi$, and $\phi \leftrightarrow \psi$) if and only if t is substitutable for x in ϕ and ψ.

4. t is substitutable for x in $\forall y \phi$ (as well as $\exists y \phi$) if and only if either (i) x does not occur free in $\forall y \phi$ (**trivial substitution**), or (ii) y does not occur in t and t is substitutable for x in ϕ.

Example 10.16: The following are in the language of rings. Let x, y, z, and w be distinct variable symbols.

1. y is substitutable for x in the formula $x + (y \cdot z) = x \rightarrow y \cdot y = y$. In fact, any term t is substitutable for each of the variables x, y, or z in this formula. This follows simply because the formula has no quantifiers.

   More generally, if ϕ is a quantifier free formula in any language, then any term t is substitutable for any variable x in ϕ.

2. The term $z \cdot z$ is substitutable for x in $\forall x(x + y = z)$ because x does not occur free in $\forall x(x + y = z)$.

   More generally, any term t is substitutable for x in $\forall x(x + y = z)$ for the same reason.

   This is really a trivial case because nothing changes here when the substitution is actually made. In other words, $\left(\forall x(x + y = z) \right)_t^x$ is just $\forall x(x + y = z)$.

3. The term $z \cdot (w + z)$ is substitutable for x in $\exists y(x \neq y)$ because y does not appear in the term $z \cdot (w + z)$ and $z \cdot (w + z)$ is substitutable for x in $x \neq y$ (it's quantifier free).

   More generally, if t contains no variables which occur in ϕ, then t is substitutable for x in ϕ.

4. A variable x is substitutable for itself in any formula.

For each formula ϕ, each variable x, and each term t such that t is substitutable for x in ϕ, we make the following a rule of inference.

$$\frac{\forall x \phi}{\phi_t^x}$$

Alternatively, we can take $\forall x \phi \rightarrow \phi_t^x$ as a logical axiom whenever t is substitutable for x in ϕ.

Validity in First-order Logic

Just like in propositional logic, a **logical argument** or **proof** consists of **premises** (formulas that we are given) and **conclusions** (formulas we are not given). A logical argument is **valid** if there is a sequence of formulas (called a **derivation** or **deduction**) such that each formula in the sequence is a premise or a conclusion that follows from the premises and conclusions above it using a rule of inference. In addition to tautologies and the rules of inference given in List 9.2, we will be allowed to use the following additional logical axioms and rules of inference involving quantifiers.

List 10.2: Here is a list of our chosen **logical axioms** that **do not** come from tautologies. Note that each member of this list consists of infinitely many formulas, each of which is a logical axiom.

(1) **(Substitution Axioms)** $\forall x \phi \rightarrow \phi_t^x$, where t is substitutable for x in ϕ

(2) **(Universal Derivation Axioms)** $\forall x(\phi \rightarrow \psi) \rightarrow (\phi \rightarrow \forall x \psi)$

(3) **(Universal Generalization Axioms)** $\phi \rightarrow \forall x \phi$, where x does not occur free in ϕ

(4) **(Equality Axioms)** $x = x$

(5) **(Variable Exchange Axioms)** $x = y \rightarrow (\phi \rightarrow \overline{\phi})$, where ϕ is an atomic formula and $\overline{\phi}$ is obtained from ϕ by replacing x in 0 or more places by y.

For any logical axiom Φ, the generalization $\forall x \Phi$ will also be considered a logical axiom.

List 10.3: Here is a list of rules of inference involving quantifiers. (The rules of inference that do not involve quantifiers are given in List 9.2.)

Universal Elimination

$$\frac{\forall x \phi}{\phi_t^x}$$

where t is substitutable for x in ϕ.

Existential Elimination

$$\frac{\exists x \phi}{\phi_c^x}$$

where c is a constant symbol that has not yet occurred in the derivation.

Universal Generalization

$$\frac{\phi}{\forall x \phi}$$

where x does not occur free in ϕ.

Existential Generalization

$$\frac{\phi(t)}{\exists x \phi(x)}$$

where x is any variable that does not occur free in ϕ and t is substitutable for x in $\phi(x)$.

Example 10.17: Let's give a derivation of the following logical argument in the language $\mathcal{L} = \{B, C, a\}$, where B and C are unary relation symbols and a is a constant symbol.

$$\forall x \big(C(x) \to B(x) \big)$$
$$\frac{\forall x \big(C(x) \big)}{B(a)}$$

Solution:

1	$\forall x \big(C(x) \to B(x) \big)$	Premise
2	$\forall x \big(C(x) \big)$	Premise
3	$C(a) \to B(a)$	Universal elimination (1)
4	$C(a)$	Universal elimination (2)
5	$B(a)$	Modus ponens (3, 4)

Note: As an alternative to using universal elimination, we can use the substitution axiom instead. The derivation would then look as follows:

1	$\forall x \big(C(x) \to B(x) \big)$	Premise
2	$\forall x \big(C(x) \big)$	Premise
3	$\forall x \big(C(x) \to B(x) \big) \to \big(C(a) \to B(a) \big)$	Substitution axiom
4	$C(a) \to B(a)$	Modus ponens (3, 1)
5	$\forall x \big(C(x) \big) \to C(a)$	Substitution axiom
6	$C(a)$	Modus ponens (5, 2)
7	$B(a)$	Modus ponens (4, 6)

Example 10.18: Let's give a derivation of the following logical argument in the language of number theory $\mathcal{L} = \{+, \cdot, S, <, 0\}$. (Recall that 1 is an abbreviation for $S(0)$ and 2 is an abbreviation for $S(S(0))$.)

$$\forall x\big(\exists y(x < y) \to \forall y(x < y)\big)$$
$$\frac{1 < 2}{1 < 0}$$

Solution:

1	$\forall x\big(\exists y(x < y) \to \forall y(x < y)\big)$	Premise
2	$1 < 2$	Premise
3	$\exists y(1 < y) \to \forall y(1 < y)$	Universal elimination (1)
4	$\exists y(1 < y)$	Existential generalization (2)
5	$\forall y(1 < y)$	Modus ponens (3, 4)
6	$1 < 0$	Universal elimination (5)

Note: At this point, we have not given any interpretation to the symbols in the language. For example, the symbol $<$ is just an arbitrary binary relation symbol.

Example 10.19: Let's give a derivation of the following logical argument in the language $\mathcal{L} = \{\equiv, a, b\}$, where $\equiv$ is a binary relation symbol and a and b are constant symbols

$$\forall x\big(\forall y(x \equiv y) \to \neg\forall y(y \equiv x)\big)$$
$$\frac{\exists x \forall y(x \equiv y)}{\exists x \exists y(x \not\equiv y)}$$

Solution:

1	$\forall x\big(\forall y(x \equiv y) \to \neg\forall y(y \equiv x)\big)$	Premise
2	$\exists x \forall y(x \equiv y)$	Premise
3	$\forall y(a \equiv y)$	Existential elimination (2)
4	$\forall y(a \equiv y) \to \neg\forall y(y \equiv a)$	Universal elimination (1)
5	$\neg\forall y(y \equiv a)$	Modus ponens (4, 3)
6	$\exists y(y \not\equiv a)$	Generalized De Morgan's law (5)
7	$b \not\equiv a$	Existential elimination (6)
8	$\exists y(b \not\equiv y)$	Existential generalization (7)
9	$\exists x \exists y(x \not\equiv y)$	Existential generalization (8)

If ϕ is a formula and Γ is a set of formulas, we write $\Gamma \vdash \phi$ if there is a derivation of ϕ from Γ. Here we are thinking of Γ as the set of premises and ϕ as the desired conclusion.

A set of formulas Γ is **inconsistent** if there is a formula ϕ such that $\Gamma \vdash \phi$ and $\Gamma \vdash \neg\phi$. Equivalently, Γ is inconsistent if for every formula ψ, $\Gamma \vdash \psi$ (see Problem 7 (part (iii)) below). Otherwise, Γ is **consistent**.

Model Theory

Recall from Lesson 4 that an **n-ary relation** on a set S is a subset of S^n. We usually use the expressions **unary**, **binary**, and **ternary** in place of 1-ary, 2-ary, and 3-ary. Note that a unary relation on S is simply a subset of S. We do not define a 0-ary relation.

Example 10.20: Let $\mathbb{Z} = \{\dots, -3, -2, -1, 0, 1, 2, 3, \dots\}$ be the set of integers. The set $\mathbb{N} = \{0, 1, 2, 3, \dots\}$ of natural numbers is a unary relation on $\mathbb{Z}$. In other words, $\mathbb{N} \subseteq \mathbb{Z}$. Some examples of binary relations on $\mathbb{Z}$ are the linear orderings $<, \leq, >$, and $\geq$ (see Example 4.5 (part 2)) and the equivalence relations $\equiv_n = \{(a, b) \in \mathbb{Z}^2 \mid n|b - a\}$ (see Example 5.1 (part 4)). $R = \{(x, y, z) \in \mathbb{Z}^3 \mid x + y = z\}$ is an example of a ternary relation on $\mathbb{Z}$ (see Example 4.8 (part (2)).

An **n-ary operation** on a set S is a function from S^n to S. We also define a 0-ary operation to simply be an element of S. We will usually call a 0-ary operation a **constant** in S (here we define S^0 to be $\{0\}$ and we identify an operation $f: \{0\} \to S$ with the element $f(0) \in S$).

Example 10.21: Let $\mathbb{R}$ be the set of real numbers. Negation is an example of a unary operation on $\mathbb{R}$. This is the operation that maps each $x \in \mathbb{R}$ to $-x$. Addition, subtraction, and multiplication are examples of binary operations on $\mathbb{R}$. 0 is an example of a 0-ary operation on $\mathbb{R}$ or a constant in $\mathbb{R}$.

A **finitary relation** is an n-ary relation for some $n \in \mathbb{N}^*$. A **finitary operation** is an n-ary operation for some $n \in \mathbb{N}$.

A **structure** or **model** is a set together with a collection of finitary relations and operations defined on the set. More specifically, we have the following:

If $\mathcal{L} = \{R_i, F_j, c_k \mid i \in I, j \in J, k \in K\}$ is a language consisting of relation symbols R_i for each $i \in I$, function symbols F_j for each $j \in J$, and constant symbols c_k for each $k \in K$, then an **$\mathcal{L}$-structure** (or **$\mathcal{L}$-model**) has the form $\mathfrak{A} = \left(A, R_i^{\mathfrak{A}}, F_j^{\mathfrak{A}}, c_k^{\mathfrak{A}}\right)_{i \in I, j \in J, k \in K}$, where A is a **nonempty** set (called the **domain** or **universe** of the structure), for each $i \in I$, $R_i^{\mathfrak{A}}$ is an n_i-ary relation on A, where n_i is the arity of the symbol R_i, for each $j \in J$, $F_j^{\mathfrak{A}}: A^{m_j} \to A$, where m_j is the arity of the function symbol F_j, and for each $k \in K$, $c_k^{\mathfrak{A}}$ is an element of A.

The **cardinality** of a model is simply the cardinality of the domain of the model. For example, when we refer to a countable model $\mathfrak{A}$, what we mean is that the domain A is countable.

Notes: (1) It's worth emphasizing that we will always assume that the domain of a model is nonempty. This assumption is necessary for many theorems in model theory to be true.

(2) A finitary operation on a set S is a function $f: S^n \to S$ for some $n \in \mathbb{N}$. There are two important facts implied by this definition:

1. The operation f is defined for every n-tuple $(a_1, a_2, \dots, a_n) \in S^n$.
2. The set S is closed under f.

(3) A finitary relation on a set S is a subset R of S^n for some $n \in \mathbb{N}$. We have more flexibility with relations than we do with operations. For example, an $(n + 1)$-ary relation can be used to define a *partial* n-ary function. Suppose we want a structure that consists of the set of integers $\mathbb{Z}$ together with the partial function defined on only the even integers that divides each even integer by 2. We can define a relation $R = \{(2k, k) \mid k \in \mathbb{Z}\}$. The structure $(\mathbb{Z}, R)$ consists of the set of integers together with the function $f: 2\mathbb{Z} \to \mathbb{Z}$ defined by $f(n) = \frac{n}{2}$ ($2\mathbb{Z}$ is the set of even integers). Notice that we defined the *unary* partial function f on $\mathbb{Z}$ by using the *binary* relation R.

Example 10.22:

1. A **monoid** is a structure of the form $(M, \star)$, where M is a set, $\star$ is an associative binary operation on M, and there is an identity $e \in M$ with respect to the operation $\star$. In Lesson 8, we proved that $(\mathbb{N}, +)$ is a commutative monoid with identity 0. $(\mathbb{Z}, +)$, $(\mathbb{Q}, +)$, and $(\mathbb{R}, +)$ are also commutative monoids with identity 0. $(\mathbb{N}, \cdot)$, $(\mathbb{Z}, \cdot)$, $(\mathbb{Q}, \cdot)$, and $(\mathbb{R}, \cdot)$ are commutative monoids with identity 1. The dedicated reader may want to prove these results using the formal definitions of $\mathbb{N}$, $\mathbb{Z}$, $\mathbb{Q}$, and $\mathbb{R}$ (see Lessons 5 and 6 for these definitions). In Lesson 15, we will prove some of these results and leave others as exercises.

   We may sometimes want to view a monoid as a structure of the form $(M, \star, e)$, where e is a constant representing the identity element of the monoid.

2. A **group** is a monoid $(G, \star)$ such that $\forall x \exists y (xy = e \land yx = e)$ (every element $x \in G$ has an **inverse** $y \in G$). If $y \in G$ is the inverse of $x \in G$, we write $y = x^{-1}$. Note that $(\mathbb{N}, +)$ is **not** a group because nonzero natural numbers do not have additive inverses. On the other hand, $(\mathbb{Z}, +)$, $(\mathbb{Q}, +)$, and $(\mathbb{R}, +)$ are commutative groups with identity 0. $(\mathbb{Q} \setminus \{0\}, \cdot)$, and $(\mathbb{R} \setminus \{0\}, \cdot)$ are commutative groups with identity 1. Once again, the dedicated reader may want to prove these results using the formal definitions of $\mathbb{Z}$, $\mathbb{Q}$, and $\mathbb{R}$ (see Lesson 15 for some details).

   We may sometimes want to view a group as a structure of the form $(G, \star, e)$ or $(G, \star, {}^{-1}, e)$, where e is the identity element of the group and $^{-1}$ is the unary inverse operator.

3. A **ring** is a structure of the form $(R, +, \cdot)$, where R is a set, $(R, +)$ is a commutative group, $(R, \cdot)$ is a monoid, and multiplication is both left and right distributive over addition in R. If multiplication is commutative, then we call $(R, +, \cdot)$ a **commutative ring**. $(\mathbb{Z}, +, \cdot)$, $(\mathbb{Q}, +, \cdot)$, and $(\mathbb{R}, +, \cdot)$ are examples of commutative rings (see Lesson 15 for details).

   Again, we may want to include additional operations. For example, we may want to view a ring as a structure of the form $(R, +, \cdot, -, 1)$, where $-$ is the unary additive inverse operator and 1 is the multiplicative identity of R.

4. A **field** is a ring $(F, +, \cdot)$ such that $(F \setminus \{0\}, \cdot)$ is a commutative group and $0 \neq 1$ (the additive and multiplicative identities are distinct). $(\mathbb{Q}, +, \cdot)$, and $(\mathbb{R}, +, \cdot)$ are examples of fields.

5. An **ordered ring** is a structure of the form $(R, +, \cdot, \leq)$, where $(R, +, \cdot)$ is a ring, and $\leq$ is a linear ordering on R that is compatible with $+$ and $\cdot$ (see Lesson 15 for details). $(\mathbb{Z}, +, \cdot, \leq)$ is an example of an ordered commutative ring. $(\mathbb{Q}, +, \cdot, \leq)$, and $(\mathbb{R}, +, \cdot, \leq)$ are examples of ordered fields (once again, see Lesson 15 for details).

6. Every set without any operations and relations is a structure. For example, $\mathbb{N}$, $\mathbb{Z}$, $\mathbb{Q}$, $\mathbb{R}$, and $\mathbb{C}$ are structures. (Notice that we abbreviate the structure (S) as S.)

We will use a fraktur letter (such as $\mathfrak{A}$, $\mathfrak{B}$, $\mathfrak{C}$) for the name of a structure if we want to be clear that we are talking about the whole structure and not just the underlying set. For example, we might write $\mathfrak{G} = (G, \star)$ for a group $\mathfrak{G}$ with underlying set G and group operation $\star$.

The language $\mathcal{L}$ is called the **type** of an $\mathcal{L}$-structure. Two structures have the same type if they are both $\mathcal{L}$-structures for some language $\mathcal{L}$.

Example 10.23:

1. $(\mathbb{Q}, \leq)$, $(\mathcal{P}(\mathbb{N}), \subseteq)$, and for each $n \in \mathbb{N}^*$, $(\mathbb{Z}, \equiv_n)$ all have the same type because they each have exactly one binary relation.

2. $(\mathbb{Z}, +)$ and $(\mathbb{Z}, +, 0)$ have different types. The first structure has one binary operation and nothing else. The second structure has a binary operation and a constant (or a 0-ary operation). Both of these are different ways of describing the group of integers under addition. The second way is specifically mentioning the identity element, while the first is not. Another structure (of yet another type) that describes the same group is $(\mathbb{Z}, +, -, 0)$, where $-$ is the unary additive inverse operator.

We would now like to define what it means for a first-order sentence to be true in a model. Since some sentences have quantifiers, accomplishing this task is a bit more tedious than one might first expect. We will need to make several preliminary definitions first and we will need to be careful that the definition we come up with is well-defined.

We begin with the following two conventions. Unless otherwise specified, we will always assume the following:

- $t(v_0, v_1, \ldots, v_k)$ represents a term whose variables form a subset of $\{v_0, v_1, \ldots, v_k\}$.

- $\phi(v_0, v_1, \ldots, v_k)$ represents a formula whose *free* variables form a subset of $\{v_0, v_1, \ldots, v_k\}$.

Example 10.24:

1. The variable v_1 can be represented by $t(v_0, v_1)$. It can also be represented by $t(v_0, v_1, v_2)$, by $t(v_0, v_1, v_2, v_3)$, and so on.

2. If c is a constant symbol, then t can be represented by $t(v_0)$, $t(v_0, v_1)$, $t(v_0, v_1, v_2)$, etc.

3. In the language of rings, the term $(v_0 + v_1) \cdot v_3$ can be represented by $t(v_0, v_1, v_2, v_3)$, $t(v_0, v_1, v_2, v_3, v_4)$, etc.

4. In the language of set theory, the atomic formula $v_0 \in v_1$ can be represented by $\phi(v_0, v_1)$. It can also be represented by $\phi(v_0, v_1, v_2)$, $\phi(v_0, v_1, v_2, v_3)$, etc.

5. Also in the language of set theory, the formula $\forall v_1 (v_0 \in v_1)$ can be represented by $\phi(v_0)$. Note that v_1 does not need to be included in the notation because v_1 is not free in $\forall v_1 (v_0 \in v_1)$. However, this formula certainly *could* be represented by $\phi(v_0, v_1)$ if we choose to do so.

Let $\mathfrak{A}$ be a structure with domain A, let $x_0, x_1, \ldots, x_m \in A$ and let $k \leq m$. The **value of a term** $t(v_0, v_1, \ldots, v_k)$ at $x_0, x_1, \ldots, x_m$, written $t[x_0, x_1, \ldots, x_m]$, is defined as follows:

1. If t is a variable, say $t = v_i$, then $t[x_0, x_1, \ldots, x_m] = x_i$.

2. If t is a constant symbol, say $t = c$, then $t[x_0, x_1, \ldots, x_m] = c^{\mathfrak{A}}$.

3. If $t = F(t_1 t_2 \cdots t_n)$, where F is an n-placed function symbol, then

$$t[x_0, x_1, \ldots, x_m] = F^{\mathfrak{A}}(t_1[x_0, x_1, \ldots, x_m], t_2[x_0, x_1, \ldots, x_m], \ldots, t_n[x_0, x_1, \ldots, x_m]).$$

Example 10.25:

1. Consider the group $(\mathbb{Z}, +, 0)$. Some elements of $\mathbb{Z}$ are $0, 1, 2, -1$, and -2, and 0 is the identity element for the group. As examples of 1, $v_0[0, 1, 2, -1, -2] = 0$, $v_1[0, 1, 2, -1, -2] = 1$, and similarly for v_2, v_3, and v_4. As examples of 2, $0[0, 1, 2, -1, -2] = 0$, $0[2, -1, -2] = 0$, and $0[1] = 0$. As examples of 3, $(v_0 + v_1)[2, -1] = v_0[2, -1] + v_1[2, -1] = 2 + (-1) = 1$, $(v_1 + 0)[-2, 1, 2] = v_1[-2, 1, 2] + 0[-2, 1, 2] = 1 + 0 = 1$. As one more example of 3, we have $\big((v_0 + v_1) + v_2\big)[0, 1, 2, -1, -2] = (0 + 1) + 2 = 1 + 2 = 3$.

2. Consider the ordered field $(\mathbb{R}, +, \cdot, \leq, 0, 1)$. Some elements of $\mathbb{R}$ are $0, 1, 5, \sqrt{2}$, and $\frac{1}{\sqrt{2}}$. The additive identity element is 0 and the multiplicative identity element is 1. As examples of 1, $v_0[\sqrt{2}, 1, 5] = \sqrt{2}$ and $v_3\left[\frac{1}{\sqrt{2}}, 1, \sqrt{2}, 5\right] = 5$. As examples of 2, $0[\sqrt{2}] = 0$, $1[\sqrt{2}] = 1$, and $0[1, 0, \sqrt{2}] = 0$. As examples of 3, $(v_0 \cdot v_1)\left[\sqrt{2}, \frac{1}{\sqrt{2}}\right] = \sqrt{2} \cdot \frac{1}{\sqrt{2}} = 1$, $(1 \cdot v_1)[\sqrt{2}, 5] = 1 \cdot 5 = 5$, and $(v_1 \cdot (v_1 + v_2) + 1)\left[\frac{1}{\sqrt{2}}, 1, \sqrt{2}, 5\right] = 1 \cdot (1 + \sqrt{2}) + 1 = (1 + \sqrt{2}) + 1 = 2 + \sqrt{2}$.

Note: In part 1 of Example 10.25, we saw that $v_0[0, 1, 2, -1, -2] = 0$. The numbers $1, 2, -1$, and -2 are irrelevant for this computation. The value of $v_0[0, 1, 2, -1, -2]$ depends only on the first input, namely 0. For example, $v_0[0] = 0$ as well (and we also have $v_0[0, 1] = 0$, and so on). In general, the definition of the value of a term allows us to evaluate terms at sequences of arbitrarily long length. However, the value of the term depends only on the variables that appear in the term. This will be stated formally and proved in Theorem 10.5 below.

Let $\phi(v_0, v_1, \ldots, v_k)$ be a formula whose *free and bound* variables form a subset of $\{v_0, v_1, \ldots, v_k\}$ and let $k \leq m$. We define "$\mathfrak{A}$ **satisfies** $\phi(v_0, v_1, \ldots, v_k)$ at $x_0, x_1, \ldots, x_m \in A$," written $\mathfrak{A} \vDash \phi[x_0, x_1, \ldots, x_m]$, as follows:

1. If $\phi(v_0, v_1, \ldots, v_k)$ is the atomic formula $R(t_1 t_2 \cdots t_n)$, where R is an n-placed relation symbol and $t_1, t_2, \ldots, t_n$ are terms, then

   $\mathfrak{A} \vDash \phi[x_0, x_1, \ldots, x_m]$ if and only if $R^{\mathfrak{A}}(t_1[x_0, x_1, \ldots, x_m], t_2[x_0, x_1, \ldots, x_m], \ldots, t_n[x_0, x_1, \ldots, x_m])$

2. If ϕ is $\neg \psi$, then $\mathfrak{A} \vDash \phi[x_0, x_1, \ldots, x_m]$ if and only if $\mathfrak{A} \nvDash \psi[x_0, x_1, \ldots, x_m]$.

3. If ϕ is $\psi \wedge \tau$, then $\mathfrak{A} \vDash \phi[x_0, x_1, \ldots, x_m]$ if and only if $\mathfrak{A} \vDash \psi[x_0, x_1, \ldots, x_m]$ and $\mathfrak{A} \vDash \tau[x_0, x_1, \ldots, x_m]$.

4. If ϕ is $\psi \vee \tau$, then $\mathfrak{A} \vDash \phi[x_0, x_1, \ldots, x_m]$ if and only if $\mathfrak{A} \vDash \psi[x_0, x_1, \ldots, x_m]$ or $\mathfrak{A} \vDash \tau[x_0, x_1, \ldots, x_m]$.

5. If ϕ is $\psi \to \tau$, then $\mathfrak{A} \vDash \phi[x_0, x_1, \ldots, x_m]$ if and only if $\mathfrak{A} \vDash \psi[x_0, x_1, \ldots, x_m]$ implies that $\mathfrak{A} \vDash \tau[x_0, x_1, \ldots, x_m]$.

6. If ϕ is $\psi \leftrightarrow \tau$, then $\mathfrak{A} \vDash \phi[x_0, x_1, \ldots, x_m]$ if and only if

$$\mathfrak{A} \vDash \psi[x_0, x_1, \ldots, x_m] \text{ if and only if } \mathfrak{A} \vDash \tau[x_0, x_1, \ldots, x_m].$$

7. If ϕ is $\forall v_i \psi$, then $\mathfrak{A} \vDash \phi[x_0, x_1, \ldots, x_m]$ if and only if for every $a \in A$, we have $\mathfrak{A} \vDash \psi[x_0, x_1, \ldots, x_{i-1}, a, x_{i+1}, \ldots, x_m]$.

8. If ϕ is $\exists v_i \psi$, then $\mathfrak{A} \vDash \phi[x_0, x_1, \ldots, x_m]$ if and only if there is an $a \in A$ such that $\mathfrak{A} \vDash \psi[x_0, x_1, \ldots, x_{i-1}, a, x_{i+1}, \ldots, x_m]$.

Example 10.26:

1. As in example 10.25, consider the group $\mathfrak{A} = (\mathbb{Z}, +, 0)$. $\mathfrak{A} \vDash (v_0 = v_1)[2, 2, 3]$ because $2 = 2$. $\mathfrak{A} \vDash (0 + v_1 = v_0 + v_2)[5, 4, -1]$ because $0 + 4 = 5 + (-1)$. $\mathfrak{A} \vDash \neg(v_0 + v_2 = v_1)[1, 2, 3]$ because $1 + 3 \neq 2$. $\mathfrak{A} \vDash \forall v_0 (v_0 + 0 = v_0)[1]$ because for all $n \in \mathbb{Z}$, $n + 0 = n$ (notice how the 1 is not used here because the variable v_0 is bound by $\forall$).

2. As in example 10.25, consider the ordered field $\mathfrak{B} = (\mathbb{R}, +, \cdot, \leq, 0, 1)$. $\mathfrak{B} \vDash (v_0 \leq v_1)[3, \pi]$ because $3 \leq \pi$. $\mathfrak{B} \vDash \left((v_2 = v_3 \cdot v_1) \wedge (1 \cdot v_1 + v_0 = v_2)\right)\left[-1, 3, 2, \frac{2}{3}\right]$ because $2 = \frac{2}{3} \cdot 3$ and $1 \cdot 3 + (-1) = 2$. $\mathfrak{A} \vDash \forall v_0 (v_0 \neq 0 \to \exists v_1 (v_0 \cdot v_1 = 1))[1, 2, 3]$ because for all nonzero $x \in \mathbb{R}$, there is $y \in \mathbb{R}$ such that $x \cdot y = 1$ (notice how the 1, 2, and 3 are not used here because the variables v_0 and v_1 are bound by $\forall$ and $\exists$, respectively, and v_2 does not appear in the formula).

Note: In part 1 of Example 10.26, we saw that $\mathfrak{A} \vDash (v_0 = v_1)[2, 2, 3]$. The number 3 is irrelevant for this computation. Determining that $\mathfrak{A} \vDash (v_0 = v_1)[2, 2, 3]$ depends only on the first two inputs. In fact, $\mathfrak{A} \vDash (v_0 = v_1)[2, 2]$ as well. In general, the definition of $\mathfrak{A} \vDash \phi[x_0, x_1, \ldots, x_m]$ allows us to check if $\mathfrak{A}$ satisfies $\phi[x_0, x_1, \ldots, x_m]$ at sequences $x_0, x_1, \ldots, x_m$ of arbitrarily long length. However, determining if the statement $\mathfrak{A} \vDash \phi[x_0, x_1, \ldots, x_m]$ is true depends only on the <u>free variables</u> that appear in the formula ϕ. This will be stated formally in Theorem 10.6 below.

Theorem 10.5: Let $t(v_0, v_1, \ldots, v_k)$ be a term and let $x_0, x_1, \ldots, x_m, y_0, y_1, \ldots, y_n \in A$ be such that $k \leq m$, $k \leq n$, and $x_i = y_i$ whenever v_i is a variable of t. Then $t[x_0, x_1, \ldots, x_m] = t[y_0, y_1, \ldots, y_n]$.

We will prove this Theorem by using the principle of induction on terms.

Proof: If $t(v_0, v_1, \ldots, v_k)$ is a variable v_i, then $t[x_0, x_1, \ldots, x_m] = x_i = y_i = t[y_0, y_1, \ldots, y_n]$. If $t(v_0, v_1, \ldots, v_k)$ is a constant symbol c, then $t[x_0, x_1, \ldots, x_m] = c^{\mathfrak{A}} = t[y_0, y_1, \ldots, y_n]$. Now, suppose that $t(v_0, v_1, \ldots, v_k)$ is $F(t_1 t_2 \cdots t_j)$, where F is a j-placed function symbol and the conclusion of the theorem holds for $t_1, t_2, \ldots, t_j$. Then

$$t[x_0, x_1, \ldots, x_m] = F^{\mathfrak{A}}\left(t_1[x_0, x_1, \ldots, x_m], t_2[x_0, x_1, \ldots, x_m], \ldots, t_j[x_0, x_1, \ldots, x_m]\right)$$
$$= F^{\mathfrak{A}}\left(t_1[y_0, y_1, \ldots, y_n], t_2[y_0, y_1, \ldots, y_n], \ldots, t_j[y_0, y_1, \ldots, y_n]\right) = t[y_0, y_1, \ldots, y_n]. \qquad \square$$

Theorem 10.6: Let $\phi(v_0, v_1, \ldots, v_k)$ be a formula all of whose free and bound variables are among $v_0, v_1, \ldots, v_k$, and let $x_0, x_1, \ldots, x_m, y_0, y_1, \ldots, y_n \in A$ be such that $k \leq m$, $k \leq n$, and $x_i = y_i$ whenever v_i is a free variable of ϕ. Then $\mathfrak{A} \vDash \phi[x_0, x_1, \ldots, x_m]$ if and only if $\mathfrak{A} \vDash \phi[y_0, y_1, \ldots, y_n]$.

Theorem 10.6 can be proved by using the principle of induction on formulas. The proof is similar to the proof of Theorem 10.5, and so, I leave it as an exercise for the reader.

Theorem 10.6 allows us to make the following definitions:

Let $\phi(v_0, v_1, \ldots, v_k)$ be a formula all of whose *free and bound* variables are among $v_0, v_1, \ldots, v_m$, where $k \leq m$, and let $x_0, x_1, \ldots, x_k \in A$. We write $\mathfrak{A} \vDash \phi[x_0, x_1, \ldots, x_k]$ (pronounced "ϕ is **satisfied** in $\mathfrak{A}$ by $x_0, x_1, \ldots, x_k$") if and only if $\mathfrak{A} \vDash \phi[x_0, x_1, \ldots, x_m]$ for every (or equivalently some) $x_{k+1}, \ldots, x_m \in A$.

Let ϕ be a sentence all of whose bound variables are among $v_0, v_1, \ldots, v_k$. Then $\mathfrak{A} \vDash \phi$ (pronounced "ϕ is **satisfied** in $\mathfrak{A}$," "$\mathfrak{A}$ **satisfies** ϕ," "$\mathfrak{A}$ is a **model** of ϕ," "$\mathfrak{A}$ **models** ϕ," or "ϕ **holds** in $\mathfrak{A}$") if and only if $\mathfrak{A} \vDash \phi[x_0, x_1, \ldots, x_k]$ for every (or equivalently some) $x_0, x_1, \ldots, x_k \in A$.

A **theory** is a set of sentences.

Example 10.27: Let $\mathcal{L} = \{<\}$. The theory of **dense linear orders without endpoints** (abbreviated as **DLO**) consists of the following sentences:

    (1) **(Transitivity)** $\forall x \forall y \forall z \big((x < y \wedge y < z) \rightarrow x < z \big)$

    (2) **(Antireflexivity)** $\forall x (x \not< x)$

    (3) **(Antisymmetry)** $\forall x \forall y \big((x < y \wedge y < x) \rightarrow x = y \big)$

    (4) **(Trichotomy)** $\forall x \forall y (x < y \vee x = y \vee y < x)$

    (5) **(Density)** $\forall x \forall y \big(x < y \rightarrow \exists z (x < z \wedge z < y) \big)$

    (6) **(No endpoints)** $\forall x \exists y \exists z (y < x \wedge x < z)$

$(\mathbb{Q}, <)$ is an example of a model of DLO. You will be asked to prove in Problem 13 below that $(\mathbb{Q}, <)$ is the only countable model of DLO, up to renaming the elements.

Recall that a set of formulas Γ is consistent if for every formula ϕ, we **do not** have both $\Gamma \vdash \phi$ and $\Gamma \vdash \neg \phi$. In the following important theorem, we will be concerned only with sets of sentences.

Theorem 10.7 (Extended Completeness Theorem): Let Σ be a theory. Then Σ is consistent if and only if Σ has a model.

The proof of Theorem 10.7 requires several steps and is quite long. We will therefore accept it as true for the purpose of this book.

The following theorem is an important consequence of the Extended Completeness Theorem.

Theorem 10.8 (Compactness Theorem): A theory Σ has a model if and only if every finite subset of Σ has a model.

Proof: If $\mathfrak{A}$ is a model of Σ, then $\mathfrak{A}$ is a model of every subset of Σ (and in particular, every *finite* subset of Σ). Conversely, suppose that every finite subset of Σ has a model. By the Extended Completeness Theorem, every finite subset of Σ is consistent. So, Σ is consistent (see the Note below for details). By the Extended Completeness Theorem again, Σ has a model. $\square$

Note: Let p be the statement "Every finite subset of Σ is consistent," and let q be the statement "Σ is consistent." Let's prove $p \to q$ in detail. By the law of the contrapositive, $p \to q$ is logically equivalent to $\neg q \to \neg p$. So we will prove $\neg q \to \neg p$ instead (recall from Lesson 3 that this is called a **proof by contrapositive**). So, let's assume that Σ is **not** consistent. Then there is a formula ϕ such that $\Sigma \vdash \phi$ and $\Sigma \vdash \neg\phi$. The derivations of ϕ and $\neg\phi$ from Σ involve only finitely many formulas from Σ. Therefore, there is a finite subset Σ^* of Σ such that $\Sigma^* \vdash \phi$ and $\Sigma^* \vdash \neg\phi$. So, Σ^* is **not** consistent. So, there is a finite subset of Σ that is not consistent, proving the result.

Let's look at a simple application of the Compactness Theorem.

Theorem 10.9: Let Σ be a theory with arbitrarily large finite models. Then Σ has an infinite model.

Proof: Suppose that Σ is a theory in a language $\mathcal{L}$ with arbitrarily large finite models. Let $\{a_0, a_1, \dots\}$ be a denumerable set of distinct constant symbols, each of which is not in the language $\mathcal{L}$, let $\mathcal{K} = \mathcal{L} \cup \{a_0, a_1, \dots\}$, and let $T = \Sigma \cup \{a_n \neq a_m \mid n < m\}$. Note that T is a theory in the language $\mathcal{K}$.

Let T' be a finite subset of T. Then T' makes use of only finitely many of the new constant symbols, say $a_0, \dots a_m$. Let $\mathfrak{A}$ be a model of Σ with at least $m + 1$ elements and let $b_0, \dots, b_m$ be distinct elements in A. Then $(\mathfrak{A}, b_0, \dots, b_m)$ is a model of T' in the language $\mathcal{L} \cup \{a_0, \dots, a_m\}$.

By the Compactness Theorem, T has a model $\mathfrak{B}$ in the language $\mathcal{K}$. Note that $\mathfrak{B}$ must be infinite. Consider the model $\mathfrak{C}$ in the language $\mathcal{L}$ that is the same as the model $\mathfrak{B}$, except that it does not interpret the new constant symbols $\{a_0, a_1, \dots\}$. Then $\mathfrak{C}$ is an infinite model of Σ. $\square$

Notes: (1) It is a common technique in model theoretic proofs to expand a language $\mathcal{L}$ to a language $\mathcal{K}$ with $\mathcal{L} \subseteq \mathcal{K}$. We did this in the first paragraph of the proof above. Specifically, we expanded our original language to include infinitely many new constant symbols.

(2) Once we have infinitely many new constant symbols, we can say things about these constant symbols by using first-order sentences. In the proof above (end of first paragraph), we wrote down the sentences saying that none of these constants are equal to each other. We then formed a new theory T in the expanded language that contained the old theory Σ together with these new sentences.

(3) The notation $(\mathfrak{A}, b_0, \dots, b_m)$ may be a little confusing. To clarify, let's look at an example. Suppose that $\mathfrak{A}$ is a model in the language $\mathcal{L} = \{<\}$, where $<$ is a binary relation symbol. Then $\mathfrak{A} = \left(A, <^{\mathfrak{A}}\right)$ for some nonempty set A and some binary relation $<^{\mathfrak{A}}$ on A. So, $(\mathfrak{A}, b_0, \dots, b_m) = \left(A, <^{\mathfrak{A}}, b_0, \dots, b_m\right)$. Notice that there is a slight abuse of notation here. The literal translation of $(\mathfrak{A}, b_0, \dots, b_m)$ would be $\left(\left(A, <^{\mathfrak{A}}\right), b_0, \dots, b_m\right)$, but we do not put in that extra set of parentheses around A and $<^{\mathfrak{A}}$.

(4) In the second paragraph, we are checking that every finite subset of this new theory T has a model. This is easy because a finite subset of T makes use of only finitely many new symbols. For example, suppose T′ is a finite subset of T making use of the 3 new constant symbols a_0, a_1, and a_2. Since Σ has arbitrarily large finite models, we can let $\mathfrak{A}$ be a model of Σ with at least 3 elements, say $s, t, u \in A$. Let $\mathfrak{B} = (\mathfrak{A}, s, t, u)$, so that $a_0^{\mathfrak{B}} = s$, $a_1^{\mathfrak{B}} = t$, and $a_2^{\mathfrak{B}} = u$. Then we have $\mathfrak{B} \vDash a_0 \neq a_1$, $\mathfrak{B} \vDash a_0 \neq a_2$, and $\mathfrak{B} \vDash a_1 \neq a_2$. So, we've succeeded in finding a model of T making use of 3 new symbols.

(5) In the last paragraph of the proof, we invoke the compactness theorem to get a model $\mathfrak{B}$ of T. There's one small issue though. $\mathfrak{B}$ is a model in the language $\mathcal{K}$ and not in the language $\mathcal{L}$. In other words, it has the wrong type. This can easily be fixed by simply "forgetting about" the extra constant symbols. This is called taking a **reduct** of the model. The reduct is still a model of Σ because Σ doesn't make use of any of those new constants.

Homomorphisms and Isomorphisms

A **homomorphism** is a function from one structure to another structure of the same type that preserves all the relations and functions of the structure (see the Note after Example 10.28 for a more rigorous definition).

Example 10.28:

1. A **semigroup** is a structure of the form $(S, \star)$, where S is a set and $\star$ is an associative binary operation on S. Every monoid is a semigroup (and therefore, every group is a semigroup). An example of a semigroup that is not a monoid is $(\mathbb{Z}^+, +)$. Indeed, $\mathbb{Z}^+$ has no additive identity.

   Let $(S, \star)$ and $(T, \circ)$ be semigroups. A **semigroup homomorphism** is a function $f: S \to T$ such that for all $a, b \in S$, $f(a \star b) = f(a) \circ f(b)$.

   For example, let $\mathfrak{A} = (\mathbb{Z}^+, +)$, $\mathfrak{B} = (\mathbb{E}, \cdot)$, and let $f: \mathbb{Z}^+ \to \mathbb{E}$ be defined by $f(n) = 2^n$. For all $n, m \in \mathbb{Z}^+$, we have $f(n + m) = 2^{n+m} = 2^n \cdot 2^m = f(n) \cdot f(m)$. Therefore, f is a semigroup homomorphism.

   As another example, let $\mathfrak{A} = (\mathbb{N}, +)$, $\mathfrak{B} = (\{T, F\}, \vee)$, and let $g: \mathbb{N} \to \{T, F\}$ be defined by $g(n) = T$. For all $n, m \in \mathbb{N}$, we have $g(n + m) = T = T \vee T = g(n) \vee g(m)$. Therefore, g is a semigroup homomorphism.

2. Let $(M, \star, e_M)$ and $(N, \circ, e_N)$ be monoids, where e_M and e_N are the identities of M and N, respectively. A **monoid homomorphism** is a function $f: M \to N$ such that for all $a, b \in M$, $f(a \star b) = f(a) \circ f(b)$ and $f(e_M) = e_N$.

   Note that we need to include the identity element of a monoid as part of the structure for a homomorphism to be a monoid homomorphism. Otherwise we get only a semigroup homomorphism. The second example in part 1 above is a semigroup homomorphism, but **not** a monoid homomorphism. Indeed, the identity of $(\mathbb{N}, +)$ is 0 and the identity of $(\{T, F\}, \vee)$ is F, but $g(0) = T \neq F$.

   On the other hand, if we change the domains of the structures in the first example from part 1 above slightly, we **do** get a monoid homomorphism. Let $\mathfrak{A} = (\mathbb{N}, +, 0)$, $\mathfrak{B} = (\mathbb{N}, \cdot, 1)$, and let $f: \mathbb{N} \to \mathbb{N}$ be defined by $f(n) = 2^n$. For all $n, m \in \mathbb{N}$, $f(n + m) = f(n) \cdot f(m)$, as we saw above, and $f(0) = 2^0 = 1$. Therefore, f is a monoid homomorphism.

3. Let $(G, \star)$ and $(H, \circ)$ be groups. A **group homomorphism** is a function $f: G \to H$ such that for all $a, b \in G$, $f(a \star b) = f(a) \circ f(b)$.

You may be asking why we are not including constant symbols for the identity like we did for monoids. After all, we certainly want f to take the identity of G to the identity of H. And you may also be asking why we are not including a unary operator symbol for taking the inverse, as we certainly want $f(a^{-1}) = \left(f(a)\right)^{-1}$. For structures $(G, \star, \,^{-1_G}, e_G)$ and $(H, \circ, \,^{-1_H}, e_H)$, we can define a group homomorphism to be a function $f: G \to H$ such that for all $a, b \in G$, $f(a \star b) = f(a) \circ f(b)$, for all $a \in G$, $f(a^{-1}) = \left(f(a)\right)^{-1}$, and $f(e_G) = e_H$. However, it turns out that this more complicated definition is equivalent to our first simpler one. In other words, if $f: G \to H$ is a group homomorphism using the simpler definition, then f already maps the identity of G to the identity of H, and f already preserves inverses. We will prove these facts in Theorems 10.10 and 10.11 below.

As an example, let $\mathfrak{A} = (\mathbb{Z}, +)$, $\mathfrak{B} = (\{1, -1\}, \cdot)$, and let $f: \mathbb{Z} \to \{1, -1\}$ be defined by $f(n) = \begin{cases} 1 & \text{if } n \text{ is even.} \\ -1 & \text{if } n \text{ is odd.} \end{cases}$ There are four cases to consider. If n and m are both even, then $n + m$ is even, and so, $f(n + m) = 1$ and $f(n) \cdot f(m) = 1 \cdot 1 = 1$. If n and m are both odd, then $n + m$ is even, and so, $f(n + m) = 1$ and $f(n) \cdot f(m) = (-1) \cdot (-1) = 1$. If n is even and m is odd, then $n + m$ is odd, and so, $f(n + m) = -1$ and $f(n) \cdot f(m) = 1 \cdot (-1) = -1$. Finally, if n is odd and m is even, then $n + m$ is odd, and so, we have $f(n + m) = -1$ and $f(n) \cdot f(m) = -1 \cdot 1 = -1$. Therefore, f is a group homomorphism.

Let's look at another example. Let $\mathfrak{A} = (\mathbb{R}, +)$, $\mathfrak{B} = (\mathbb{R}, +)$, and let $g: \mathbb{R} \to \mathbb{R}$ be defined by $g(x) = x^2$. Then g is **not** a group homomorphism. To see this, we just need a single counterexample. We have $g(1) = 1^2 = 1$, $g(2) = 2^2 = 4$, $g(1 + 2) = g(3) = 3^2 = 9$, and $g(1) + g(2) = 1 + 4 = 5$. Since $g(1 + 2) \neq g(1) + g(2)$, g fails to be a homomorphism.

4. Let $(R, +_R, \cdot_R, 1_R)$ and $(S, +_S, \cdot_S, 1_S)$ be rings, where 1_R and 1_S are the multiplicative identities of R and S, respectively. A **ring homomorphism** is a function $f: R \to S$ such that for all $a, b \in R$, $f(a +_R b) = f(a) +_S f(b)$, $f(a \cdot_R b) = f(a) \cdot_S f(b)$, and $f(1_R) = 1_S$.

Notice that we did not include constant symbols for the additive identities of the rings and we did not include unary operator symbols for taking the additive inverses of elements in the rings. We will see in Theorems 10.10 and 10.11 below that with f defined as above, it follows that for all $a \in R$, $f(-a) = -f(a)$, and $f(0_R) = 0_S$.

Let's look at an example. First note that if R is a ring, then $R \times R$ with addition and multiplication defined componentwise is also a ring. That is, for $a, b, c, d \in R$, we define addition and multiplication by $(a, b) + (c, d) = (a + c, b + d)$ and $(a, b)(c, d) = (ac, bd)$. The verification that $R \times R$ is a ring with these definitions is straightforward. Let $\mathfrak{A} = (\mathbb{Z} \times \mathbb{Z}, +, \cdot, (1, 1))$, $\mathfrak{B} = (\mathbb{Z}, +, \cdot, 1)$, and let $f: \mathbb{Z} \times \mathbb{Z} \to \mathbb{Z}$ be defined by $f((n, m)) = n$. Then for all $n, m, j, k \in \mathbb{Z}$, we have $f((n, m) + (j, k)) = f((n + j, m + k)) = n + j$ and $f((n, m)) + f((j, k)) = n + j$. We also have $f((n, m) \cdot (j, k)) = f((nj, mk)) = nj$ and $f((n, m)) \cdot f((j, k)) = nj$. Finally, $f((1, 1)) = 1$. Therefore, f is a ring homomorphism.

Let's look at another example. Let $\mathfrak{A} = \mathfrak{B} = (\mathbb{Z}, +, \cdot, 1)$, and let $g: \mathbb{Z} \to \mathbb{Z}$ be defined by $g(n) = 2n$. Then g is **not** a ring homomorphism. To see this, we just need a single counterexample. $g(3) = 2 \cdot 3 = 6$, $g(5) = 2 \cdot 5 = 10$, $g(3 \cdot 5) = g(15) = 2 \cdot 15 = 30$, and $g(3) \cdot g(5) = 6 \cdot 10 = 60$. Since $g(3 \cdot 5) \neq g(3) \cdot g(5)$, g fails to be a ring homomorphism. Note, however, that g **is** a group homomorphism from $(\mathbb{Z}, +)$ to itself. Indeed, if $n, m \in \mathbb{Z}$, then $g(n + m) = 2(n + m) = 2n + 2m = g(n) + g(m)$.

5. A **field homomorphism** is the same as a ring homomorphism. The multiplicative inverse is automatically preserved (see Theorem 10.11 below), and so, nothing additional needs to be added to the definition.

6. Let $(A, \leq_A)$ and $(B, \leq_B)$ be partially ordered sets. An **order homomorphism** (also known as a **monotonic function**) is a function $f: A \to B$ such that for all $x, y \in A$, $x \leq_A y$ if and only if $f(x) \leq_B f(y)$.

    For example, let $\mathfrak{A} = \mathfrak{B} = (\mathbb{N}, \leq)$ and let $f: \mathbb{N} \to \mathbb{N}$ be defined by $f(n) = n + 3$. For all $n, m \in \mathbb{N}$, we have $n \leq m$ if and only if $n + 3 \leq m + 3$ if and only if $f(n) \leq f(m)$. Therefore, f is an order homomorphism.

    As another example, let $\mathfrak{A} = (\mathbb{Z}, \geq)$, $\mathfrak{B} = (\mathcal{P}(\mathbb{Z}), \subseteq)$, and let $g: \mathbb{Z} \to \mathcal{P}(\mathbb{Z})$ be defined by $g(n) = \{k \in \mathbb{Z} \mid n \leq k\}$. Let $m, n \in \mathbb{Z}$. We will show that $m \geq n$ if and only if the relationship $\{k \in \mathbb{Z} \mid m \leq k\} \subseteq \{k \in \mathbb{Z} \mid n \leq k\}$ holds. Suppose that $m \geq n$ and let $j \in \{k \in \mathbb{Z} \mid m \leq k\}$. Then $j \geq m$. Since $m \geq n$, $j \geq n$, and so, $j \in \{k \in \mathbb{Z} \mid n \leq k\}$. Now, let $\{k \in \mathbb{Z} \mid m \leq k\} \subseteq \{k \in \mathbb{Z} \mid n \leq k\}$. Since $m \leq m$, we have $m \in \{k \in \mathbb{Z} \mid m \leq k\}$. So, $m \in \{k \in \mathbb{Z} \mid n \leq k\}$. Thus, $n \leq m$, or equivalently, $m \geq n$. Therefore, g is an order homomorphism.

Note: Here is a more rigorous definition of a homomorphism.

If $\mathfrak{A}$ and $\mathfrak{B}$ are structures of the same type with underlying domains A and B, then a homomorphism from $\mathfrak{A}$ to $\mathfrak{B}$ is a function $f: A \to B$ such that for each $n \in \mathbb{N}$ and all $a_1, a_2, \ldots, a_n \in A$,

1. if R is an n-ary relation, then $R_A(a_1, a_2, \ldots, a_n)$ if and only if $R_B(f(a_1), f(a_2), \ldots, f(a_n))$.

2. If F is an n-ary function, then $f(F_A(a_1, a_2, \ldots, a_n)) = F_B(f(a_1), f(a_2), \ldots, f(a_n))$.

In particular, 2 implies that if c is a constant, then $f(c_A) = c_B$.

Theorem 10.10: Let $(G, \star)$ and $(H, \circ)$ be groups with identities e_G and e_H, respectively, and let $f: G \to H$ be a group homomorphism. Then $f(e_G) = e_H$.

Proof: Since $e_G = e_G \star e_G$, we have $f(e_G) = f(e_G \star e_G) = f(e_G) \circ f(e_G)$. So,

$$f(e_G) = f(e_G) \circ e_H = f(e_G) \circ \left(f(e_G) \circ (f(e_G))^{-1} \right)$$
$$= (f(e_G) \circ f(e_G)) \circ (f(e_G))^{-1} = f(e_G) \circ (f(e_G))^{-1} = e_H. \qquad \square$$

Notes: (1) The computations in the proof take place in the group $(H, \circ)$. In particular, $f(e_G) \in H$ and $e_H \in H$. If the proof seems confusing because $f(e_G)$ appears so often, try making the substitutions $h = f(e_G)$ and $e = e_H$. Notice that $h, e \in H$ and by the first line of the proof, $h = h \circ h$. The rest of the proof then looks like this:

$$h = h \circ e = h \circ (h \circ h^{-1}) = (h \circ h) \circ h^{-1} = h \circ h^{-1} = e.$$

Remember that $h = f(e_G)$ and $e = e_H$. So, we have $f(e_G) = e_H$, as desired.

(2) $h = h \circ e$ because e is the identity for H.

(3) $e = h \circ h^{-1}$ by the definition of inverse and because e is the identity for H. From this equation, it follows that $h \circ e = h \circ (h \circ h^{-1})$.

(4) $h \circ (h \circ h^{-1}) = (h \circ h) \circ h^{-1}$ because $\circ$ is associative in H.

(5) $h \circ h = h$ from the first line of the proof (this is equivalent to $f(e_G) \circ f(e_G) = f(e_G)$). It follows that $(h \circ h) \circ h^{-1} = h \circ h^{-1}$.

(6) Finally, $h \circ h^{-1} = e$, again by the definition of inverse and because e is the identity for H.

(7) If the group operation is addition, then we usually use the symbols 0_G and 0_H for the identities.

Theorem 10.11: Let $(G, \star)$ and $(H, \circ)$ be groups and let $f \colon G \to H$ be a group homomorphism. Then for all $g \in G$, $f(g^{-1}) = \left(f(g)\right)^{-1}$.

Proof: By Theorem 10.10, we have $f(e_G) = e_H$. So, for $g \in G$, we have
$$e_H = f(e_G) = f(g \star g^{-1}) = f(g) \circ f(g^{-1}).$$
Since $f(g) \circ f(g^{-1}) = e_H$, $f(g^{-1}) = \left(f(g)\right)^{-1}$. $\qquad \square$

Notes: (1) $e_G = g \star g^{-1}$ by the definition of inverse and because e_G is the identity for G. From this equation, it follows that $f(e_G) = f(g \star g^{-1})$.

(2) $f(g \star g^{-1}) = f(g) \circ f(g^{-1})$ because f is a homomorphism.

(3) In a group with identity e, if $xy = e$ and $yx = e$, then $y = x^{-1}$. We actually need to verify only one of the equations $xy = e$ or $yx = e$ to determine that $y = x^{-1}$ (Prove this!). Letting $x = f(g)$, $y = f(g^{-1})$, and $e = e_H$, we showed in the proof that $xy = e$. It follows that $y = x^{-1}$. That is, $f(g^{-1}) = \left(f(g)\right)^{-1}$.

An **isomorphism** is a bijective homomorphism. If there is an isomorphism from a structure $\mathfrak{A}$ to a structure $\mathfrak{B}$, then we say that $\mathfrak{A}$ and $\mathfrak{B}$ are **isomorphic**, and we write $\mathfrak{A} \cong \mathfrak{B}$. Mathematicians generally consider isomorphic structures to be the same. Indeed, they behave identically. The only difference between them is the "names" of the elements.

Example 10.29:

1. For $n \in \mathbb{Z}^+$, the function $f \colon \mathbb{Z} \to n\mathbb{Z}$ defined by $f(k) = nk$ is an isomorphism between the groups $(\mathbb{Z}, +)$ and $(n\mathbb{Z}, +)$. It's easy to see that f is injective ($j \neq k \to nj \neq nk$) and surjective (if $nk \in n\mathbb{Z}$, then $f(k) = nk$). If $j, k \in \mathbb{Z}$, then $f(j + k) = n(j + k) = nj + nk = f(j) + f(k)$. It follows that $(\mathbb{Z}, +) \cong (n\mathbb{Z}, +)$.

Note that this map is **not** a ring isomorphism for $n > 1$. First, $(n\mathbb{Z}, +, \cdot)$ is technically not even a ring for $n > 1$ because $1 \notin n\mathbb{Z}$. But it is "almost a ring." In fact, the multiplicative identity property is the only property that fails. We will say that $(R, +, \cdot)$ is **almost a ring** if all the ring properties hold, **except** the existence of a multiplicative identity.

Let's show that for $n > 1$, f is **not** an isomorphism between the "almost rings" $(\mathbb{Z}, +, \cdot)$ and $(n\mathbb{Z}, +, \cdot)$. Let's use $2, 3 \in \mathbb{Z}$ to provide a counterexample: $f(2 \cdot 3) = f(6) = n \cdot 6 = 6n$ and $f(2) \cdot f(3) = (n \cdot 2)(n \cdot 3) = 6n^2$. If $f(2 \cdot 3) = f(2) \cdot f(3)$, then $6n = 6n^2$, so that $n = n^2$. This equation is equivalent to $n^2 - n = 0$, or $n(n - 1) = 0$. So, $n = 0$ or $n = 1$.

In fact, as "almost rings," $(\mathbb{Z}, +, \cdot)$ is **not** isomorphic to $(n\mathbb{Z}, +, \cdot)$ at all for $n > 1$. If $f\colon \mathbb{Z} \to n\mathbb{Z}$ were an isomorphism, then $f(1) = nm$ for some $m \in \mathbb{Z}$. But also, since f is a homomorphism, $f(1) = f(1 \cdot 1) = f(1)f(1) = (nm)(nm) = n^2m^2$. So, $nm = n^2m^2$, and thus, $m = 0, n = 0$, or $1 = nm$. If $m = 0$, then $f(1) = 0$, and so, $f(2) = f(1 + 1) = f(1) + f(1) = 0 + 0 = 0$. So, f is not injective. Since $n > 1$, $n \neq 0$ and $1 \neq nm$.

2. The function $g\colon \mathbb{Z} \to \mathbb{Z}$ defined by $g(n) = n + 2$ is an isomorphism from the linearly ordered set $(\mathbb{Z}, <)$ to itself. It's easy to see that g is injective ($j \neq k \to j + 2 \neq k + 2$) and surjective (if $n \in \mathbb{Z}$, then $f(n - 2) = (n - 2) + 2 = n$). If $j, k \in \mathbb{Z}$, then $j < k$ if and only if $j + 2 < k + 2$. Thus, g is a homomorphism. Therefore, g is a bijective homomorphism, and so, g is an isomorphism.

Note: The figure below provides a visual representation of the isomorphism g from part 2 of Example 10.29.

An isomorphism from a structure to itself is called an **automorphism**. The identity function is always an automorphism from any structure to itself. In the previous example, we described a nontrivial automorphism from $\mathbb{Z}$ to $\mathbb{Z}$.

We finish this lesson with a theorem that tells us that homomorphisms preserve truth.

Theorem 10.12 (Homomorphism Theorem): Let $\mathfrak{A}$ and $\mathfrak{B}$ be structures with domains A and B, respectively, and let $h\colon A \to B$ be a homomorphism. Then for any term $t(v_0, v_1, \ldots, v_k)$ and $a_0, a_1, \ldots, a_k \in A$, $h\big(t^{\mathfrak{A}}[a_0, a_1, \ldots, a_k]\big) = t^{\mathfrak{B}}[h(a_0), h(a_1), \ldots, h(a_k)]$. Furthermore, for any quantifier-free formula $\phi(v_0, v_1, \ldots, v_k)$ not containing the equality relation and $a_0, a_1, \ldots, a_k \in A$, $\mathfrak{A} \vDash \phi[a_0, a_1, \ldots, a_k]$ if and only if $\mathfrak{B} \vDash \phi[h(a_0), h(a_1), \ldots, h(a_k)]$. If h is injective, we can eliminate the restriction "not containing the equality relation." If h is surjective, we can eliminate the restriction "quantifier-free."

Theorem 10.12 can be proved using induction on terms and formulas. I leave the proof to the reader (see Problem 15 below).

Problem Set 10

LEVEL 1

1. Let $\mathcal{L} = \{+, \cdot, S, <, 0\}$ be the language of number theory and let ϕ be the following formula: $\left(\left(2 \cdot (v_0 + 3)\right) + (1 + 0)\right) < \left((0 + 1) \cdot v_1\right) \wedge \forall v_0(v_0 \cdot 0 = 0)$. The formula ϕ is abbreviated. Write ϕ in its unabbreviated form.

2. Let $\mathcal{L} = \{\in\}$ be the language of set theory. Determine whether each occurrence of each variable in the following formula is free or bound: $\forall v_0 \exists v_1(v_0 \in v_1 \rightarrow v_1 = v_2) \wedge \exists v_0 \forall v_2(v_1 \in v_2)$

LEVEL 2

3. Give an example of sentences ϕ and ψ and expressions α and β in the language of set theory such that $(\phi \wedge \psi) = (\alpha \wedge \beta)$ but $\phi \neq \alpha$.

4. Determine if each of the following is a logical axiom:

   (i) $\forall x \exists y(x < y) \rightarrow \exists y(y < y)$

   (ii) $\forall y\big(C(y) \rightarrow C(y)\big) \rightarrow \big(C(a) \rightarrow C(a)\big)$

   (iii) $\forall x\big(C(y) \rightarrow C(x)\big) \rightarrow \big(C(y) \rightarrow \forall x C(x)\big)$

   (iv) $\left[\left(\forall x\big(S(x)\big) \rightarrow \forall y\big(S(y)\big)\right) \rightarrow S(z)\right] \rightarrow \left[\forall x\big(S(x)\big) \rightarrow \left(\forall y\big(S(y)\big) \rightarrow S(z)\right)\right]$

LEVEL 3

5. Recall that a set of statements Σ of sentential logic **tautologically implies** a statement ϕ if and only if every truth assignment for the propositional variables in Σ and ϕ that satisfies every element of Σ also satisfies ϕ. Let Γ be an arbitrary set of first-order formulas, let $\Phi = \{\phi_1, \phi_2, \ldots, \phi_n\}$ be a set of n first-order formulas, and let ψ be a first-order formula. Suppose that Φ tautologically implies ψ and for each $k = 1, 2, \ldots, n$, $\Gamma \vdash \phi_k$. Prove that $\Gamma \vdash \psi$.

6. Let Λ be the set of logical axioms, let Γ be a set of first-order formulas, and let ϕ be a first-order formula. Suppose that $\Lambda \cup \Gamma$ tautologically implies ϕ. Prove that $\Gamma \vdash \phi$. (Hint: Use Problem 13 from Problem Set 9.)

7. Let Γ be a set of first-order formulas and let ϕ, ψ be first-order formulas. Prove each of the following:

   (i) $\Gamma \vdash \phi \rightarrow \psi$ if and only if $\Gamma \cup \{\phi\} \vdash \psi$.

   (ii) $\Gamma \cup \{\phi\} \vdash \neg\psi$ if and only if $\Gamma \cup \{\psi\} \vdash \neg\phi$.

   (iii) The following are equivalent: (a) There is a formula ϕ such that $\Gamma \vdash \phi$ and $\Gamma \vdash \neg\phi$. (b) For every formula ψ, $\Gamma \vdash \psi$.

8. Let Γ be a set of first-order formulas and let ϕ be a first-order formula. Suppose that $\Gamma \cup \{\phi\}$ is inconsistent. Prove that $\Gamma \vdash \neg\phi$.

LEVEL 4

9. Prove that for any formula ϕ, $\vdash \exists x \forall y \phi \rightarrow \forall y \exists x \phi$.

10. Determine whether each of the following logical arguments is valid or invalid. A and B are unary relation symbols and a and b are constant symbols. If the argument is valid, provide a deduction. If the argument is invalid, provide a counterexample.

I
$$\frac{\exists x (A(x))}{\forall x (A(x))}$$

II
$$\frac{\forall x (A(x) \vee B(x))}{\exists x \neg A(x)}$$
$$\frac{}{\exists x (B(x))}$$

III
$$\forall x (A(x) \vee B(x))$$
$$\forall x (A(x) \rightarrow C(x))$$
$$\frac{\forall x (B(x) \rightarrow C(x))}{C(a) \wedge C(b)}$$

IV
$$\exists x (A(x))$$
$$\frac{B(a)}{\exists x (A(x) \wedge B(x))}$$

LEVEL 5

11. Prove Unique Readability for Formulas (Theorem 10.4).

12. Let x and y be variables. Prove that if y does not occur in ϕ, then x is substitutable for y in ϕ_y^x and $\left(\phi_y^x\right)_x^y = \phi$. Then provide a counterexample to show that $\left(\phi_y^x\right)_x^y$ does not necessarily equal ϕ.

CHALLENGE PROBLEMS

13. Prove that the theory DLO has only one countable model up to isomorphism.

14. Let $\mathcal{L} = \{\star, e\}$ be the language of groups and let T be the theory of groups. In other words, T consists of the following sentences:

    (1) **(Associativity)** $\forall x \forall y \forall z (x \star (y \star z) = (x \star y) \star z)$

    (2) **(Identity)** $\forall x (x \star e = x \wedge e \star x = x)$

    (3) **(Inverse)** $\forall x \exists y (x \star y = e \wedge y \star x = e)$

If $\mathfrak{G} = (G, \star)$ is a group and $g \in G$, then the **order** of g is the least $n \in \mathbb{N}$ such that $x^n = e$ (where $x^0 = e$ and for $n \geq 0$, x^{n+1} is $x \star x^n$). If no such n exists, then we say that g has infinite order. Let Σ be a theory containing T with models that contain elements of arbitrarily large finite order. Prove that Σ has a model that is a group with an element of infinite order.

15. Prove the Homomorphism Theorem.

LESSON 11
AXIOMATIC SET THEORY

The Axioms of ZF

Recall that an **axiom** is simply a statement that is assumed to be true. Set theorists, logicians, and philosophers have spent a lot of time and energy trying to decide upon the "correct" collection of axioms. However, deciding whether a statement should be true is a philosophical question and not a mathematical one. More than one axiomatic system has been developed over the years, but we will stick with one of the more popular and basic ones. Unless otherwise specified, we will be working within the axiomatic system ZFC (Zermelo-Fraenkel set theory **with** Choice). In fact, we have essentially been assuming these axioms throughout this book.

Let's start by writing down each of the axioms of ZF (Zermelo-Fraenkel set theory **without** Choice). We will describe each axiom informally, and then write down the appropriate first-order formula. Our first-order formulas will be coming from the language of set theory. Therefore, aside from the equality relation, "$=$," the only other relation we will use is the membership relation, "$\in$." As usual with first-order logic, our first-order formulas can contain the connectives $\land$, $\lor$, $\to$, $\leftrightarrow$, and $\neg$, as well as the quantifiers $\forall$ and $\exists$, and finitely many variables. For easier readability, we will always abbreviate $\neg x = y$ as $x \neq y$ and $\neg x \in y$ as $x \notin y$. We will also leave out parentheses that make a formula harder to read. See Lesson 10 for details.

Axiom 0 (Empty set): This axiom says that there is a set with no elements. We call this set the empty set, and we use the symbol $\emptyset$ to represent it. Some authors use the symbol $\{\ \}$ instead. Symbolically, the axiom looks like this:

$$\exists x \forall y (y \notin x)$$

Set theorists identify the empty set with the natural number 0, so that $0 = \emptyset$.

Axiom 1 (Extensionality): This axiom says that two sets are equal if and only if they have the same elements. Symbolically, the axiom looks like this:

$$\forall x \forall y \big(x = y \leftrightarrow \forall z (z \in x \leftrightarrow z \in y) \big)$$

Note that the Axiom of Extensionality implies that the empty set is unique. To see this, let x and y both be empty sets. Then $\forall z (z \in x \leftrightarrow z \in y)$ is vacuously true. Therefore, by the Axiom of Extensionality, $x = y$.

Axiom 2 (Pairing): This axiom says that given two sets x and y, there is a set whose only elements are x and y. We write this set as $\{x, y\}$. If $x \neq y$, then $\{x, y\}$ has exactly two elements. If $x = y$, then $\{x, y\} = \{x, x\} = \{x\}$, a set with just one element. Symbolically, the axiom looks like this:

$$\forall x \forall y \exists z \forall w \big(w \in z \leftrightarrow (w = x \lor w = y) \big)$$

Example 11.1:

1. If we let $x = 0$ and $y = 0$ (where $0 = \emptyset$), then the pairing axiom gives us the set $\{0, 0\} = \{0\}$. Set theorists identify this set with the natural number 1, so that $1 = \{\emptyset\} = \{0\}$.

2. We can now let $x = 0$ and $y = 1$. The pairing axiom then gives us the set $\{0, 1\} = \{\emptyset, \{\emptyset\}\}$. Set theorists identify this set with the natural number 2. So, $2 = \{\emptyset, \{\emptyset\}\} = \{0, 1\}$.

3. Here is an example that doesn't have a special identification. Since 1 and 2 are sets, we can use the pairing axiom to form the set $\{1, 2\}$. In its unabbreviated form, $\{1, 2\} = \left\{\{\emptyset\}, \{\emptyset, \{\emptyset\}\}\right\}$.

4. Given sets x and y, by the pairing axiom, we get the set $\{x, y\}$. Again, using the pairing axiom, we get the set $\{x, x\} = \{x\}$. Using the pairing axiom one more time, we get the set $\{\{x\}, \{x, y\}\}$. We call this set an **ordered pair** and we abbreviate it as (x, y). So, $(x, y) = \{\{x\}, \{x, y\}\}$. In Theorem 4.1 from Lesson 4, we saw that ordered pairs have the property that $(x, y) = (z, w)$ if and only if $x = z$ and $y = w$.

Axiom 3 (Union): This axiom says that given any set x, there is a set whose only elements are the elements of elements of x. We write this set as $\bigcup x$. If x consists of just two sets a and b, then we write $\bigcup x$ as $a \cup b$ (see part 1 of Example 3.4). Symbolically, the axiom looks like this:

$$\forall x \exists y \forall z \big(z \in y \leftrightarrow \exists w (w \in x \wedge z \in w)\big)$$

Example 11.2:

1. If we let $x = \{2, \{1, 2\}\}$ (this is a set by the pairing axiom), the union axiom gives us the set

$$\bigcup\{2, \{1, 2\}\} = 2 \cup \{1, 2\} = \{\emptyset, \{\emptyset\}\} \cup \left\{\{\emptyset\}, \{\emptyset, \{\emptyset\}\}\right\} = \left\{\emptyset, \{\emptyset\}, \{\emptyset, \{\emptyset\}\}\right\} = \{0, 1, 2\}.$$

   Set theorists identify this set with the natural number 3. So, $3 = \left\{\emptyset, \{\emptyset\}, \{\emptyset, \{\emptyset\}\}\right\} = \{0, 1, 2\}$.

   We can also see that 3 is a set as follows. Since 2 is a set, by the pairing axiom, $\{2, 2\} = \{2\}$ is a set. Then $\bigcup\{2, \{2\}\} = 2 \cup \{2\} = \{\emptyset, \{\emptyset\}\} \cup \left\{\{\emptyset, \{\emptyset\}\}\right\} = \left\{\emptyset, \{\emptyset\}, \{\emptyset, \{\emptyset\}\}\right\}$ is a set by the union axiom. As before, this is the set $3 = \{0, 1, 2\}$.

2. We can now use the principle of mathematical induction to define the set $n = \{0, 1, \ldots, n - 1\}$ for each natural number n. We do this as follows. For $k \geq 1$, given that $k = \{0, 1, \ldots, k - 1\}$ is a set, by the pairing axiom, $\{k, k\} = \{k\}$ is a set. Then by the union axiom, we get the set

$$\bigcup\{k, \{k\}\} = k \cup \{k\} = \{0, 1, \ldots, k - 1\} \cup \{k\} = \{0, 1, \ldots, k - 1, k\} = k + 1.$$

Axiom 4 (Power Set): This axiom says that given any set x, there is a set whose only elements are the subsets of x. We write this set as $\mathcal{P}(x)$. Symbolically, the axiom looks like this:

$$\forall x \exists y \forall z (z \in y \leftrightarrow z \subseteq x)$$

Recall that $z \subseteq x$ is an abbreviation for $\forall w (w \in z \rightarrow w \in x)$. So, in its unabbreviated form, the power set axiom looks like this:

$$\forall x \exists y \forall z \big(z \in y \leftrightarrow \forall w (w \in z \rightarrow w \in x)\big)$$

Example 11.3: Since $2 = \{\emptyset, \{\emptyset\}\}$ is a set, by the power set axiom, we get the set

$$\mathcal{P}(2) = \mathcal{P}(\{\emptyset, \{\emptyset\}\}) = \{\emptyset, \{\emptyset\}, \{\{\emptyset\}\}, \{\emptyset, \{\emptyset\}\}\}$$

Observe that $\mathcal{P}(2)$ contains the natural numbers 0, 1, and 2, but it also contains the set $\{\{\emptyset\}\}$, which is not equal to a natural number. It follows that $\mathcal{P}(2)$ is **not** a natural number.

Axiom 5 (Infinity): This axiom says that there is a set x such that $\emptyset \in x$ and whenever $y \in x$, the **successor** of y is also in x, where we define the successor of y to be $S(y) = y \cup \{y\}$. Symbolically, in an abbreviated, easy to read form, the axiom looks like this:

$$\exists x \big(\emptyset \in x \wedge \forall y (y \in x \to y \cup \{y\} \in x) \big)$$

Just for fun, let's write this axiom in its fully unabbreviated form.

To start, note that $\emptyset \in x$ is an abbreviation for $\exists y \big(y \in x \wedge \forall z (z \notin y) \big)$.

Also, $y \cup \{y\} \in x$ is an abbreviation for $\exists z \big(z \in x \wedge \forall w \big(w \in z \leftrightarrow (w \in y \vee w = y) \big) \big)$.

So, the fully unabbreviated form of this axiom is the following:

$$\exists x \left(\exists y \big(y \in x \wedge \forall z (z \notin y) \big) \wedge \forall y \left(y \in x \to \exists z \left(z \in x \wedge \forall w \big(w \in z \leftrightarrow (w \in y \vee w = y) \big) \right) \right) \right)$$

The axiom of infinity provides us with a set that contains all the natural numbers. We can see this from the definition. We are told that $0 = \emptyset \in x$. It then follows that $S(0) = 0 \cup \{0\} = \{0\} = 1 \in x$. And then we have $S(1) = 1 \cup \{1\} = \{0, 1\} = 2 \in x$, and so on. Formally, we can use the principle of mathematical induction to prove that $n \in x$ for each natural number n.

What about the set of natural numbers itself? How can we show that it exists? One way to do this is to use the axiom of infinity together with one instance of the next axiom.

Axiom Schema 6 (Bounded Comprehension Schema): This is a collection of axioms (the word "schema" indicates that this is more than one axiom), which says that given sets $b_1, b_2, \ldots, b_n, a$ and a first-order formula ϕ with free variables $w, y_1, y_2, \ldots, y_n, x$, there is a set consisting of all the elements of a that satisfy the formula $\phi(w, y_1, y_2, \ldots, y_n, x)$ when $y_1, y_2, \ldots, y_n, x$ are replaced by $b_1, b_2, \ldots, b_n, a$, respectively. We write this set as $\{w \in a \mid \phi(w, b_1, b_2, \ldots, b_n, a)\}$. The sets $b_1, b_2, \ldots, b_n, a$ are often called **parameters**. Symbolically, given ϕ and parameters $b_1, b_2, \ldots, b_n, a$, the axiom looks like this:

$$\forall x \forall y_1 \forall y_2 \cdots \forall y_n \exists z \forall w \left(w \in z \leftrightarrow \big(w \in x \wedge \phi(w, y_1, y_2, \ldots, y_n, x) \big) \right)$$

Note that the "Unbounded Comprehension Schema"

$$\forall y_1 \forall y_2 \cdots \forall y_n \exists z \forall w \big(w \in z \leftrightarrow \phi(w, y_1, y_2, \ldots, y_n) \big)$$

cannot be a collection of axioms (notice how we left out the variable x and "$w \in x$"). If we let $\phi(x)$ be the formula $x \notin x$, we encounter Russell's Paradox (see Problem 9 from Problem Set 2). In general, the collection $\{w \mid \phi(w, b_1, b_2, \ldots, b_n)\}$ is called a **class**. Every set is a class, but not every class is a set. A class that is not a set is called a **proper class**. For example, the class $\{x \mid x \notin x\}$ is a proper class. However, if a is a set, then the class $\{w \in a \mid \phi(w, b_1, b_2, \ldots, b_n, a)\}$ **is** a set. This follows from the Bounded Comprehension Schema.

Example 11.4:

1. Let $b_1 = 0 = \emptyset$, $b_2 = 1 = \{\emptyset\}$, $b_3 = 2 = \{\emptyset, \{\emptyset\}\}$, and $a = 100 = \{0, 1, \ldots, 99\}$. Also, let $\phi(w, y_1, y_2, y_3, a)$ be $(w \neq y_1 \wedge y_2 \notin w) \vee y_3 \in w$. By bounded comprehension, we get the set $\{w \in 100 \mid (w \neq 0 \wedge 1 \notin w) \vee 2 \in w\} = \{1\} \cup \{3, 4, \ldots, 99\} = \{1, 3, 4, \ldots, 99\}$.

2. Let's use the axiom of infinity together with bounded comprehension to form the set of natural numbers. By the axiom of infinity, we can let x be a set containing the natural numbers.

   Let $\phi(n)$ be the formula $\forall m(m \notin n) \vee \exists k \forall m(m \in n \leftrightarrow (m \in k \vee m = k))$. This formula expresses that $n = \emptyset$ or $n = S(k)$ for some k.

   Let $\psi(n)$ be $\forall k \left(k \in n \rightarrow \left(\forall m(m \notin k) \vee \exists m(m \in n \wedge \forall j(j \in k \leftrightarrow (j \in m \vee j = m))) \right) \right)$. This formula expresses that for every $k \in n$, $k = \emptyset$ or $k = S(m)$ for some $m \in n$.

   Let $\tau(n)$ be the formula $\phi(n) \wedge \psi(n)$.

   We now use bounded comprehension to form the set $\omega = \{n \in x \mid \tau(n)\}$. In problem 8 below, you will be asked to prove that under the axioms of ZFC, this set is the set of natural numbers.

   The symbol "ω" represents a Greek letter that is pronounced "omega." It is the standard symbol that set theorists use for the set of natural numbers. In other words, $\omega = \mathbb{N}$.

3. Given sets b_1 and b_2, we can define the set $b_1 \cap b_2$ as $\{w \in b_1 \cup b_2 \mid w \in b_1 \wedge w \in b_2\}$. Here, we have used the formula $\phi(w, y_1, y_2, x)$ defined by $w \in y_1 \wedge w \in y_2$, together with the parameters b_1 and b_2. The "bounding set" is $b_1 \cup b_2$. We know this is a set by the union axiom. (note that the bounding set $b_1 \cup b_2$ is not being used as a parameter here because x does not appear in the formula $w \in y_1 \wedge w \in y_2$).

   If b is any nonempty set, then we can define the set $\cap b = \{w \in \cup b \mid \forall z(z \in b \wedge w \in z)\}$. Here, we have used the formula $\phi(w, y, x)$ defined by $\forall z(z \in y \wedge w \in z)$, together with the parameter b. The "bounding set" is $\cup b$, which we know is a set by the union axiom.

Axiom Schema 7 (Replacement Schema): This is a collection of axioms, which says that the image of a set under a function is also a set. A formula $\phi(x, z)$ represents a function if

$$\forall x \forall w \forall v \left((\phi(x, w) \wedge \phi(x, v)) \rightarrow w = v \right).$$

The replacement schema will allow parameters (just like the bounded comprehension schema). Therefore, the expression that ϕ represents a function should technically be written as follows:

$$\forall x \forall w \forall v \forall y_1 \forall y_2 \cdots \forall y_n \left((\phi(x, w, y_1, y_2, \ldots, y_n) \wedge \phi(x, v, y_1, y_2, \ldots, y_n)) \rightarrow w = v \right)$$

We will abbreviate this formula by simply writing "$\phi(x, z)$ is a function." Note that there may be other variables in the formula even though we are not mentioning them explicitly.

Informally, the replacement schema will then say "If $\phi(x, z)$ is a function, then for any given set A acting as the domain of the function, the image of A under the function is a set. We can write this more formally as follows:

$$\phi(x, z) \text{ is a function} \rightarrow \forall A \exists B \forall s(s \in B \leftrightarrow \exists t(t \in A \wedge \phi(t, s)))$$

Just for fun, let's write the unabbreviated form of this formula. To save space, let's let $\boldsymbol{y}$ represent $y_1, y_2, \ldots, y_n$ and $\forall \boldsymbol{y}$ represent $\forall y_1 \forall y_2 \cdots \forall y_n$. The axiom then looks like this:

$$\forall x \forall w \forall v \forall \boldsymbol{y} \left(\left(\phi(x, w, \boldsymbol{y}) \wedge \phi(x, v, \boldsymbol{y}) \right) \to w = v \right) \to \forall A \forall \boldsymbol{y} \exists B \forall s \left(s \in B \leftrightarrow \exists t \left(t \in A \wedge \phi(t, s, \boldsymbol{y}) \right) \right)$$

In branches of mathematics outside of set theory, it's hard to find much use for the replacement schema. However, for set theorists, it is useful, as it is needed to show that every ordinal is a set. We will learn about the ordinals in Lesson 12.

Axiom 8 (Foundation): This axiom says that every nonempty set has an $\in$-least element. Symbolically, the axiom looks like this:

$$\forall x (\exists z (z \in x) \to \exists z (z \in x \wedge \forall y (y \in z \to y \notin x)))$$

Like the replacement schema, the axiom of foundation is not used much outside of set theory, and in fact much of set theory can be developed without it. Some mathematicians actually take the opposite approach and adopt an axiom called "the axiom of antifoundation." One interesting consequence of antifoundation is that there exists a unique set x such that $x = \{x\}$. This set is quite strange (and it does not exist under the axiom of foundation). Clearly, we have $x \in x$. This leads to an infinite descending $\in$-chain $x \ni x \ni x \ni x \ni \cdots$ (if the backwards "epsilon" confuses you, we can also write this sequence as $\cdots \in x \in x \in x \in x$).

Axioms 0 through 8 form an axiom system known as ZF. This stands for "Zermelo-Fraenkel." Sometimes one may wish to leave out the axiom of foundation. In this case, we have the axiom system ZF^-.

The Axiom of Choice

We complete our list of axioms with one that has caused much controversy over the years.

Axiom 9 (Axiom of Choice): One version of this axiom says that for every set X of nonempty pairwise disjoint sets, there is a set Y that contains exactly one element from each set in X. The set Y is sometimes called a **selector** for X.

Let's try to write out the unabbreviated first-order formula. First, let ϕ be the statement "X is a set of nonempty pairwise disjoint sets." Then ϕ can be written as follows:

$$\forall x (x \in X \to \exists y (y \in x)) \wedge \forall x \forall y ((x \in X \wedge y \in X \wedge x \neq y) \to \forall z (z \notin x \vee z \notin y)).$$

Now, let ψ be the statement "There is a set Y that contains exactly one element from each set in X." Then ψ can be written as follows:

$$\exists Y \forall x (x \in X \to \exists! y (y \in x \wedge y \in Y)).$$

The exclamation point (!) is an abbreviation used for uniqueness. $\exists! y$ is read "there is a unique y." In general, $\exists! y \left(\tau(y) \right)$ is an abbreviation for $\exists y \left(\tau(y) \wedge \forall z (\tau(z) \to z = y) \right)$. So, $\exists! y (y \in x \wedge y \in Y)$ is an abbreviation for $\exists y \left(y \in x \wedge y \in Y \wedge \forall z ((z \in x \wedge z \in Y) \to z = y) \right)$.

Putting this all together, the unabbreviated formula expressing the axiom of choice is the following:

$$\forall X \Big(\big((\forall x(x \in X \to \exists y(y \in x)) \land \forall x \forall y((x \in X \land y \in X \land x \neq y) \to \forall z(z \notin x \lor z \notin y)) \big) \to$$

$$\exists Y \forall x \Big(x \in X \to \exists y \big(y \in x \land y \in Y \land \forall z((z \in x \land z \in Y) \to z = y) \big) \Big) \Big) \Big).$$

The axiom of choice can be phrased as follows: "For every set X of nonempty pairwise disjoint sets, there is a set Y such that for each $x \in X$, there is a unique $y_x \in x$ such that $y_x \in Y$. Notice that $Y \subseteq \bigcup X$. So, we can define a function $f: X \to \bigcup X$ by letting $f(x) = y_x$. This function is called a **choice function**. It chooses one element from each set in X.

In fact, the axiom of choice is equivalent to the following statement: "For every set X of nonempty sets, there is a choice function $f: X \to \bigcup X$" (notice the absence of the phrase "pairwise disjoint"). You will be asked to prove that this statement is equivalent to AC in Problem 5 below.

Example 11.5:

1. Let $X = \{\{0, 1, 2\}, \{a, b, c, d\}, \{\Delta, \boxdot\}\}$ and let $f = \{(\{0, 1, 2\}, 1), (\{a, b, c, d\}, d), (\{\Delta, \boxdot\}, \Delta)\}$. We see that $f: X \to \bigcup X$ satisfies $f(\{0, 1, 2\}) = 1$, $f(\{a, b, c, d\}) = d$, and $f(\{\Delta, \boxdot\}) = \Delta$. This function f is a choice function. The corresponding selector Y is $\{1, d, \Delta\}$. Note that the axiom of choice is **not** needed to provide a choice function for this example. In fact, whenever X is a finite set of sets, we can always find a choice function without resorting to the axiom of choice.

2. Let $X = \mathcal{P}(\mathbb{N}) \setminus \{\emptyset\}$ and define $f: X \to \mathbb{N}$ by $f(S) = $ the least element of S. Then f is a choice function. For example, if $\mathbb{O}$ is the set of odd natural numbers, then $f(\mathbb{O}) = 1$. If $\mathbb{P}$ is the set of primes, then $f(\mathbb{P}) = 2$. The axiom of choice is **not** needed for this example. In this case, we could define a choice function by using the Well Ordering Principle of $\mathbb{N}$ (see Lesson 8).

    More generally, if a set A can be ordered in such a way that every subset of S has a least element, then the axiom of choice will not be needed to define a choice function on $\mathcal{P}(A) \setminus \{\emptyset\}$. Once, again, we can simply define $f: \mathcal{P}(A) \setminus \{\emptyset\} \to A$ by $f(S) = $ the least element of S.

3. For each natural number n, let A_n be a set with two distinct elements and let $X = \{A_n \mid n \in \mathbb{N}\}$. Can we *explicitly define* a choice function $f: X \to \bigcup X$? The answer is no. Even though all the sets in X are finite, we do not have enough information about the sets to explicitly describe a choice function. However, if we assume the axiom of choice, then we can say that a choice function exists. Furthermore, we can feel free to use this choice function to prove other results. This example gives a little insight into why the axiom of choice was so controversial when it was first introduced. It's like magic. All of a sudden, we have this function that we can't describe. We weren't able to come up with the function ourselves, so we simply said, "No big deal—the axiom of choice will take care of this for us. Here's your choice function." Someone might ask, "Well, what does it look like?" And you would have to respond, "I have no idea, but here it is."

    We can replace the natural numbers with any set here. For example, we can let A_r be a set with two distinct elements for each $r \in \mathbb{R}$. Even though $\mathbb{R}$ is uncountable, the axiom of choice still gives us a choice function $f: X \to \bigcup X$. The axiom of choice is indeed very powerful.

Axioms 0 through 9 form the axiom system known as ZFC. This stands for "Zermelo-Fraenkel with Choice."

There are many statements that are equivalent to the Axiom of Choice. We will discuss one of the most popular ones known as Zorn's Lemma. Before stating Zorn's Lemma, we will need some preliminary definitions.

Recall that a **partially ordered set** (or **poset**) is a pair $(P, \leq)$, where P is a set and $\leq$ is a reflexive, antisymmetic, and transitive relation on P. See Example 4.9 from Lesson 4 for examples of partially ordered sets.

A **linearly ordered set** is a poset $(P, \leq)$ that satisfies the **comparability condition** (for all $x, y \in P$, either $x \leq y$ or $y \leq x$).

If $(P, \leq)$ is a partially ordered set, then $(C, \leq)$ is a **chain** in P if $C \subseteq P$ and $(C, \leq)$ is linearly ordered. An **upper bound** of the chain $(C, \leq)$ in P is an element $s \in P$ such that for all $y \in C$, $y \leq s$. An element $m \in P$ is a **maximal element** of $(P, \leq)$ if there is no $y \in P$ such that $m < y$.

Example 11.6:

1. Let $A = \{a, b, c\}$. Then $(\mathcal{P}(A), \subseteq)$ is a partially ordered set that is not linearly ordered (see part 2 of Example 4.10). An example of a chain in $\mathcal{P}(A)$ is $(X, \subseteq)$, where $X = \{\emptyset, \{a\}, \{a, b\}, \{a, b, c\}\}$. Another example is $(Y, \subseteq)$, where $Y = \{\{b\}, \{b, c\}\}$. The set $\{a, b, c\}$ is an upper bound of the chain $(X, \subseteq)$. The chain $(Y, \subseteq)$ has two upper bounds, namely $\{b, c\}$ and $\{a, b, c\}$. The element $\{a, b, c\} \in \mathcal{P}(A)$ is a maximal element of $(\mathcal{P}(A), \subseteq)$ (and A is the only maximal element in this case).

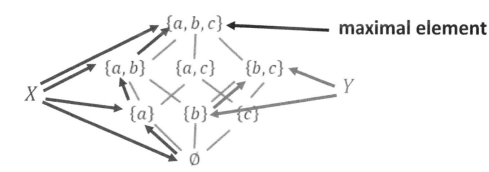

2. More generally, given any set A with at least two elements, $(\mathcal{P}(A), \subseteq)$ is a partially ordered set that is not linearly ordered. If $(C, \subseteq)$ is a chain in P, then $\bigcup C$ is an upper bound of $(C, \subseteq)$ in $\mathcal{P}(A)$. The element $A \in \mathcal{P}(A)$ is a maximal element of $(\mathcal{P}(A), \subseteq)$

Zorn's Lemma (ZL): Let $(P, \leq)$ be a poset such that each chain in P has an upper bound in P. Then P contains at least one maximal element.

Before we discuss the equivalence of ZL and AC, let's look at a simple application of Zorn's Lemma.

Example 11.7: Let $\mathcal{D} = \{\mathcal{A} \subseteq \mathcal{P}(\mathbb{N}) \mid \mathcal{A} \text{ is pairwise disjoint}\}$. For example, if $\mathcal{B} = \{\{0, 1\}, \{1, 2\}\}$ and $\mathcal{C} = \{\{0, 1, 2\}, \{3, 4, 5\}, \{6, 7\}\}$, then $\mathcal{B} \notin \mathcal{D}$ and $\mathcal{C} \in \mathcal{D}$. Since $\subseteq$ is transitive, reflexive, and antisymmetric, $(\mathcal{D}, \subseteq)$ is a partially ordered set. An example of a chain in $\mathcal{D}$ is

$$\{\{0\}\} \subseteq \{\{0\}, \{1\}\} \subseteq \{\{0\}, \{1\}, \{2\}\} \subseteq \cdots \subseteq \{\{0\}, \{1\}, \{2\}, \dots, \{n\}\} \subseteq \cdots$$

133

The union of all these sets is $\{\{k\} \mid k \in \mathbb{N}\}$, and clearly this collection is an upper bound of this chain. Does every chain in the poset $(\mathcal{D}, \subseteq)$ have an upper bound? The answer is Yes! If $\mathcal{C} \subseteq \mathcal{D}$ is a chain, then $\bigcup \mathcal{C} \in \mathcal{D}$. To see this, let $A, B \in \bigcup \mathcal{C}$. Then there are $\mathcal{A}, \mathcal{B} \in \mathcal{C}$ with $A \in \mathcal{A}$ and $B \in \mathcal{B}$. Since $\mathcal{C}$ is a chain, we must have $\mathcal{A} \subseteq \mathcal{B}$ or $\mathcal{B} \subseteq \mathcal{A}$. Without loss of generality, assume that $\mathcal{A} \subseteq \mathcal{B}$. Then $A, B \in \mathcal{B}$. Since $\mathcal{B}$ is pairwise disjoint, $A \cap B = \emptyset$. Since $A, B \in \bigcup \mathcal{C}$ were arbitrary, we have shown that $\bigcup \mathcal{C} \in \mathcal{D}$.

By Zorn's Lemma, $\mathcal{D}$ has at least one maximal element.

It's actually not too difficult in this example to find maximal elements of $\mathcal{D}$ without resorting to Zorn's Lemma. For example, $\mathcal{X} = \{\emptyset\} \cup \{\{k\} \mid k \in \mathbb{N}\}$ is a maximal element of $\mathcal{D}$. To see this, let $A \in \mathcal{P}(\mathbb{N})$ be arbitrary. Since $\emptyset \in \mathcal{X}$, we may assume that $A \neq \emptyset$. Since $A \neq \emptyset$, there is $k \in \mathbb{N}$ with $k \in A$. Then $k \in A \cap \{k\}$, and so $A \cap \{k\} \neq \emptyset$. Thus, $\mathcal{A} \cup \{A\} \notin \mathcal{D}$. Since $A \in \mathcal{P}(\mathbb{N})$ was arbitrary, $\mathcal{D}$ is maximal.

There are many other maximal elements of $\mathcal{D}$. In fact, the maximal elements of $\mathcal{D}$ are precisely the collections $P \cup \{\emptyset\}$, where P is a partition of $\mathbb{N}$. See Problem 10 below for a less trivial example.

Theorem 11.1: $\mathrm{ZL} \to \mathrm{AC}$.

Proof: Assume that Zorn's Lemma is true and let X be a set of nonempty sets. We make the following definition: $F = \{f \mid (f \text{ is a function with } \mathrm{dom}\, f \subseteq X) \land \forall A \in \mathrm{dom}\, f\ (f(A) \in A)\}$. Then $(F, \subseteq)$ is a partially ordered set. This follows from parts 2 and 3 of Example 4.9.

Let $(C, \subseteq)$ be a chain in F and let $g = \bigcup C$.

We first show that $g \in F$. Suppose that $(A, y), (A, z) \in g$. Then $(A, y) \in f_1$ and $(A, z) \in f_2$ for some f_1, $f_2 \in C$. Since C is linearly ordered, either $f_1 \subseteq f_2$ or $f_2 \subseteq f_1$. Without loss of generality, assume that $f_1 \subseteq f_2$. Then $(A, y), (A, z) \in f_2$. Since $f_2 \in F$, f_2 is a function, and therefore, $y = z$. So, g is a function. If $A \in \mathrm{dom}\, g$, then there is $y \in \bigcup X$ such that $(A, y) \in g$. So, there is $f \in C$ with $(A, y) \in f$. Since $C \subseteq F$, $f \in F$. So, $\mathrm{dom}\, f \subseteq X$ and $f(A) \in A$. Since $A \in \mathrm{dom}\, f$, $A \in X$. Also, $g(A) = f(A)$. Since $A \in \mathrm{dom}\, g$ was arbitrary, $\mathrm{dom}\, g \subseteq X$ and $\forall A \in \mathrm{dom}\, g\ (g(A) \in A)$. Thus, $g \in F$.

Next, we show that g is an upper bound of $(C, \subseteq)$. Let $f \in C$. Then $f \subseteq \bigcup C$ by part (i) of Problem 9 in Problem Set 3. So, $f \subseteq g$. Therefore, g is an upper bound of $(C, \subseteq)$.

By Zorn's Lemma, $(F, \subseteq)$ has a maximal element h. Since h is in F, h is a choice function on $\mathrm{dom}\, h \subseteq X$. We need to show that $\mathrm{dom}\, h = X$. Since we already know that $\mathrm{dom}\, h \subseteq X$, we need only show that $X \subseteq \mathrm{dom}\, h$. Assume toward contradiction that there is some set A in $X \setminus \mathrm{dom}\, h$. Since A is nonempty, there is $a \in A$. Let $k = h \cup \{(A, a)\}$. Then $k \in F$ and $h \subset k$ (h is a proper subset of k), contradicting the maximality of h. Therefore, $X \subseteq \mathrm{dom}\, h$, as desired. $\qquad\square$

It is also true that the Axiom of Choice implies Zorn's Lemma (and so, the two statements are equivalent). However, the proof of this is more challenging and requires the use of ordinals. You will be asked to prove this in Problem 11 in Problem Set 12. We will learn about ordinals in the next lesson.

Problem Set 11

LEVEL 1

1. Prove from the axioms of ZF that for all $n \geq 2$, every n-tuple of n sets is a set.

2. Prove that Zorn's Lemma is equivalent to the following statement: Let $(P, \leq)$ be a poset with nonempty domain such that each chain in P with nonempty domain has an upper bound in P. Then P contains at least one maximal element.

LEVEL 2

3. Prove from the axioms of ZF that the cartesian product of two sets is a set.

4. Prove that Zorn's Lemma is equivalent to the following statement: If X is a set of sets such that, for each $Y \subseteq X$ such that $(Y, \subseteq)$ is a linearly ordered set, $\bigcup Y \in X$, then $(X, \subseteq)$ has at least one maximal element.

LEVEL 3

5. Prove that the following two versions of AC are equivalent: (i) If X is a set of nonempty sets, then there is a function $f: X \to \bigcup X$ such that for each $x \in X$, $f(x) \in x$; (ii) If X is a set of nonempty pairwise disjoint sets, then there is a set Y that contains exactly one element from each set in X.

6. We say that a set of sets X has **finite character** if the following holds: $A \in X$ if and only if every finite subset of A is in X. Prove that Zorn's Lemma is equivalent to the following statement: If X is a set of sets with finite character, then $(X, \subseteq)$ has at least one maximal element (This statement is known as **Tukey's Lemma**).

LEVEL 4

7. Prove that the bounded comprehension schema follows from the replacement schema.

8. Let $\tau(n)$ be the formula $\phi(n) \wedge \psi(n)$, where

$$\phi(n) \equiv \forall m(m \notin n) \vee \exists k \forall m\big(m \in n \leftrightarrow (m \in k \vee m = k)\big)$$

and

$$\psi(n) \equiv \forall k \left(k \in n \to \Big(\forall m(m \notin k) \vee \exists m\big(m \in n \wedge \forall j(j \in k \leftrightarrow (j \in m \vee j = m))\big) \Big) \right)$$

Use the axiom of infinity, the bounded comprehension schema, and the axiom of foundation to prove that $\{n \mid \tau(n)\}$ is the set of natural numbers. Then prove that if there is a set x such that $x = \{x\}$, then $\{n \mid \tau(n)\}$ is **not** the set of natural numbers.

LEVEL 5

9. Prove that the set of natural numbers exists using only the axiom of infinity and the bounded comprehension schema.

10. Prove that for every partially ordered set $(P, \leq_P)$, there is a linearly ordered set $(P, \leq_L)$ such that $\leq_P \subseteq \leq_L$.

CHALLENGE PROBLEM

11. Prove that the statement given in Problem 10 is **not** equivalent to the Axiom of Choice.

Lesson 12
Ordinals

Transitive Sets

In Example 2.5 from Lesson 2, we saw that the membership relation $\in$ is **not** transitive in general. Nonetheless, we make the following definition.

A set x is **transitive** if every element of x is also a subset of x. Symbolically, we can write

$$\forall y(y \in x \to y \subseteq x), \quad \text{or equivalently,} \quad \forall y \, \forall z \left((z \in y \land y \in x) \to z \in x\right).$$

Example 12.1:

1. $0 = \emptyset$ is transitive. Indeed, $\emptyset$ has no elements, and so, it is vacuously true that every element of $\emptyset$ is a subset of $\emptyset$.

2. $1 = \{\emptyset\}$ is transitive. To see this, note that the only element of $\{\emptyset\}$ is $\emptyset$, and $\emptyset$ is a subset of every set. In particular, $\emptyset \subseteq \{\emptyset\}$.

3. $2 = \{\emptyset, \{\emptyset\}\}$ is transitive. The elements of $\{\emptyset, \{\emptyset\}\}$ are $\emptyset$ and $\{\emptyset\}$. As in 2, we observe that $\emptyset$ is a subset of every set, and so, $\emptyset \subseteq \{\emptyset, \{\emptyset\}\}$. The only element of $\{\emptyset\}$ is $\emptyset$, and $\emptyset \in \{\emptyset, \{\emptyset\}\}$. Therefore, $\{\emptyset\} \subseteq \{\emptyset, \{\emptyset\}\}$.

4. $\{\emptyset, \{\{\emptyset\}\}\}$ is **not** transitive. We have $\{\emptyset\} \in \{\{\emptyset\}\} \in \{\emptyset, \{\{\emptyset\}\}\}$, but $\{\emptyset\} \notin \{\emptyset, \{\{\emptyset\}\}\}$. Therefore, $\{\{\emptyset\}\} \in \{\emptyset, \{\{\emptyset\}\}\}$, but $\{\{\emptyset\}\} \not\subseteq \{\emptyset, \{\{\emptyset\}\}\}$.

5. $\mathcal{P}(\{\emptyset, \{\emptyset\}\}) = \{\emptyset, \{\emptyset\}, \{\{\emptyset\}\}, \{\emptyset, \{\emptyset\}\}\}$ is transitive. The elements of $\{\emptyset, \{\emptyset\}, \{\{\emptyset\}\}, \{\emptyset, \{\emptyset\}\}\}$ are $\emptyset$, $\{\emptyset\}$, $\{\{\emptyset\}\}$, and $\{\emptyset, \{\emptyset\}\}$. By the same reasoning as in 3, $\emptyset$ and $\{\emptyset\}$ are subsets of $\{\emptyset, \{\emptyset\}, \{\{\emptyset\}\}, \{\emptyset, \{\emptyset\}\}\}$. The only element of $\{\{\emptyset\}\}$ is $\{\emptyset\}$, which is in $\{\emptyset, \{\emptyset\}, \{\{\emptyset\}\}, \{\emptyset, \{\emptyset\}\}\}$. The set $\{\emptyset, \{\emptyset\}\}$ has two elements: $\emptyset$ and $\{\emptyset\}$, both of which are in $\{\emptyset, \{\emptyset\}, \{\{\emptyset\}\}, \{\emptyset, \{\emptyset\}\}\}$.

6. Every natural number is a transitive set. We saw in 1, 2, and 3 above that $0 = \emptyset$, $1 = \{\emptyset\}$, and $2 = \{\emptyset, \{\emptyset\}\}$ are transitive. Let's use induction to show that n is transitive for all $n \in \omega$. Assuming that k is transitive, let $j \in k + 1 = k \cup \{k\}$ and $m \in j$. Then $j \in k$ or $j \in \{k\}$. If $j \in k$, then we have $m \in j \in k$. Since k is transitive, $m \in k$. So, $m \in k \cup \{k\} = k + 1$. If $j \in \{k\}$, then $j = k$. So, $m \in k$, and again, we have $m \in k \cup \{k\} = k + 1$.

7. The set of natural numbers, $\omega = \{0, 1, 2, \dots\}$ is a transitive set. We can prove this by induction. The base case is $0 = \emptyset \subseteq \omega$. For the inductive step, we assume that $k \in \omega \to k \subseteq \omega$. Since $k \in \omega$, we have $\{k\} \subseteq \omega$, and therefore, $k + 1 = k \cup \{k\} \subseteq \omega$.

8. If A is a transitive set, then $\mathcal{P}(A)$ is also transitive. To see this, let $B \in \mathcal{P}(A)$ and let $c \in B$. By the definition of $\mathcal{P}(A)$, $B \subseteq A$. Since $c \in B$ and $B \subseteq A$, we have $c \in A$. Since A is transitive, $c \subseteq A$. Thus, $c \in \mathcal{P}(A)$. Since $c \in B$ was arbitrary, $B \subseteq \mathcal{P}(A)$.

9. If A is a transitive set, then $\bigcup A$ is also transitive. To see this, let $b \in \bigcup A$. Then $b \in X$ for some $X \in A$. Since A is transitive, $b \in A$. By part (i) of Problem 9 from Problem Set 3, $b \subseteq \bigcup A$.

137

Well-ordered Sets

Recall from Lesson 4 that a **strict linearly ordered set** is a pair $(L, <)$, where L is a set, $<$ is **antireflexive** on L $(\forall x \in L(x \not< x))$, **antisymmetric** on L $(\forall x, y \in L(x < y \wedge y < x \rightarrow x = y))$, and **transitive** on L $(\forall x, y, z \in L(x < y \wedge y < z \rightarrow x < z))$, and such that $(L, <)$ satisfies trichotomy $(\forall x, y \in L(x < y \vee x = y \vee y < x))$.

A strict linearly ordered set $(L, <)$ is called **well-ordered** if for every nonempty subset $A \subseteq L$, there is an element $a \in A$ such that for all $b \in A$ with $b \neq a$, $a < b$. This element $a \in A$ is called the $<$**-least element** of A.

Example 12.2:

1. $(\mathbb{N}, <)$ is well-ordered. This is precisely the statement of the Well Ordering Principle from Lesson 8. A rigorous proof of this using the formal set-theoretic definition of $\mathbb{N}$ will be given below in part 6 of this example.

2. $(\mathbb{Z}, <)$, $(\mathbb{Q}, <)$, and $(\mathbb{R}, <)$ are **not** well-ordered. None of $\mathbb{Z}$, $\mathbb{Q}$, or $\mathbb{R}$ have a $<$-least element.

3. $([0, 1], <)$ is **not** well-ordered. Although $[0, 1]$ has the $<$-least element 0, the subset $(0, 1)$ has no $<$-least element. Note that when we write an interval such as $[0, 1]$ without any additional comments, we are usually thinking of this interval as a subset of $\mathbb{R}$. We will write $[0, 1] \cap \mathbb{Q}$ for the corresponding subset of $\mathbb{Q}$. It's worth noting that $[0, 1] \cap \mathbb{Q}$ is not well-ordered either.

4. Define the relation $<_*$ on $\mathbb{N}$ by

   $$<_* = \{(m, n) \mid (m \text{ and } n \text{ have the same parity and } m < n) \vee (m \text{ is even and } n \text{ is odd})\}$$

   We can visualize this ordering as follows:

   $$0 <_* 2 <_* 4 <_* 6 <_* 8 <_* \cdots <_* 1 <_* 3 <_* 5 <_* \cdots$$

   In words, we are insisting that all even natural numbers are less than all odd natural numbers, while the evens and odds themselves are placed in their usual order within themselves.

   Let's show that $(\mathbb{N}, <_*)$ is well-ordered. It is very easy to check that $(\mathbb{N}, <_*)$ is linearly ordered and so, I leave this to the reader. Suppose that $A \subseteq \mathbb{N}$ is nonempty. If A contains any even natural numbers, let m be the $<$-least one. Since $m <_* n$ for every odd natural number (by the definition of $<_*$), m is the $<_*$-least element of A. If A does not contain any even natural numbers, let m be the $<$-least odd natural number of A. Then m is also the $<_*$-least element of A. In either case, A has a $<_*$-least element. This proves that $(\mathbb{N}, <_*)$ is well-ordered.

   Recall from Lesson 10 that a **homomorphism** from a strict partially ordered set $(A, <_A)$ to a strict partially ordered set $(B, <_B)$ is a function $f: A \rightarrow B$ such that for all $x, y \in A$, $x <_A y$ if and only if $f(x) <_B f(y)$. An **isomorphism** is a bijective homomorphism.

   Let's show that $(\mathbb{N}, <_*)$ is **not** isomorphic to $(\mathbb{N}, <)$, where $<$ is the usual ordering on $\mathbb{N}$. Suppose that $f: \mathbb{N} \rightarrow \mathbb{N}$ satisfies $n < m$ if and only if $f(n) <_* f(m)$. Suppose also that $1 \in \operatorname{ran} f$. Let $a \in \mathbb{N}$ satisfy $f(a) = 1$. If $a = 0$, then $\operatorname{ran} f$ contains no even integers, and so, f is not surjective. If $a \neq 0$, let $f(a - 1) = b$. Since $a - 1 < a$, $b <_* 1$. So, b is even. Therefore, $b + 2$ is also even. So, $b <_* b + 2 <_* 1$. It follows that $b + 2 \notin \operatorname{ran} f$. So, once again, f is not surjective. Therefore, f is not an isomorphism, and so, $(\mathbb{N}, <)$ is **not** isomorphic to $(\mathbb{N}, <_*)$.

5. Recall that $0 = \emptyset$, $1 = \{\emptyset\} = \{0\}$, $2 = \{\emptyset, \{\emptyset\}\} = \{0, 1\}$, and so on for each natural number. In general, we have $n + 1 = n \cup \{n\}$. You will be asked to prove in Problem 4 below that each natural number is well-ordered by $\in$.

6. Let's show that $\omega = \{0, 1, 2, 3, \ldots\}$ is well-ordered by $\in$.

   To see that $\in$ is antireflexive on ω, let $n \in \omega$. Then $n \in n + 1$. Since $n + 1$ is well-ordered by $\in$ (by 5), $\in$ is antireflexive on $n + 1$. So, $n \notin n$.

   To see that $\in$ is antisymmetric on ω, let $j, k \in \omega$, and choose $m \in \omega$ with $j, k \in m$. If $j \in k$ and $k \in j$, then by transitivity of $\in$ on m, we have $j \in j$. But this contradicts that $\in$ is a strict partial order on m. So, we cannot have $j \in k$ and $k \in j$. So, antisymmetry is vacuously satisfied by $\in$ on ω.

   To see that $\in$ is transitive on ω, let $j, k, l \in \omega$, and choose $m \in \omega$ with $j, k, l \in m$. If $j \in k$ and $k \in l$, then by transitivity of $\in$ on m, we have $j \in l$.

   To see that $(\omega, \in)$ satisfies trichotomy, let $j, k \in \omega$, and choose $m \in \omega$ with $j, k \in m$. Since $(m, \in)$ satisfies trichotomy, $j \in k$, $j = k$, or $k \in j$.

   Finally, let A be a nonempty subset of ω, and choose $n \in A$. If $n \cap A = \emptyset$, then n is the $\in$-least element of A (If $m \in A$ with $m \in n$, then $m \in n \cap A$, contradicting $n \cap A = \emptyset$). Otherwise, $n \cap A$ is a nonempty subset of n, and since n is well-ordered by $\in$, $n \cap A$ has an $\in$-least element m. Then m is the $\in$-least element of A (If $k \in A$ with $k \in m$, then $k \in n$ because n is transitive, and so, m is not the $\in$-least element of $n \cap A$).

The collection of all well-ordered sets has a particularly nice structure. As we will soon see, any two well-ordered sets are either isomorphic or one is isomorphic to an "initial segment" of the other.

Let $(W, <)$ be a well-ordered set with least element a. If $b \in W$ with $b \neq a$, then the set of **predecessors** of b is $\text{pred}(W, b) = [a, b) = \{x \in W \mid x < b\}$. The set of predecessors of a is $\emptyset$. That is, $\text{pred}(W, a) = [a, a) = \emptyset$. A subset $S \subseteq W$ is an **initial segment** of W if for all $b \in S$, $[a, b) \subseteq S$ (or equivalently, $\text{pred}(W, b) \subseteq S$).

Example 12.3:

1. Consider $\omega = \{0, 1, 2, \ldots\}$ ordered by the $\in$ relation. The set of predecessors of 0 is $\emptyset$. The set of predecessors of 1 is $[0, 1) = \{0\}$. The set of predecessors of 2 is $[0, 2) = \{0, 1\}$. In general, the set of predecessors of n is $[0, n) = \{0, 1, 2, \ldots, n - 1\}$. Each $n \in \omega$ is an initial segment of ω. The set $A = \{0, 1, 3, 4, 5, 6\}$ is **not** an initial segment of ω because $3 \in A$, but the set of predecessors of 3 is $[0, 3) = \{0, 1, 2\}$, which is not a subset of A because $2 \in [0, 3)$, but $2 \notin A$.

2. Consider the well-ordered set $(\mathbb{N}, <_*)$ from Part 4 of Example 12.2. Recall that the well ordering $<_*$ is defined on $\mathbb{N}$ by

   $$<_* = \{(m, n) \mid (m \text{ and } n \text{ have the same parity and } m < n) \vee (m \text{ is even and } n \text{ is odd})\}.$$

   Once again, we can visualize this ordering as follows:

   $$0 <_* 2 <_* 4 <_* 6 <_* 8 <_* \cdots <_* 1 <_* 3 <_* 5 <_* \cdots$$

   The set of predecessors of 8 is $[0, 8) = \{0, 2, 4, 6\}$. The set of predecessors of 5 is $\{0, 2, 4, 6, \ldots, 1, 3\} = \mathbb{E} \cup \{1, 3\}$, where $\mathbb{E}$ is the set of even natural numbers.

Notice that there is an isomorphism f from $(\omega, \in)$ to an initial segment of $(\mathbb{N}, <_*)$ defined by $f(n) = 2n$. It's easy to show that f is injective, $n \in m$ if and only if $f(n) <_* f(m)$, and $f[\omega] = \mathbb{E}$.

3. Given a well-ordered set $(W, <)$, W is trivially an initial segment of W.

If S is an initial segment of W and $S \neq W$, we call S a **proper initial segment** of W.

Theorem 12.1: Let $(W, <)$ be a well-ordered set and let S be a proper initial segment of W. Then there is $b \in W$ such that $S = \text{pred}(W, b)$.

Analysis: The idea of the proof is simple. Since the initial segment S is not equal to W, just take the least element of W not in S. Let's call this least element b. Then S consists of everything less than b.

Proof: Since S is a *proper* initial segment of W, $W \setminus S$ is a nonempty subset of W. Let b be the $<$-least element of $W \setminus S$. We will show that $S = \text{pred}(W, b)$.

Let $c \in \text{pred}(W, b)$. Then $c < b$. Since b is the $<$-least element of $W \setminus S$, $c \notin W \setminus S$. So, $c \in S$. Since $c \in \text{pred}(W, b)$ was arbitrary, we have $\forall c(c \in \text{pred}(W, b) \to c \in S)$. Therefore, $\text{pred}(W, b) \subseteq S$.

If $c \notin \text{pred}(W, b)$, then $c \not< b$. Since $(W, <)$ is a linearly ordered set, $b = c$ or $b < c$. If $b = c$, then $c \in W \setminus S$ (because b was chosen to be in $W \setminus S$). So, $c \notin S$. If $b < c$, then $c \in S$ would imply $b \in S$ because S is an initial segment of W. So, $c \notin S$. So, $\forall c(c \notin \text{pred}(W, b) \to c \notin S)$. By the law of the contrapositive, $\forall c(c \in S \to c \in \text{pred}(W, b))$. That is, $S \subseteq \text{pred}(W, b)$.

Since $\text{pred}(W, b) \subseteq S$ and $S \subseteq \text{pred}(W, b)$, we have $S = \text{pred}(W, b)$. $\square$

Note: Recall from Lesson 9 that the law of the contrapositive says that $\neg q \to \neg p$ is logically equivalent to $p \to q$. If we let p be the statement "$c \in S$" and we let q be the statement "$c \in \text{pred}(W, b)$," we get that "$c \notin \text{pred}(W, b) \to c \notin S$" is logically equivalent to "$c \in S \to c \in \text{pred}(W, b)$."

If $(A, <_1)$ and $(B, <_2)$ are partially ordered sets, then a function $f: A \to B$ is said to be **increasing** if for all $x, y \in A$, $x <_1 y \to f(x) \leq_2 f(y)$. The function f is said to be **strictly increasing** if for all $x, y \in A$, $x <_1 y \to f(x) <_2 f(y)$. For example, every homomorphism from A to B is strictly increasing.

Theorem 12.2: Let $(W, <)$ be a well-ordered set and let $f: W \to W$ be a strictly increasing function. Then for all $x \in W$, $f(x) \geq x$.

Analysis: Let's think about trying to construct a strictly increasing function by starting with the least element of W and working our way up through the well-ordered set. If a is the least element of W, then $f(a)$ must be at least as big as a simply because there is nothing in W smaller than a. So, we have $f(a) \geq a$. The second element, let's call it b, must satisfy $f(b) > f(a)$ because f is strictly increasing. Since $f(a) \geq a$ and $f(b) > f(a)$, we have $f(b) > a$. So, $f(b) \geq b$. We can continue in this fashion to show that $f(x) \geq x$ for the third element, the fourth element, ... and so on.

Now, the argument in the previous paragraph gives strong evidence that the result is true at "successor stages." But what about "limit stages?" For example, consider the well-ordered set $(\mathbb{N}, <_*)$ from Part 4 of Example 12.2 where all the evens are less than all the odds.

$$0 <_* 2 <_* 4 <_* 6 <_* 8 <_* \cdots <_* 1 <_* 3 <_* 5 <_* \cdots$$

There is one "limit stage" to consider in this example. The number 1 is **not** the successor of any other natural number. How do we know that $f(1)$ can't be less than 1? Well, if it were, then $f(1)$ would be equal to an even natural number. If $f(1) = 0$, then we would have $f(0) \geq_* 0 = f(1)$, which is impossible because f is strictly increasing. Similarly, if $f(1) = 2$, then $f(2) \geq_* 2 = f(1)$, which is again impossible for the same reason (remember that $2 <_* 1$). And so on. So, we must have $f(1) \geq_* 1$.

We will prove Theorem 12.2 rigorously by contradiction. If we let b be the least element where the conclusion of the theorem fails (so that $f(b) < b$), we simply observe that $f(f(b))$ is a smaller element than $f(b)$ and the conclusion fails for $f(b)$ as well.

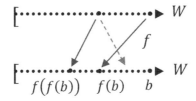

The figure above shows two identical copies of a well-ordered set $(W, <)$ together with a strictly increasing function f with $f(b) < b$. Notice how $f(f(b))$ is forced to be less than $f(b)$. The dashed arrow would violate f being strictly increasing.

Let's write out the proof.

Proof: Let $S = \{x \in W \mid f(x) < x\}$. Assume toward contradiction that $S \neq \emptyset$. Since $S \subseteq W$ and $(W, <)$ is well-ordered, S has a $<$-least element b. Since $b \in S$, $\boldsymbol{f(b)} < \boldsymbol{b}$. Since f is strictly increasing, $f(f(b)) < f(b)$. It follows that $\boldsymbol{f(b)} \in \boldsymbol{S}$, contradicting b being the $<$-least element of S. It follows that $S = \emptyset$. Since trichotomy holds in $(W, <)$, for all $x \in W$, $f(x) \geq x$. $\qquad\square$

Theorem 12.3: Let $(W, <)$ be a well-ordered set and let S be a proper initial segment of W. Then $(W, <)$ is **not** isomorphic to $(S, <)$.

Analysis: S must have the form $\text{pred}(W, b)$. So, if $f: W \cong S$, then $f(b) < b$. But an isomorphism between two well-ordered sets is a strictly increasing function. This contradicts Theorem 12.2.

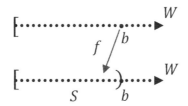

Proof: Let S be a proper initial segment of W and assume toward contradiction that $f: W \to S$ is an isomorphism. By Theorem 12.1, there is $b \in W$ such that $S = \text{pred}(W, b)$. Since f is a homomorphism, whenever $x, y \in W$ with $x < y$, we have $f(x) < f(y)$. So, f is a strictly increasing function. Since $b \in W$, $f(b) \in S = \text{pred}(W, b)$. So, $f(b) < b$, contradicting Theorem 12.2. Therefore, there is no isomorphism from W to S. $\qquad\square$

Theorem 12.4: Let $(W, <)$ be a well-ordered set. The only automorphism of W is the identity function.

Recall: An **automorphism** of a well-ordered set $(W, <)$ is an isomorphism from W to itself.

For example, the identity function $i_W: W \to W$ is an automorphism of $(W, <)$.

Let $f: W \to W$ be an automorphism of $(W, <)$. Recall that $f^{-1}: W \to W$ is defined by $f^{-1}(x) = y$ if and only if $f(y) = x$. Since f is a bijection, f^{-1} exists and is also a bijection (see Lesson 6). Furthermore, if $x, y \in W$, then since f is a homomorphism, $f^{-1}(x) < f^{-1}(y)$ if and only if $f\big(f^{-1}(x)\big) < f\big(f^{-1}(y)\big)$ if and only if $x < y$. It follows that f^{-1} is also an automorphism of $(W, <)$.

We are now ready to prove Theorem 12.4.

Proof: Let $f: W \to W$ be an automorphism. By Theorem 12.2, for all $x \in W$, $f(x) \geq x$. Since f is an automorphism, so is f^{-1}. Again, by Theorem 12.2, for all $x \in W$, $f^{-1}(x) \geq x$. So, for all $x \in W$, $f\big(f^{-1}(x)\big) \geq f(x)$. Since $f\big(f^{-1}(x)\big) = x$, for all $x \in W$, $x \geq f(x)$. So, for all $x \in W$, $f(x) = x$. Therefore, f is the identity function. $\qquad\square$

In general, when two structures are isomorphic, there may be many isomorphisms between them.

As a simple example, let's look at the two sets $A = \{0, 1, 2\}$ and $B = \{a, b, c\}$. An isomorphism from one set to another is simply a bijection and two finite sets are isomorphic precisely when they have the same number of elements. The function $\{(0, a), (1, b), (2, c)\}$ is an isomorphism (bijection) from A to B. But there are others. For example, $\{(0, a), (1, c), (2, b)\}$ is another isomorphism from A to B. All together there are 6 isomorphisms from A to B.

As a less trivial example, consider the linear order $(\mathbb{Z}, <)$. There are infinitely many automorphisms from $\mathbb{Z}$ to itself. In fact, for any integer n, there is a unique automorphism sending 0 to n. Just define $f_n: \mathbb{Z} \to \mathbb{Z}$ by $f_n(k) = k + n$. It is easy to verify that f_n is an automorphism for each n. A visualization of f_2 is shown below.

As we just proved, there is only one automorphism of a well-ordered set. We will now use this result to show that if two well-ordered sets are isomorphic, there is only one isomorphism from one to the other.

Theorem 12.5: Let $(W_1, <_1)$ and $(W_2, <_2)$ be isomorphic well-ordered sets. Then there is exactly one isomorphism $f: W_1 \to W_2$.

Proof: Let $f, g: W_1 \to W_2$ be isomorphisms. Then $g^{-1} \circ f$ is an automorphism of W_1. By Theorem 12.4, $g^{-1} \circ f = id_{W_1}$. Therefore, $f = g$. □

If $f: X \to Y$ is a function and $Z \subseteq X$, the **restriction** of f to Z is the function $g: Z \to f[Z]$ defined by $g(z) = f(z)$ for all $z \in Z$.

Theorem 12.6: Let $f: X \to Y$ be an isomorphism from the well-ordered set $(X, <_1)$ to the well-ordered set $(Y, <_2)$, let $x \in X$, and let $g: \mathrm{pred}(X, x) \to \mathrm{pred}(Y, f(x))$ be the restriction of f to $\mathrm{pred}(X, x)$. Then g is an isomorphism. Furthermore, g is the **only** isomorphism from $\mathrm{pred}(X, x)$ to $\mathrm{pred}(Y, f(x))$.

Proof: First note that if $z \in \mathrm{pred}(X, x)$, then $z <_1 x$. Since f is a homomorphism, $f(z) <_2 f(x)$. So, $g(z) = f(z) \in \mathrm{pred}(Y, f(x))$. Therefore, g maps into $\mathrm{pred}(Y, f(x))$.

Suppose that $g(z) = g(w)$. Then $f(z) = g(z) = g(w) = f(w)$. Since f is injective, $z = w$. Therefore, g is injective.

Let $y \in \mathrm{pred}(Y, f(x))$. Then $y <_2 f(x)$. Since f is an isomorphism, there is $z \in X$ with $f(z) = y$. So, we have $z, x \in X$ with $f(z) <_2 f(x)$. Since f is a homomorphism, $z <_1 x$. Therefore, $z \in \mathrm{pred}(X, x)$, and so, $g(z) = f(z) = y$. Thus, g is surjective.

Let $z, w \in \mathrm{pred}(X, x)$. Then $z <_1 w$ if and only if $f(z) <_2 f(w)$ if and only if $g(z) <_2 g(w)$. So, g is a homomorphism.

Since g is a bijective homomorphism, g is an isomorphism. By Theorem 12.5, g is the **only** isomorphism from $\mathrm{pred}(X, x)$ to $\mathrm{pred}(Y, f(x))$. □

The next theorem tells us that any two well-ordered sets can be compared. If two well-ordered sets are not isomorphic, then one of them is *essentially* just an initial segment of the other one.

Theorem 12.7: Let $(W_1, <_1)$ and $(W_2, <_2)$ be well-ordered sets. Then exactly one of the following holds: (i) $(W_1, <_1) \cong (W_2, <_2)$; (ii) $(W_1, <_1) \cong (T, <_2)$ for some proper initial segment T of W_2; (iii) $(W_2, <_2) \cong (S, <_1)$ for some proper initial segment S of W_1.

Analysis: The idea is that all well-ordered sets are built up the same way. There's a least element, then a next element, then a third element, and so on... until we get to the first "limiting element." This is an element that is greater than the first countably many elements. Let's call this the ωth (pronounced "omegeth") element. We then continue to the "omega plus first" element, ... and so on.

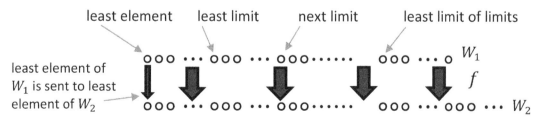

least element   least limit   next limit   least limit of limits

least element of W_1 is sent to least element of W_2

W_1

f

W_2

We can begin building an isomorphism f from W_1 to W_2 by sending the least element a_0 of W_1 to the least element b_0 of W_2. So, $(a_0, b_0) \in f$. Notice that $\{a_0\} = \text{pred}(W_1, a_1)$ and $\{b_0\} = \text{pred}(W_2, b_1)$, where a_1 and b_1 are the successors of a_0 and b_0, respectively. Thus, so far f is an isomorphism from $\text{pred}(W_1, a_1)$ to $\text{pred}(W_2, b_1)$. But now we can send a_1 to b_1, extending f to an isomorphism from $\text{pred}(W_1, a_2)$ to $\text{pred}(W_2, b_2)$.

More generally, we can just let $(x, y) \in f$ precisely if we have $\text{pred}(W_1, x) \cong \text{pred}(W_2, y)$.

The figure above gives a nice visual interpretation of "the beginning" of f. In the proof below, we will show that f is a strictly increasing function from an initial segment of W_1 to an initial segment of W_2, and then verify that at least one of these initial segments is **not** proper. I think we are ready to write the proof.

Proof: Let $f = \{(x, y) \in W_1 \times W_2 \mid \text{pred}(W_1, x) \cong \text{pred}(W_2, y)\}$.

We first show that f is a function. To see this, suppose that $(x, y), (x, z) \in f$. It then follows that $\text{pred}(W_1, x) \cong \text{pred}(W_2, y)$ and $\text{pred}(W_1, x) \cong \text{pred}(W_2, z)$. So, $\text{pred}(W_2, y) \cong \text{pred}(W_2, z)$. Without loss of generality, assume that $y \leq_2 z$. Then $\text{pred}(W_2, y)$ is an initial segment of $\text{pred}(W_2, z)$ (if $t <_2 y$, then since $y \leq_2 z$, by the transitivity of $\leq_2$ in W, $t <_2 z$). By Theorem 12.3, $\text{pred}(W_2, y)$ is **not** a **proper** initial segment of $\text{pred}(W_2, z)$. Therefore, $y = z$.

A similar argument shows that f is injective.

We now show that f is a homomorphism. To see this, let $x, t \in \text{dom } f$ with $x <_1 t$. By the definition of f, there are isomorphisms $g \colon \text{pred}(W_1, t) \cong \text{pred}(W_2, f(t))$ and $h \colon \text{pred}(W_1, x) \cong \text{pred}(W_2, f(x))$. Since $x <_1 t$, $g(x) <_2 f(t)$. Let $k \colon \text{pred}(W_1, x) \to \text{pred}(W_2, g(x))$ be the restriction of g to $\text{pred}(W_1, x)$. By Theorem 12.6, k is an isomorphism. So, $\text{pred}(W_2, g(x)) \cong \text{pred}(W_2, f(x))$. Using the same argument as in the first paragraph, $g(x) = f(x)$. Since $g(x) <_2 f(t)$, we have $f(x) <_2 f(t)$. Now, let $x, t \in \text{dom } f$ with $f(x) <_2 f(t)$. If $t <_1 x$, then by the previous argument, we would have $f(t) <_2 f(x)$, violating the trichotomy of $(W_2, <_2)$. If $x = t$, then we would have $f(x) = f(t)$, once again violating the trichotomy of $(W_2, <_2)$. So, $x <_1 t$.

Next, we show that $\text{dom } f$ is an initial segment of W_1. If $t \in \text{dom } f$, there is an isomorphism $g \colon \text{pred}(W_1, t) \cong \text{pred}(W_2, f(t))$. By Theorem 12.6, g is the restriction of f to $\text{pred}(W_1, t)$. If $x <_1 t$, then by Theorem 12.6 again, $\text{pred}(W_1, x) \cong \text{pred}(W_2, g(x))$. So, $x \in \text{dom } f$.

Similarly, we can show that $\text{ran } f$ is an initial segment of W_2. If $y \in \text{ran } f$, say $y = f(t)$, then there is an isomorphism $g \colon \text{pred}(W_1, t) \cong \text{pred}(W_2, y)$. If $z <_2 y$, then since g is an isomorphism, there is $x \in \text{pred}(W_1, t)$ with $g(x) = z$. By Theorem 12.6, $\text{pred}(W_1, x) \cong \text{pred}(W_2, z)$. So, $z \in \text{ran } f$.

If $\text{dom } f = W_1$ and $\text{ran } f = W_2$, then (i) holds.

If $\text{dom } f = W_1$ and $\text{ran } f \neq W_2$, then (ii) holds.

If $\text{dom } f \neq W_1$ and $\text{ran } f = W_2$, then (iii) holds.

Suppose toward contradiction that dom $f \neq W_1$ and ran $f \neq W_2$. Then there is $a \in W_1$ and $b \in W_2$ such that dom $f = \operatorname{pred}(W_1, a)$ and ran $f = \operatorname{pred}(W_2, b)$. So, $\operatorname{pred}(W_1, a) \cong \operatorname{pred}(W_2, b)$. Therefore, $(a, b) \in f$. But $a \notin \operatorname{pred}(W_1, a) = \operatorname{dom} f$. This is a contradiction.

Now, if (i) and (ii) both hold, then $(W_2, <_2) \cong (W_1, <_1) \cong (T, <_2)$, contradicting Theorem 12.3. If (i) and (iii) both hold, then $(W_1, <_1) \cong (W_2, <_2) \cong (S, <_1)$, again contradicting Theorem 12.3. Finally, if (ii) and (iii) both hold, then $(W_1, <_1) \cong (T, <_2)$ and $(W_2, <_2) \cong (S, <_1)$. Let $f: W_1 \cong T$ and let g be the restriction of f to S. Then $g: S \cong f[S]$. So, $(W_2, <_2) \cong (f[S], <_2)$. Since $f[S] \subseteq T$, $f[S]$ is a proper initial segment of W_2. This again contradicts Theorem 12.3. It follows that exactly one of (i), (ii), or (iii) holds. $\qquad \square$

Ordinals

A set x is an **ordinal** if and only if x is transitive and well-ordered by $\in$. We generally use letters from the beginning of the Greek alphabet such as α (alpha), β (beta), and γ (gamma) to represent arbitrary ordinals. We use ω (omega) to represent the set of natural numbers when we are thinking of this set as an ordinal.

Technical note: If a set is linearly ordered by $\in$, then by the axiom of foundation, the set is automatically well-ordered by $\in$. So, if we are assuming ZF or ZFC, we can define a set to be an ordinal if and only if it is transitive and linearly ordered by $\in$. However, we will not take that approach here. In this way, we can always be sure that the axiom of foundation is not required for any of the theory we develop.

Example 12.4:

1. By part 6 of Example 12.1, every natural number is a transitive set. By part 5 of Example 12.2 and Problem 4 below, every natural number is well-ordered by $\in$. Therefore, every natural number is an ordinal. The natural numbers are the **finite ordinals** with 0 being the least ordinal, 1 being the next ordinal after 0, and so on.

$$0 \in 1 \in 2 \in 3 \in \cdots$$

   Except for the ordinal 0, each natural number is a **successor ordinal**. A successor ordinal has the form $\alpha \cup \{\alpha\}$ for some ordinal α.

   For example, $0 \cup \{0\} = \{0\} = 1$. So, 1 is a successor ordinal. It is the successor of 0.

   Similarly, 2 is a successor ordinal because $1 \cup \{1\} = \{0\} \cup \{1\} = \{0, 1\} = 2$.

   In general, we have $n \cup \{n\} = \{0, 1, \dots, n-1\} \cup \{n\} = \{0, 1, \dots, n\} = n + 1$, showing that $n + 1$ is a successor ordinal.

2. By part 7 of Example 12.1, the set of natural numbers, $\omega = \{0, 1, 2, \dots\}$ is a transitive set. By part 6 of Example 12.2, ω is well-ordered by $\in$. Therefore, ω is an ordinal. ω is the **least infinite ordinal**. It is the set containing all the finite ordinals. Note that ω is **not** a successor ordinal. Indeed, for all $n \in \omega$, $n \cup \{n\} = n + 1 \in \omega$. We say that ω is a **limit ordinal**. In fact, ω is the **least limit ordinal**.

3. If α is an ordinal, then the **successor** of α is $\alpha + 1 = \alpha \cup \{\alpha\}$. You will be asked to show in part (i) of Problem 5 below that for any ordinal α, $\alpha + 1$ is also an ordinal.

For example, we have $\omega + 1 = \omega \cup \{\omega\} = \{0, 1, 2, \dots, \omega\}$. More generally, we can use induction to show that for each $n \in \omega$, $\omega + n = \{0, 1, 2, \dots, \omega, \omega + 1, \omega + 2, \dots, \omega + (n-1)\}$ is an ordinal. Indeed, assuming that $\omega + k$ is an ordinal, $\omega + (k+1) = (\omega + k) \cup \{\omega + k\}$ is an ordinal by part (i) of Problem 5 below.

4. An ordinal $\alpha \neq 0$ is a **limit ordinal** if $\alpha = \bigcup\alpha$. For example, let's show that ω is a limit ordinal. First, if $n \in \omega$, then $n \in n + 1$. Since $n + 1 \in \omega$, $n \in \bigcup\omega$. Since $n \in \omega$ was arbitrary, $\omega \subseteq \bigcup\omega$. Now, let $n \in \bigcup\omega$. Then there is $k \in \omega$ with $n \in k$. Since ω is transitive, $n \in \omega$. Since $n \in \bigcup\omega$ was an arbitrary ordinal, $\bigcup\omega \subseteq \omega$. Since $\omega \subseteq \bigcup\omega$ and $\bigcup\omega \subseteq \omega$, $\omega = \bigcup\omega$.

   More generally, a nonzero ordinal is a limit ordinal if and only if it is **not** a successor ordinal.

   To see this, first suppose that α is a limit ordinal. Then $\alpha = \bigcup\alpha$. Assume toward contradiction that $\alpha = \beta + 1$ for some ordinal β. Then $\beta \in \alpha$. Since $\alpha = \bigcup\alpha$, there is $\gamma \in \alpha$ with $\beta \in \gamma$. So, $\beta \in \gamma \in \beta + 1 = \beta \cup \{\beta\}$. If $\gamma \in \beta$, then we have $\beta \in \beta$ by the transitivity of β. If $\gamma = \beta$, then we also have $\beta \in \beta$. Since $\beta \in \beta$ is impossible, α is **not** a successor ordinal.

   Now suppose that α is not a successor ordinal. $\bigcup\alpha \subseteq \alpha$ is always true. To see this, let $\beta \in \bigcup\alpha$. Then there is $\gamma \in \alpha$ with $\beta \in \gamma$. By the transitivity of α, $\beta \in \alpha$. So, we need only show $\alpha \subseteq \bigcup\alpha$. Let $\beta \in \alpha$. Since $\alpha \neq \beta + 1$, by part (ii) of Problem 7 below, either $\alpha \in \beta + 1$ or $\beta + 1 \in \alpha$. If $\alpha \in \beta + 1$, then $\beta \in \alpha \in \beta + 1$. This is impossible—the argument is given in the last paragraph. So, we have $\beta + 1 \in \alpha$. Since $\beta + 1 \in \alpha$ and $\beta \in \beta + 1$, $\beta \in \bigcup\alpha$. Since $\beta \in \alpha$ was an arbitrary ordinal, $\alpha \subseteq \bigcup\alpha$. Since $\bigcup\alpha \subseteq \alpha$ and $\alpha \subseteq \bigcup\alpha$, $\alpha = \bigcup\alpha$. Therefore, α is a limit ordinal.

5. Define ω_1 to be the set of countable ordinals. We show that ω_1 is an ordinal. To see that ω_1 is transitive, let $\alpha \in \omega_1$ and let $\beta \in \alpha$. Since α is an ordinal, by part (ii) of Problem 5 below, β is an ordinal. Since α is transitive, $\beta \subseteq \alpha$. Since α is countable, so is β. Therefore, $\beta \in \omega_1$. So, ω_1 is transitive.

   We now show that ω_1 is well-ordered by $\in$.

   To see that $\in$ is antireflexive on ω_1, let $\alpha \in \omega_1$. Then α is an ordinal, and so, $\alpha \notin \alpha$.

   To see that $\in$ is antisymmetric on ω_1, let $\alpha, \beta \in \omega_1$. Then α and β are ordinals. By part (ii) of Problem 7 below, we cannot have both $\alpha \in \beta$ and $\beta \in \alpha$. So, antisymmetry is vacuously satisfied by $\in$ on ω_1.

   To see that $\in$ is transitive on ω_1, let $\alpha, \beta, \gamma \in \omega_1$ with $\alpha \in \beta$ and $\beta \in \gamma$. Since α, β, and γ are ordinals, by Problem 2 below, $\alpha \in \gamma$.

   To see that $(\omega_1, \in)$ satisfies trichotomy, let $\alpha, \beta \in \omega_1$. Since α and β are ordinals, by part (ii) of Problem 7 below, exactly one of the following holds: $\alpha = \beta$, $\alpha \in \beta$, or $\beta \in \alpha$.

   Finally, let A be a nonempty subset of ω_1, and choose $\alpha \in A$. If $\alpha \cap A = \emptyset$, then α is the $\in$-least element of A (If $\beta \in A$ with $\beta \in \alpha$, then $\beta \in \alpha \cap A$, contradicting $\alpha \cap A = \emptyset$). Otherwise, $\alpha \cap A$ is a nonempty subset of α, and since α is well-ordered by $\in$ (because α is an ordinal), $\alpha \cap A$ has an $\in$-least element β. Then β is the $\in$-least element of A (If $\gamma \in A$ with $\gamma \in \beta$, then $\gamma \in \alpha$ because α is transitive, and so, β is not the $\in$-least element of $\alpha \cap A$).

   It follows that ω_1 is an ordinal. ω_1 is the least uncountable ordinal.

6. Define **ON** to be the **class** of all ordinals. So, **ON** $= \{\alpha \mid \alpha$ is an ordinal$\}$. Although **ON** satisfies all the properties of being an ordinal (see Problems 2, 5, 7, and Theorem 12.10 below) it is too large to be a set. Indeed, if **ON** were an ordinal, we would have **ON** $\in$ **ON**. This contradicts the fact that $\in$ is a **strict** linear ordering. **ON** is a proper class. Notice that there is no "bounding set" in the definition of **ON**, and so, the Bounded Comprehension Schema cannot be used to show that **ON** is a set.

The next theorem is arguably the most important result about ordinals. It essentially says that every well-ordered set "looks" exactly like one and only one ordinal. It allows us to take the class of ordinals to be the natural representatives for all well-ordered sets. The proof of this theorem is similar to the proof of Theorem 12.7 and so, we leave it as an exercise (see Problem 10 below).

Theorem 12.8: Let $(W, <)$ be a well-ordered set. There is a unique ordinal α such that $W \cong \alpha$.

Ordinal Arithmetic

We now extend the definitions of addition, multiplication, and exponentiation on the natural numbers (from Lesson 8) to the class of ordinals.

We define the **sum** $\alpha + \beta$ of the ordinals α and β as follows:

(i) If $\beta = 0$, then $\alpha + \beta = \alpha$.

(ii) If $\beta = \gamma + 1$, then $\alpha + \beta = (\alpha + \gamma) + 1$.

(iii) If $\beta = \bigcup \beta$, then $\alpha + \beta = \bigcup\{\alpha + \gamma \mid \gamma \in \beta\}$.

Note: This is an example of a **definition by transfinite recursion**. See Example 12.8 below for its justification.

Example 12.5:

1. The definition of addition agrees with the definition we are already familiar with on the natural numbers. Only (i) and (ii) are needed to add two natural numbers because all natural numbers occur before the first limit ordinal.

2. $1 + \omega = \bigcup\{1 + n \mid n \in \omega\} = \omega$ because

    $$\bigcup\{1 + n \mid n \in \omega\} = 1 \cup 2 \cup 3 \cup \cdots = \{0\} \cup \{0, 1\} \cup \{0, 1, 2\} \cup \cdots = \{0, 1, 2, \ldots\} = \omega.$$

    We can think of $\alpha + \beta$ as follows: If we have α almonds and β berries, we can visualize $\alpha + \beta$ by placing the α almonds followed by the β berries.

    For $1 + \omega$, we place 1 almond followed by ω berries. The result looks just like the ordering of the natural numbers (after placement, we no longer make a distinction between almonds and berries).

    $$\lozenge \, \text{o o o o o o o o o o o} \ \cdots$$

3. $\omega + 1 = \{0, 1, 2, \ldots, \omega\}$ is the successor of ω. Notice that $\omega + 1 \neq 1 + \omega$. In fact, they are very different from each other. $\omega + 1$ is a successor ordinal, whereas $1 + \omega = \omega$ is a limit ordinal.

This time we place ω almonds followed by 1 berry. This ordering looks like the natural numbers followed by one additional element that is larger than all the natural numbers.

◇ ◇ ◇ ◇ ◇ ◇ ◇ ◇ ◇ ◇ ◇   · · ·   ○

We define the **product** $\alpha\beta$ of the ordinals α and β as follows:

(i)   If $\beta = 0$, then $\alpha\beta = 0$.

(ii)   If $\beta = \gamma + 1$, then $\alpha\beta = \alpha\gamma + \alpha$.

(iii)   If $\beta = \bigcup\beta$, then $\alpha\beta = \bigcup\{\alpha\gamma \mid \gamma \in \beta\}$.

Note: This is another example of a **definition by transfinite recursion**. See Example 12.9 below for its justification.

Example 12.6:

1. As with addition, the definition of multiplication agrees with the definition we are already familiar with on the natural numbers. Only (i) and (ii) are needed to multiply two natural numbers because all natural numbers occur before the first limit ordinal.

2. $2\omega = \bigcup\{2n \mid n \in \omega\} = \omega$ because

    $$\bigcup\{2n \mid n \in \omega\} = 0 \cup 2 \cup 4 \cup \cdots = \emptyset \cup \{0,1\} \cup \{0,1,2,3\} \cup \cdots = \{0,1,2,\dots\} = \omega.$$

    We can think of $\alpha\beta$ as follows: If we have α almonds in each of β many bags, we can visualize $\alpha\beta$ by lining up the β bags, while leaving the α many almonds in order in each bag.

    For 2ω, we have ω many bags, each with 2 almonds. When we line them up, the result looks just like the ordering of the natural numbers (after placement, we no longer pay attention to the bags).

    ▢▢ ▢▢ ▢▢ ▢▢ ▢▢ ▢▢   · · ·

3. $\omega \cdot 2 = \omega \cdot 1 + \omega = \omega + \omega = \bigcup\{\omega + n \mid n \in \omega\} = \{0,1,2,\dots,\omega,\omega+1,\omega+2,\dots\}$. This is the next limit ordinal after ω. Notice that $\omega \cdot 2 \neq 2\omega$. Indeed, $\omega \cdot 2$ is the second limit ordinal, whereas $2\omega = \omega$ is the least limit ordinal.

    This time we have just 2 bags, each with ω many almonds. This ordering looks like the natural numbers followed by a second copy of the natural numbers.

    ▢○○○○○○○○○○○○ · · ·▢ ▢○○○○○○○○○○○○ · · ·▢

    Similarly, we have $\omega \cdot 3 = \{0,1,2,\dots,\omega,\omega+1,\omega+2,\dots,\omega+\omega,\omega+\omega+1,\omega+\omega+2,\dots\}$. This is the next limit ordinal after $\omega \cdot 2$. Notice that $\omega \cdot 3 \neq 3\omega$. Indeed, $\omega \cdot 3$ is the third limit ordinal, whereas $3\omega = \omega$ is the least limit ordinal. $\omega \cdot 3$ can be visualized as 3 bags in a row, each bag filled up with ω many almonds all lined up in order.

    ▬▬▬   ▬▬▬   ▬▬▬

    In the figure above, I used 3 solid rectangles to indicate 3 bags, each containing ω many almonds, all lined up in a row.

Continuing in this fashion, we see that $\omega \cdot n$ is the nth limit ordinal. It can be visualized as n bags in a row, each bag filled up with ω many almonds, all lined up in order.

4. $\omega \cdot \omega = \bigcup\{\omega \cdot n \mid n \in \omega\}$. This is the limit of the limit ordinals of the form $\omega \cdot n$ for $n \in \mathbb{N}$. We can visualize $\omega \cdot \omega$ as ω bags, each bag filled up with ω many almonds.

We define the **power** α^β of the ordinals α and β as follows:

(i) If $\beta = 0$, then $\alpha^\beta = 1$.

(ii) If $\beta = \gamma + 1$, then $\alpha^\beta = \alpha^\gamma \cdot \alpha$.

(iii) If $\beta = \bigcup\beta$, then $\alpha^\beta = \bigcup\{\alpha^\gamma \mid \gamma \in \beta\}$.

Note: This is another example of a **definition by transfinite recursion**. See Example 12.10 below for its justification.

Example 12.7:

1. As with addition and multiplication, the definition of power (or **exponentiation**) agrees with the definition of power on the natural numbers. Only (i) and (ii) are needed to raise a natural number to the power of another natural number because all natural numbers occur before the first limit ordinal.

2. We have $\omega^0 = 1$, $\omega^1 = \omega^0 \cdot \omega = 1 \cdot \omega = \omega$, and $\omega^2 = \omega^1 \cdot \omega = \omega \cdot \omega$. We already saw a visual representation of $\omega^2 = \omega \cdot \omega$ in part 4 of Example 12.6.

   I leave it to the reader to explore possible visualizations of ω^n for $n > 2$ and ω^ω. Be careful here. You may find it useful to look at ordinals such as $\omega^2 \cdot 2$, $\omega^2 \cdot 3$,... and so on, to help understand ω^3. And similarly, for higher powers of ω.

3. $2^\omega = \bigcup\{2^n \mid n \in \omega\} = 1 \cup 2 \cup 4 \cup 8 \cup 16 = \omega$. More generally, $k^\omega = \omega$ for every $k \in \omega$.

Note: Readers that are somewhat familiar with cardinal arithmetic might be very suspicious of the equation $2^\omega = \omega$. Isn't 2^ω uncountable? Unfortunately, the standard definitions for ordinal and cardinal arithmetic are very different from each other. Cardinals and cardinal exponentiation will be defined in Lesson 13.

The Well Ordering Axiom

Recall that one version of the **Axiom of Choice (AC)** says that every set of nonempty sets has a choice function. In other words, if X is a set of nonempty sets, then there is a function $f \colon X \to \bigcup X$ such that for each $x \in X$, $f(x) \in x$.

If X is an arbitrary set, recall that $\mathcal{P}(X)$ (the power set of X) is the set of all subsets of X. AC **cannot** be applied to $\mathcal{P}(X)$ because $\emptyset \in \mathcal{P}(X)$. However, if we remove the empty set, AC gives us a choice function $f \colon \mathcal{P}(X) \setminus \{\emptyset\} \to \bigcup(\mathcal{P}(X) \setminus \{\emptyset\})$.

Note that $\bigcup(\mathcal{P}(X) \setminus \{\emptyset\}) = X$. To see this, let $y \in \bigcup(\mathcal{P}(X) \setminus \{\emptyset\})$. Then there is $z \in \mathcal{P}(X) \setminus \{\emptyset\}$ with $y \in z$. Since $z \in \mathcal{P}(X)$, $z \subseteq X$. Therefore, $y \in X$. Conversely, if $y \in X$, then since $X \in \mathcal{P}(X) \setminus \{\emptyset\}$, we have $y \in \bigcup(\mathcal{P}(X) \setminus \{\emptyset\})$.

So, AC implies that for any set X, there is a choice function $f: \mathcal{P}(X) \setminus \{\emptyset\} \to X$.

The **Well Ordering Axiom (WA)** says that every set can be well-ordered.

As it turns out, WA is yet another statement that is equivalent to AC .

Theorem 12.9: $AC \leftrightarrow WA$.

The proof that WA implies AC is straightforward.

Proof that WA implies AC: Assume WA, let $\mathcal{F}$ be a set of nonempty sets, and let $A = \bigcup \mathcal{F}$. Then A is a set by the Union Axiom. By WA, there is a well-ordering $<$ on A. We can now define a choice function $f: \mathcal{F} \to \bigcup \mathcal{F}$ by $f(S) =$ the $<$-least element of S. Since $\mathcal{F}$ was an arbitrary set of nonempty sets, AC holds. □

The proof that AC implies WA is a bit more involved, but the main idea isn't hard to understand. Let's start with a nonempty set X (If $X = \emptyset$, then X is well-ordered by the empty relation). Then $\mathcal{P}(X) \setminus \{\emptyset\}$ is a set of nonempty sets.

By AC, there is a choice function $f: \mathcal{P}(X) \setminus \{\emptyset\} \to X$. We will use this choice function to construct a well-ordering on X. Since f is a choice function and $X \in \mathcal{P}(X)$, $f(X) \in X$. Let $x_0 = f(X)$. We will let x_0 be the least element of our well ordering. Now, $X \setminus \{x_0\} \in \mathcal{P}(X)$ and $f(X \setminus \{x_0\}) \in X \setminus \{x_0\}$. Let $x_1 = f(X \setminus \{x_0\})$. We will let x_1 be the immediate successor of x_0 in our well ordering. Similarly, we let $x_2 = f(X \setminus \{x_0, x_1\})$ be the immediate successor of x_1, ... and so on. But we don't just do this for natural numbers. We proceed all the way up through the class of ordinals until we run out of elements in X. We must run out eventually because if we don't, we will get a surjection from the **set** X to the **proper class** ON, which is impossible. Here are the details.

Proof that AC implies WA: Assume AC and let X be any set. If $X = \emptyset$, then $\emptyset$ is a well-ordering of X. Suppose that $X \neq \emptyset$. By AC, there is a choice function $f: \mathcal{P}(X) \setminus \{\emptyset\} \to X$. Assume that for each $\beta \in \alpha$, x_β has been selected from X such that $\beta \neq \gamma \to x_\beta \neq x_\gamma$. If $\{x_\beta \mid \beta \in \alpha\} \neq X$, we define $x_\alpha \in X$ by $x_\alpha = f(X \setminus \{x_\beta \mid \beta \in \alpha\})$. There must be an ordinal δ such that $\{x_\beta \mid \beta \in \delta\} = X$ because if $\{x_\beta \mid \beta \in \delta\} \neq X$ for all $\delta \in ON$, then we can define a surjection $g: X \to ON$ by $g(x_\beta) = \beta$. By the axiom of replacement, ON would be a set, which is a contradiction. Let α be the least ordinal such that $\{x_\beta \mid \beta \in \alpha\} = X$. We can define a well-ordering $<$ on X by $x_\beta < x_\gamma$ if and only if $\beta \in \gamma \in \alpha$. □

Transfinite Induction

In Lesson 8, we learned about the Well Ordering Principle and the Principle of Mathematical Induction—these are both principles that are satisfied by the set of natural numbers. These principles can be generalized to work for **any** well-ordered set. Since every well-ordered set is isomorphic to an ordinal, we may as well just prove the ordinal versions of these two principles. We do this now.

Theorem 12.10 (Ordinal Well Ordering Principle): Let S be a nonempty subclass of **ON**. Then S contains an $\in$-least element.

Proof: Since $S \neq \emptyset$, there is $\alpha \in S$. If α is **not** the $\in$-least element of S, then there is $\beta \in S$ with $\beta \in \alpha$. So, $\beta \in \alpha \cap S$, and therefore, $\alpha \cap S \neq \emptyset$. Also, since $\alpha \cap S \subseteq \alpha$, $\alpha \cap S$ is a nonempty **set** of ordinals. Since α is well-ordered by $\in$, $\alpha \cap S$ has an $\in$-least element γ. If $\delta \in S$ with $\delta \in \gamma$, then by the transitivity of α, $\delta \in \alpha$. So, $\delta \in \alpha \cap S$, contradicting that γ is $\in$-least in $\alpha \cap S$. So, γ is the $\in$-least element of S. $\square$

Theorem 12.11 (Transfinite Induction): Let S be a subclass of **ON** such that (i) $0 \in S$, (ii) if $\alpha \in S$, then $\alpha + 1 \in S$, and (iii) if α is a limit ordinal and $\beta \in S$ for all $\beta \in \alpha$, then $\alpha \in S$. Then $S = $ **ON**.

Notes: (1) Recall from Lesson 8 how the Principle of Mathematical Induction works like a chain reaction. Transfinite induction works similarly. We know that $0 \in S$ (this is condition (i)). Substituting 0 in for α in the expression "$\alpha \in S \rightarrow \alpha + 1 \in S$" (condition (ii)) gives us $0 \in S \rightarrow 1 \in S$. So, we have that 0 is in the set S, and "if 0 is in the set S, then 1 is in the set S." So, $1 \in S$ must also be true. We can then substitute 1 in for α in (ii) to get $2 \in S$, ... and so on. We get the following chain reaction:

$$0 \in S \rightarrow 1 \in S \rightarrow 2 \in S \rightarrow 3 \in S \rightarrow \cdots$$

This shows that S contains every natural number.

(2) Now what about ω? For this we use condition (iii). Since S contains every natural number, condition (iii) gives us that $\omega \in S$. So, our chain now looks like this:

$$0 \in S \rightarrow 1 \in S \rightarrow 2 \in S \rightarrow 3 \in S \rightarrow \cdots \rightarrow \omega \in S$$

(3) Now that we have $\omega \in S$, we can start using condition (ii) again to get $\omega + 1 \in S$, then $\omega + 2 \in S$, ... and so on.

$$0 \in S \rightarrow 1 \in S \rightarrow 2 \in S \rightarrow 3 \in S \rightarrow \cdots \rightarrow \omega \in S \rightarrow \omega + 1 \in S \rightarrow \omega + 2 \in S \rightarrow \cdots$$

(4) The next time we will need to apply condition (iii) is at $\omega + \omega = \omega \cdot 2$. Then again at $\omega \cdot 3$ ... and so on.

I hope that the "argument" presented in Notes 1 through 4 above convinces you that Transfinite Induction should be true. Now let's give a proof using the Ordinal Well Ordering Principle.

Proof of Theorem 12.11: Let S be a subclass of **ON** such that $0 \in S$ (condition (i)), if $\alpha \in S$, then $\alpha + 1 \in S$ (condition (ii)), and if α is a limit ordinal and $\beta \in S$ for all $\beta \in \alpha$, then $\alpha \in S$ (condition (iii)). Assume towards contradiction that $S \neq $ **ON**. Let $A = \{\alpha \in $ **ON** $\mid \alpha \notin S\}$ (so, A is the class of ordinals **not** in S). Since $S \neq $ **ON**, A is nonempty. So, by the Ordinal Well Ordering Principle, A has an $\in$-least element, let's call it β. $\beta \neq 0$ because $0 \in S$ and $\beta \notin S$. If $\beta = \gamma + 1$, then since β is the $\in$-least ordinal in A, $\gamma \in S$. By (ii), $\beta = \gamma + 1 \in S$. So, β is **not** a successor ordinal. Therefore, β must be a limit ordinal. If $\gamma \in \beta$, then $\gamma \in S$, again because β is the $\in$-least element in A. Then by (iii), $\beta \in S$. This is a contradiction, and so, $S = $ **ON**. $\square$

Transfinite Recursion

The definitions of the sum, product, and power given above are examples of **recursive definitions** on **ON**. The following theorem gives us permission to define functions in this way. In the following theorem, **V** is the proper class of all sets.

Theorem 12.12 (Transfinite Recursion Theorem): Let $\mathbf{G}, \mathbf{H}, \mathbf{K}: \mathbf{V} \times \mathbf{V} \to \mathbf{V}$. Then there is a unique $\mathbf{F}: \mathbf{V} \times \mathbf{ON} \to \mathbf{V}$ such that

   (i) $\mathbf{F}(x, 0) = \mathbf{G}(x, \emptyset)$.

   (ii) $\mathbf{F}(x, \alpha + 1) = \mathbf{H}\big(x, \mathbf{F}(x, \alpha)\big)$ for all $\alpha \in \mathbf{ON}$.

   (iii) $\mathbf{F}(x, \alpha) = \mathbf{K}\big(x, \mathbf{F} \restriction (\{x\} \times \alpha)\big)$ for all limit ordinals α.

Notes: (1) Since $\mathbf{V}$ and $\mathbf{ON}$ are proper classes, so are $\mathbf{F}, \mathbf{G}, \mathbf{H},$ and $\mathbf{K}$.

(2) $\mathbf{F} \restriction (\{x\} \times \alpha)$ is the **restriction** of $\mathbf{F}$ to $\{x\} \times \alpha$. In other words, $\big(\mathbf{F} \restriction (\{x\} \times \alpha)\big)(x, \beta) = \mathbf{F}(x, \beta)$ for all $\beta < \alpha$.

Before we discuss the proof of Theorem 12.12, let's look at some examples to help us understand how it works.

Example 12.8: Let $\mathbf{G}, \mathbf{H}, \mathbf{K}: \mathbf{V} \times \mathbf{V} \to \mathbf{V}$ be defined as follows: $\mathbf{G}(x, v) = x$, $\mathbf{H}(x, v) = v + 1$, and $\mathbf{K}(x, v) = \begin{cases} \bigcup \operatorname{ran} v & \text{if } v \text{ is a function.} \\ 0 & \text{if } v \text{ is not a function.} \end{cases}$ Then the Transfinite Recursion Theorem gives us $\mathbf{F}: \mathbf{V} \times \mathbf{ON} \to \mathbf{V}$ such that for all x,

   (i) $\mathbf{F}(x, 0) = \mathbf{G}(x, \emptyset) = x$.

   (ii) $\mathbf{F}(x, \beta + 1) = \mathbf{H}\big(x, \mathbf{F}(x, \beta)\big) = \mathbf{F}(x, \beta) + 1$ for all $\beta \in \mathbf{ON}$.

   (iii) $\mathbf{F}(x, \beta) = \mathbf{K}\big(x, \mathbf{F} \restriction (\{x\} \times \beta)\big) = \bigcup \operatorname{ran}\big(\mathbf{F} \restriction (\{x\} \times \beta)\big) = \bigcup\{\mathbf{F}(x, \gamma) \mid \gamma < \beta\}$ for all limit ordinals β.

This gives us the definition of the sum of two ordinals. Indeed, if α and β are ordinals and we abbreviate $\mathbf{F}(\alpha, \beta)$ as $\alpha + \beta$, then (i), (ii), and (iii) above are equivalent to

   (i) $\alpha + 0 = \alpha$.

   (ii) $\alpha + (\beta + 1) = (\alpha + \beta) + 1$ for all $\beta \in \mathbf{ON}$.

   (iii) $\alpha + \beta = \bigcup\{\alpha + \gamma \mid \gamma < \beta\}$ for all limit ordinals β.

Example 12.9: Let $\mathbf{G}, \mathbf{H}, \mathbf{K}: \mathbf{V} \times \mathbf{V} \to \mathbf{V}$ be defined as follows: $\mathbf{G}(x, v) = 0$, $\mathbf{H}(x, v) = v + x$, and $\mathbf{K}(x, v) = \begin{cases} \bigcup \operatorname{ran} v & \text{if } v \text{ is a function.} \\ 0 & \text{if } v \text{ is not a function.} \end{cases}$ Then the Transfinite Recursion Theorem gives us $\mathbf{F}: \mathbf{V} \times \mathbf{ON} \to \mathbf{V}$ such that for all x,

   (i) $\mathbf{F}(x, 0) = \mathbf{G}(x, \emptyset) = 0$.

   (ii) $\mathbf{F}(x, \beta + 1) = \mathbf{H}\big(x, \mathbf{F}(x, \beta)\big) = \mathbf{F}(x, \beta) + x$ for all $\beta \in \mathbf{ON}$.

   (iii) $\mathbf{F}(x, \beta) = \mathbf{K}\big(x, \mathbf{F} \restriction (\{x\} \times \beta)\big) = \bigcup \operatorname{ran}\big(\mathbf{F} \restriction (\{x\} \times \beta)\big) = \bigcup\{\mathbf{F}(x, \gamma) \mid \gamma < \beta\}$ for all limit ordinals β.

This gives us the definition of the product of two ordinals. Indeed, if α and β are ordinals and we abbreviate $\mathbf{F}(\alpha, \beta)$ as $\alpha\beta$, then (i), (ii), and (iii) above are equivalent to

(i) $\alpha \cdot 0 = \alpha$.

(ii) $\alpha \cdot (\beta + 1) = \alpha\beta + \alpha$ for all $\beta \in \mathbf{ON}$.

(iii) $\alpha\beta = \bigcup\{\alpha\gamma \mid \gamma < \beta\}$ for all limit ordinals β.

Example 12.10: Let $\mathbf{G}, \mathbf{H}, \mathbf{K} \colon \mathbf{V} \times \mathbf{V} \to \mathbf{V}$ be defined as follows: $\mathbf{G}(x, v) = 1$, $\mathbf{H}(x, v) = vx$, and $\mathbf{K}(x, v) = \begin{cases} \bigcup \operatorname{ran} v & \text{if } v \text{ is a function.} \\ 0 & \text{if } v \text{ is not a function.} \end{cases}$ Then the Transfinite Recursion Theorem gives us $\mathbf{F} \colon \mathbf{V} \times \mathbf{ON} \to \mathbf{V}$ such that for all x,

(i) $\mathbf{F}(x, 0) = \mathbf{G}(x, \emptyset) = 1$.

(ii) $\mathbf{F}(x, \beta + 1) = \mathbf{H}\big(x, \mathbf{F}(x, \beta)\big) = \mathbf{F}(x, \beta) \cdot x$ for all $\beta \in \mathbf{ON}$.

(iii) $\mathbf{F}(x, \beta) = \mathbf{K}\big(x, \mathbf{F} \restriction (\{x\} \times \beta)\big) = \bigcup \operatorname{ran}\big(\mathbf{F} \restriction (\{x\} \times \beta)\big) = \bigcup\{\mathbf{F}(x, \gamma) \mid \gamma < \beta\}$ for all limit ordinals β.

This gives us the definition of the power of two ordinals. Indeed, if α and β are ordinals and we abbreviate $\mathbf{F}(\alpha, \beta)$ as α^β, then (i), (ii), and (iii) above are equivalent to

(i) $\alpha^0 = 1$.

(ii) $\alpha^{\beta+1} = \alpha^\beta \cdot \alpha$ for all $\beta \in \mathbf{ON}$.

(iii) $\alpha^\beta = \bigcup\{\alpha^\gamma \mid \gamma < \beta\}$ for all limit ordinals β.

The proof of Theorem 12.12 is similar to the proof of Theorem 8.10. It requires several steps. I will give a brief outline of those steps and leave the details as an exercise for the reader (see Problem 12 below).

Proof outline for Theorem 12.12: Let $\mathbf{G}, \mathbf{H}, \mathbf{K} \colon \mathbf{V} \times \mathbf{V} \to \mathbf{V}$. For each $x \in \mathbf{V}$ and $\beta \in \mathbf{ON}$, let $f_{x,\beta} \colon \{x\} \times \beta \to \mathbf{V}$ be defined by

- $f_{x,\beta}(x, 0) = \mathbf{G}(x, \emptyset)$.

- $f_{x,\beta}(x, \alpha + 1) = \mathbf{H}\Big(x, f_{x,\beta}(x, \alpha)\Big)$ for all α such that $0 < \alpha + 1 < \beta$.

- $f_{x,\beta}(x, \alpha) = \mathbf{K}\Big(x, f_{x,\beta} \restriction (\{x\} \times \alpha)\Big)$ for all limit ordinals $\alpha < \beta$.

Step 1: Prove that for each $x \in \mathbf{V}$ and $\beta \in \mathbf{ON}$, $f_{x,\beta} \colon \{x\} \times \beta \to \mathbf{V}$ is the only function with the given definition above (use transfinite induction on $\alpha < \beta$).

Step 2: Prove that if $\gamma \leq \delta$, then $x \in \mathbf{V}$ and $0 \leq \alpha < \gamma$ implies that $f_{x,\gamma}(x, \alpha) = f_{x,\delta}(x, \alpha)$.

Step 3: Let $g = \{f_{x,\beta} \mid n \in \mathbb{N}\}$ and let $\mathbf{F} = \bigcup g$. Prove that $\mathbf{F} \colon \mathbf{V} \times \mathbf{ON} \to \mathbf{V}$.

Step 4: Prove that $\mathbf{F}$ satisfies (i), (ii), and (iii).

Step 5: Prove that $\mathbf{F}$ is unique by assuming $\mathbf{F}'$ also satisfies (i), (ii), and (iii) and then using transfinite induction to prove that $\mathbf{F}' = \mathbf{F}$.

Completing these steps will prove the theorem.   □

LEVEL 1

1. Prove each of the following or provide a counterexample:

    (i)   Every transitive set is an ordinal.

    (ii)   Every set that is well-ordered by $\in$ is an ordinal.

2. Let α, β, and γ be ordinals with $\alpha \in \beta$ and $\beta \in \gamma$. Prove that $\alpha \in \gamma$.

LEVEL 2

3. Strong Transfinite Induction is the following statement:

    If S is a subclass of **ON** such that for all $\alpha \in$ **ON**, $\forall \beta < \alpha \ (\beta \in S) \to \alpha \in S$, then $S =$ **ON**.

    Use Theorem 12.10 (Ordinal Well Ordering Principle) to prove Strong Transfinite Induction.

4. Prove that each natural number is well-ordered by $\in$, and use this to conclude that each natural number is an ordinal.

LEVEL 3

5. Let α be an ordinal. Prove each of the following:

    (i) $\alpha + 1 = \alpha \cup \{\alpha\}$ is also an ordinal.

    (ii)   If $x \in \alpha$, then x is an ordinal and $x = \text{pred}(\alpha, x)$.

6. Let $\boldsymbol{P} = \{P_0, P_1, \dots\}$ be a partition of $\mathbb{N}$ into infinitely many infinite sets (see part (i) of Problem 5 from Problem Set 7). Define $\lhd$ on $\mathbb{N}$ by

$$\lhd = \big\{(m, n) \big| (\exists k \in \mathbb{N}(m, n \in P_k \wedge m < n) \vee \exists j, k \in \mathbb{N}(j < k \wedge m \in P_j \wedge n \in P_k)\big\}.$$

Prove that $(\mathbb{N}, \lhd)$ is a well-ordered set isomorphic to the ordinal $\omega \cdot \omega$.

LEVEL 4

7. Let α and β be ordinals. Prove each of the following:

    (i)   If α is isomorphic to β, then $\alpha = \beta$.

    (ii)   Exactly one of the following holds: $\alpha = \beta$, $\alpha \in \beta$, or $\beta \in \alpha$.

8. Prove that a transitive set of ordinals in an ordinal.

9. Let X be a set of ordinals. Prove the following:

    (i) $\bigcup X$ is the least ordinal greater than or equal to all elements of X.

    (ii)   If $X \neq \emptyset$, then $\bigcap X$ is the least ordinal in X.

10. Let $(W, <)$ be a well-ordered set. Prove that there is a unique ordinal α such that $W \cong \alpha$.

CHALLENGE PROBLEMS

11. Prove that the Axiom of Choice implies Zorn's Lemma.

12. Prove the Transfinite Recursion Theorem.

LESSON 13
CARDINALS

The Basics

For this lesson, it is essential that we are assuming AC. By Theorem 12.9, it follows from AC that every set can be well-ordered. We can now define the **cardinality** of a set A, written $|A|$, to be the least ordinal α such that $(A, <) \cong \alpha$, where $<$ is some well ordering of A.

An ordinal α is a **cardinal** if and only if $|\alpha| = \alpha$.

We generally use letters from the middle of the Greek alphabet such as κ (kappa), λ (lambda), and μ (mu) to represent cardinals.

Note: If α and β are ordinals, we may write $\alpha < \beta$ or $\beta > \alpha$ instead of $\alpha \in \beta$. $\alpha \leq \beta$ is an abbreviation for $\alpha \in \beta$ or $\alpha = \beta$. Similarly, $\beta \geq \alpha$ has the same meaning as $\alpha \leq \beta$. We are most likely to use $<$ and $\leq$ (instead of $\in$) when comparing cardinals. However, when comparing cardinals (or ordinals), $<$ and $\in$ have the same exact meaning.

Example 13.1:

1. Each natural number $n \in \omega$ is a cardinal, as there is no bijection from a natural number to a smaller natural number.

2. ω is a cardinal because ω is infinite, while any smaller ordinal is finite.

    Many authors use the Hebrew letter $\aleph$ (pronounced "aleph") with a subscript of 0 to represent the least infinite cardinal. In other words, when thinking of ω as a cardinal, $\aleph_0$ (pronounced "aleph naught") is often used. We will continue to use ω or ω_0. For all practical purposes, $\mathbb{N}$, ω, ω_0, and $\aleph_0$ all represent the same set with the same natural ordering.

3. $\omega_1 = \{\alpha \mid \alpha \text{ is a countable ordinal}\}$ is a cardinal because ω_1 is uncountable, while any smaller ordinal is countable. Many authors use $\aleph_1$ (pronounced "aleph one") to represent the least uncountable cardinal. We will continue to use ω_1 for this purpose. As in 2 with ω, for all practical purposes, ω_1 and $\aleph_1$ both represent the same set with the same ordering.

4. $\omega + 1$ is **not** a cardinal because it is equinumerous with the smaller ordinal ω. We can define a bijection $f: \omega + 1 \to \omega$ by $f(\alpha) = \begin{cases} \alpha + 1 & \text{if } \alpha \in \omega. \\ 0 & \text{if } \alpha = \omega. \end{cases}$

5. If α is an ordinal, then α^+ is the least cardinal such that $\alpha \in \alpha^+$. For example, if n is a natural number, then $n^+ = n + 1$. As another example, $\omega^+ = \omega_1$. We also have $(\omega + 1)^+ = \omega_1$, and in fact, for any ordinal α with $\omega \in \alpha \in \omega_1$, $\alpha^+ = \omega_1$.

    A cardinal κ is a **successor cardinal** if and only if there is an ordinal α such that $\kappa = \alpha^+$. Any infinite cardinal that isn't a successor cardinal is called a **limit cardinal**.

    So, each natural number except 0 is a successor cardinal, whereas ω is a limit cardinal.

156

We define $\omega_2 = \omega_1^+$, $\omega_3 = \omega_2^+,...$, and in general, $\omega_{n+1} = \omega_n^+$. By definition, the cardinals $\omega_1, \omega_2, \omega_3, ...$ are all successor cardinals.

We can then define $\omega_\omega = \bigcup\{\omega_n | n \in \omega\}$. ω_ω is a cardinal. To see this, assume toward contradiction that $f: \omega_\omega \to \alpha$ is a bijection for some $\alpha \in \omega_\omega$. Then there is $n \in \omega$ with $\alpha \in \omega_n$. So, $|\omega_\omega| \le \alpha < \omega_n$, and therefore, $|\omega_\omega| < \omega_n$. Since $\omega_n \subseteq \omega_\omega$, $|\omega_n| \le |\omega_\omega|$. So, $|\omega_n| < \omega_n$, contradicting that ω_n is a cardinal.

A similar argument can be used to show that ω_ω is **not** a successor cardinal. Indeed, if $\omega_\omega = \omega_n^+$, then we have $|\omega_\omega| = |\omega_n^+| = \omega_n^+ = \omega_{n+1} < \omega_{n+2}$. So, $|\omega_\omega| < \omega_{n+2}$. Since $\omega_{n+2} \subseteq \omega_\omega$, $|\omega_{n+2}| \le |\omega_\omega|$. So, $|\omega_{n+2}| < \omega_{n+2}$, contradicting that ω_{n+2} is a cardinal. So, ω_ω is a limit cardinal. It is the second limit cardinal.

6. For each ordinal α, we define the cardinal ω_α as follows:

   (i) $\omega_0 = \omega$.

   (ii) $\omega_{\alpha+1} = (\omega_\alpha)^+$.

   (iii) $\omega_\gamma = \bigcup\{\omega_\alpha \mid \alpha < \gamma\}$ if γ is a limit ordinal.

The transfinite recursion theorem (Theorem 12.12) can be used to justify this definition.

For each ordinal α, ω_α is a cardinal. To see this, suppose toward contradiction that this is not the case, and let β be the least ordinal such that ω_β is not a cardinal. Clearly β is not 0 or a successor ordinal. Therefore, $\omega_\beta = \bigcup\{\omega_\alpha \mid \alpha < \beta\}$. Let $f: \omega_\beta \to \delta$ be a bijection for some $\delta \in \omega_\beta$. Then there is $\alpha < \beta$ with $\delta \in \omega_\alpha$. So, $|\omega_\beta| \le \delta < \omega_\alpha$, and therefore, $|\omega_\beta| < \omega_\alpha$. Since $\omega_\alpha \subseteq \omega_\beta$, $|\omega_\alpha| \le |\omega_\beta|$. So, $|\omega_\alpha| < \omega_\alpha$. Therefore, ω_α is not a cardinal. Since $\alpha < \beta$, this contradicts our assumption that β is the least ordinal such that ω_β is not a cardinal. Thus, for every ordinal α, ω_α is a cardinal.

Conversely, given any cardinal κ, there is an ordinal α such that $\kappa = \omega_\alpha$. I leave the proof of this to the reader.

Let's prove by transfinite induction on β that $\alpha < \beta \to \omega_\alpha < \omega_\beta$. If $\beta = 0$, then $\alpha < \beta$ never occurs. Let $\beta = \gamma + 1$, assume that $\alpha < \gamma \to \omega_\alpha < \omega_\gamma$, and let $\alpha < \beta$. Then $\alpha < \gamma + 1$. If $\alpha = \gamma$, then $\omega_\beta = (\omega_\gamma)^+ > \omega_\gamma = \omega_\alpha$. If $\alpha < \gamma$, then $\omega_\beta = (\omega_\gamma)^+ > \omega_\gamma > \omega_\alpha$. Finally, let β be a limit ordinal, assume that for all $\delta < \beta$, $\alpha < \delta \to \omega_\alpha < \omega_\delta$, and let $\alpha < \beta$. Since β is a limit ordinal, there is $\delta < \beta$ such that $\alpha < \delta$. So, $\omega_\alpha < \omega_\delta$. Since $\omega_\delta \subseteq \bigcup\{\omega_\gamma \mid \gamma < \beta\}$, we have $\omega_\alpha < \bigcup\{\omega_\gamma \mid \gamma < \beta\} = \omega_\beta$.

If α is a successor ordinal, say $\alpha = \beta + 1$, then $\omega_\alpha = \omega_{\beta+1} = (\omega_\beta)^+$, showing that ω_α is a successor cardinal. Conversely, if ω_α is a successor cardinal, say $\omega_\alpha = (\omega_\beta)^+$, then $\omega_\alpha > \omega_\beta$. If $\alpha < \beta$, then by the previous paragraph, $\omega_\alpha < \omega_\beta$, contradicting that $<$ is antisymmetric. So, $\beta \le \alpha$. If $\beta = \alpha$, then $\omega_\beta = \omega_\alpha = (\omega_\beta)^+$, another contradiction. If $\alpha > \beta + 1$, then again by the previous paragraph, we have $\omega_\alpha > (\omega_\beta)^+$, yet another contradiction. So, $\alpha = \beta + 1$. Thus, α is a successor ordinal. So, we proved that α is a successor ordinal if and only if ω_α is a successor cardinal.

If γ is a limit ordinal, then $\omega_\gamma = \bigcup\{\omega_\alpha \mid \alpha < \gamma\}$. If $\omega_\gamma = (\omega_\alpha)^+$, then $\omega_\gamma = \omega_{\alpha+1} < \omega_{\alpha+2} \le \omega_\gamma$. This contradicts that $<$ is a strict linear order, and so, ω_γ is a a limit cardinal. Conversely, if ω_γ is a limit cardinal, but $\gamma = \beta + 1$, then $\omega_\gamma = \bigcup\{\omega_\alpha \mid \alpha < \beta + 1\} = \bigcup\{\omega_\alpha \mid \alpha \le \beta\} = \omega_\beta$, a contradiction. Therefore, γ is a limit ordinal. So, we proved that α is a limit ordinal if and only if ω_α is a limit cardinal.

Cardinal Arithmetic

We define addition, multiplication, and exponentiation of cardinals as follows:

$$\kappa + \lambda = |(\kappa \times \{0\}) \cup (\lambda \times \{1\})| \qquad \kappa \cdot \lambda = |\kappa \times \lambda| \qquad \kappa^\lambda = |^\lambda\kappa|$$

Notes: (1) The choice of using $\kappa \times \{0\}$ and $\lambda \times \{1\}$ in the definition of $\kappa + \lambda$ is somewhat arbitrary. We can define $\kappa + \lambda$ to be $|A \cup B|$, where A and B are **any** two **disjoint** sets such that $|A| = \kappa$ and $|B| = \lambda$.

(2) Recall that $\kappa \times \lambda$ is the **Cartesian product** of κ and λ. See Lesson 4 for details.

(3) Recall that $^\lambda\kappa$ is the set of functions from λ to κ. See Lesson 6 for details.

Example 13.2:

1. $\omega + \omega = |A \cup B|$, where $A = \omega \times \{0\}$ and $B = \omega \times \{1\}$. Since A and B are both countably infinite, $A \cup B$ is countably infinite (see part (ii) of Problem 5 from Problem Set 7). Therefore, $|A \cup B| = \omega$. So, $\omega + \omega = \omega$.

2. $\omega \cdot \omega = |\omega \times \omega| = \omega$ by part (i) of Problem 7 from Problem Set 7.

3. For any cardinal κ, $\kappa^0 = |\{f \mid f : 0 \to \kappa\}| = |1| = 1$.

4. For any cardinal κ, $\kappa^1 = |\{f \mid f : \{0\} \to \kappa\}| = |\kappa| = \kappa$.

5. $2^\omega = |^\omega 2| = |\{f \mid f : \omega \to \{0, 1\}\}|$. Some other sets that have the same size as 2^ω are $\mathcal{P}(\omega)$, $\mathbb{R}$, and ω^ω. We proved that many of these sets were equinumerous in Lesson 7 (and the problems in Problem Set 7). We also know by Theorem 7.2 from Lesson 7 that 2^ω is strictly larger than ω. In particular, 2^ω is uncountable.

    Exactly how big is 2^ω? The **Continuum Hypothesis (CH)** is the statement $2^\omega = \omega_1$. In other words, CH says that 2^ω is the least uncountable cardinal. This is equivalent to saying that there is no set A such that $|\mathbb{N}| < |A| < |\mathbb{R}|$. As it turns out, CH is **independent** of the axioms of ZFC. It can neither be proved nor disproved using only the axioms we described in Lesson 11. Proving that CH is independent of ZFC is beyond the scope of this book. It is best left for the interested reader to investigate "independently."

Our next goal is to show that if κ is an infinite cardinal, then $\kappa \cdot \kappa = \kappa$. To do this, we will need to define an appropriate well-ordering of $\kappa \times \kappa$.

Lemma 13.1: Let κ be an infinite cardinal. Define the relation $\lhd$ on $\kappa \times \kappa$ by $(\alpha, \beta) \lhd (\gamma, \delta)$ if and only if

(i) $\max\{\alpha, \beta\} \in \max\{\gamma, \delta\}$; or

(ii) $\max\{\alpha, \beta\} = \max\{\gamma, \delta\}$ and $\alpha \in \gamma$; or

(iii) $\max\{\alpha, \beta\} = \max\{\gamma, \delta\}$ and $\alpha = \gamma$ and $\beta \in \delta$.

Then $(\kappa \times \kappa, \lhd)$ is a well-ordered set.

You will be asked to prove Lemma 13.1 in Problem 6 below.

Notes: (1) Let's write out the beginning of the ordering $(\omega \times \omega, \lhd)$:

$$(0,0) \lhd (0,1) \lhd (1,0) \lhd (1,1) \lhd (0,2) \lhd (1,2) \lhd (2,0) \lhd (2,1) \lhd (2,2)$$
$$\lhd (0,3) \lhd (1,3) \lhd (2,3) \lhd (3,0) \lhd (3,1) \lhd (3,2) \lhd (3,3)$$
$$\lhd (0,4) \lhd (1,4) \lhd (2,4) \lhd (3,4) \lhd (4,0) \lhd (4,1) \lhd (4,2) \lhd (4,3) \lhd (4,4)$$
$$\lhd (0,5) \lhd (1,5) \lhd (2,5) \lhd (3,5) \lhd (4,5) \lhd (5,0) \lhd (5,1) \lhd \cdots$$

Observe how for each $n \in \omega$, there are only finitely many pairs (j, k) with $n = \max\{j, k\}$. For example, if $n = 0$, then there is only 1 such pair, namely $(0, 0)$. If $n = 1$, there are 3 pairs: $(0, 1)$, $(1, 0)$, and $(1, 1)$. In general, there are $2n + 1$ pairs (j, k) with $n = \max\{j, k\}$. So, we see that $(\omega \times \omega, \lhd) \cong \omega$. Since an isomorphism is also a bijection, this shows that $\omega \cdot \omega = \omega$.

(2) Let's write out the beginning of the ordering $(\omega_1 \times \omega_1, \lhd)$. Since $(\omega \times \omega, \lhd)$ is a proper initial segment of $(\omega_1 \times \omega_1, \lhd)$, let's begin after all pairs (i, j) such that $\max\{i, j\}$ is a natural number.

$$\cdots (0, \omega) \lhd (1, \omega) \lhd (2, \omega) \lhd (3, \omega) \lhd \cdots \lhd (\omega, 0) \lhd (\omega, 1) \lhd (\omega, 2) \lhd \cdots \lhd (\omega, \omega)$$
$$\lhd (0, \omega + 1) \lhd (1, \omega + 1) \lhd (2, \omega + 1) \lhd \cdots \lhd (\omega, \omega + 1) \lhd (\omega + 1, 0) \lhd (\omega + 1, 1) \lhd$$
$$\cdots \lhd (\omega + 1, \omega) \lhd (\omega + 1, \omega + 1) \lhd (0, \omega + 2) \lhd (1, \omega + 2) \lhd \cdots$$

Since $(\omega_1 \times \omega_1, \lhd)$ is a well-ordered set, there is a unique ordinal ξ such that $\xi \cong (\omega_1 \times \omega_1, \lhd)$ (By Theorem 12.8). If $\alpha, \beta \in \omega_1$, then α and β are both smaller than $\eta = \max\{\alpha, \beta\} + 1$. Since $|\alpha|, |\beta| \leq \omega$, it follows that $|\eta| \leq \omega$. By Note 1, $|\eta \times \eta| = \big||\eta| \times |\eta|\big| \leq |\omega \times \omega| = \omega$. It follows that (α, β) has countably many predecessors in $(\omega_1 \times \omega_1, \lhd)$. If $\omega_1 < \xi$, then the image of ω_1 under the isomorphism from ξ to $(\omega_1 \times \omega_1, \lhd)$ would have uncountably many predecessors. Since we just showed that this cannot happen, it follows that $\xi \leq \omega_1$. Therefore, $|\omega_1 \times \omega_1| = |\xi| \leq \xi \leq \omega_1$. Since $\omega_1 \leq |\omega_1 \times \omega_1|$ is also true (for example, the function $f : \omega_1 \to \omega_1 \times \omega_1$ defined by $f(\alpha) = (\alpha, \alpha)$ is an injection), we have $|\omega_1 \times \omega_1| = \omega_1$. In other words, $\omega_1 \cdot \omega_1 = \omega_1$.

We now generalize the results from Notes 1 and 2 above to arbitrary infinite cardinals.

Theorem 13.2: Let κ be an infinite cardinal. Then $\kappa \cdot \kappa = \kappa$.

We will use **strong transfinite induction** (see Problem 3 from Problem Set 12) to prove this theorem.

Proof: We saw in Note 1 above (or part 2 of Example 13.2) that $\omega \cdot \omega = \omega$.

Let $\kappa > \omega$ and suppose that for all cardinals $\lambda < \kappa$, $\lambda \cdot \lambda \leq \max\{\lambda, \omega\}$.

Let $(\kappa \times \kappa, \lhd)$ be the well-ordered set from Lemma 13.1. Since $(\kappa \times \kappa, \lhd)$ is a well-ordered set, by Theorem 12.8 there is a unique ordinal ξ such that $\xi \cong (\kappa \times \kappa, \lhd)$. Let $f: \xi \to (\kappa \times \kappa, \lhd)$ be an isomorphism.

If $(\alpha, \beta) \in \kappa \times \kappa$, then α and β are both smaller than $\eta = \max\{\alpha, \beta\} + 1$. Since κ is an infinite cardinal, κ is a limit ordinal. Therefore, since $|\alpha|, |\beta| < \kappa$, we have $|\eta| < \kappa$. By the inductive hypothesis, $|\eta \times \eta| = ||\eta| \times |\eta|| \leq \max\{|\eta|, \omega\} < \kappa$. It follows that (α, β) has less than κ predecessors in $(\kappa \times \kappa, \lhd)$. If $\kappa < \xi$, then $f(\kappa)$ would have κ many predecessors. Since we just showed that this cannot happen, it follows that $\xi \leq \kappa$. Therefore, $|\kappa \times \kappa| = |\xi| \leq \xi \leq \kappa$. Since $\kappa \leq |\kappa \times \kappa|$ is also true (for example, $f: \kappa \to \kappa \times \kappa$ defined by $f(\alpha) = (\alpha, \alpha)$ is an injection), we have $|\kappa \times \kappa| = \kappa$. In other words, $\kappa \cdot \kappa = \kappa$. $\square$

Theorem 13.2 gives us the machinery we need to do basic arithmetic with infinite cardinals. For example, in Problem 1 below, you will be asked to prove that both the sum and product of two infinite cardinals is simply the bigger of the two cardinals. So, $\omega + \omega_1 = \omega_1$ simply because ω_1 is larger.

Cofinality

Let α and β be ordinals. A function $f: \alpha \to \beta$ is **cofinal** if and only if for every $\delta \in \beta$, there is $\gamma \in \alpha$ such that $\delta \leq f(\gamma)$.

In other words, $f: \alpha \to \beta$ cofinal means that the range of f is unbounded in β. In simple terms, a cofinal function "cuts" all the way through its target ordinal.

The **cofinality** of an ordinal β, written $cf(\beta)$, is the least ordinal α such that there exists a cofinal function $f: \alpha \to \beta$.

Example 13.3:

1. If β is a successor ordinal, then $cf(\beta) = 1 = \{0\}$. To see this, note that there is an ordinal γ such that $\beta = \gamma + 1$. Define $f: \{0\} \to \beta$ by $f(0) = \gamma$. Then f is cofinal.

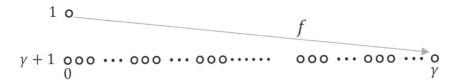

2. For any ordinal β, the identity function $i: \beta \to \beta$ defined by $i(\gamma) = \gamma$ for all $\gamma \in \beta$ is cofinal. It follows that $cf(\beta) \leq \beta$.

3. If n is a natural number, then there is no cofinal function from n to ω. So, by 2, $cf(\omega) = \omega$.

   ω is an example of a **regular** cardinal. In general, a cardinal κ is called regular if $cf(\kappa) = \kappa$.

4. ω_1 is also a regular cardinal. To see this, let $f: \alpha \to \omega_1$ be a cofinal map. Then we have $\omega_1 = \bigcup\{f(\beta) | \beta \in \alpha\}$. If $\alpha < \omega_1$, then this is a countable union of countable sets, and so, by part (ii) of Problem 5 from Problem Set 7, ω_1 would be countable. Since ω_1 is uncountable, $\omega_1 \leq \alpha$. It follows that $cf(\omega_1) = \omega_1$.

In fact, every infinite successor cardinal is regular. You will be asked to prove this in Problem 7 below. So, in particular, the following are all regular: $\omega_1, \omega_2, \omega_3,\dots$ and so on.

5. An infinite cardinal that is **not** regular is called **singular**. Since $cf(\kappa) \leq \kappa$, an infinite cardinal κ is singular if and only if $cf(\kappa) < \kappa$.

   For example, ω_ω is singular. We can define a cofinal map $f: \omega \to \omega_\omega$ by $f(n) = \omega_n$. It follows that $cf(\omega_\omega) \leq \omega$. In fact, it's easy to see that $cf(\omega_\omega) = \omega$, as there can certainly be no cofinal map from a natural number to ω_ω, simply because ω_ω is infinite.

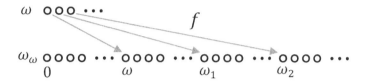

In part 5 of Example 13.2, we discussed what we know about the size of 2^ω. The axioms of ZFC imply that $2^\omega > \omega$. If CH holds, then we know that the exact value of 2^ω is ω_1, the first uncountable cardinal. As we already mentioned, CH is independent of ZFC. So, it is consistent with ZFC that $2^\omega = \omega_1$ and it is also consistent with ZFC that $2^\omega \neq \omega_1$. So, the next natural question is, "For which uncountable cardinals κ is it consistent that $2^\omega = \kappa$?" As it turns out, the possible values for κ for which $2^\omega = \kappa$ is unbounded in **ON**. So, not only can we not determine the size of 2^ω using the axioms of ZFC, but we cannot even put a bound on the size of 2^ω.

We will not attempt here to determine all the values κ for which it is consistent that $2^\omega = \kappa$. However, using the next theorem, we will be able to determine certain values of κ such that $2^\omega \neq \kappa$.

Specifically, we will show that $cf(2^\omega) > \omega$. So, for example, since $cf(\omega_\omega) = \omega$, $2^\omega \neq \omega_\omega$.

Theorem 13.3 (König's Theorem): Let κ be an infinite cardinal. Then $\kappa < \kappa^{cf(\kappa)}$.

Proof: Let $f: cf(\kappa) \to \kappa$ be a cofinal function and let $F: \kappa \to {}^{cf(\kappa)}\kappa$ be any function. We will prove that F is **not** surjective. For each $\alpha < cf(\kappa)$, we have $|\{F(\gamma)(\alpha) \mid \gamma < f(\alpha)\}| \leq |f(\alpha)| < \kappa$. Therefore, $\kappa \setminus \{F(\gamma)(\alpha) \mid \gamma < f(\alpha)\} \neq \emptyset$. So, we can choose an element $\beta_\alpha \in \kappa \setminus \{F(\gamma)(\alpha) \mid \gamma < f(\alpha)\}$. We define a function $h: cf(\kappa) \to \kappa$ by $h(\alpha) = \beta_\alpha$.

We now show that $h \notin \text{ran } F$. Assume toward contradiction that $h \in \text{ran } F$. Then there is $\gamma < \kappa$ such that $F(\gamma) = h$. Choose $\alpha < cf(\kappa)$ such that $\gamma < f(\alpha)$. Then $h(\alpha) = \beta_\alpha \neq F(\gamma)(\alpha)$. This contradiction shows that $h \notin \text{ran } F$, so that F is not surjective. Therefore, $\kappa < \kappa^{cf(\kappa)}$. $\quad\square$

Example 13.4: Since $(2^\omega)^\omega = 2^{\omega \cdot \omega} = 2^\omega$, by letting $\kappa = 2^\omega$ in Theorem 13.3, we see that $cf(2^\omega)$ cannot be equal to ω. In particular, $2^\omega \neq \omega_\omega$.

Problem Set 13

LEVEL 1

1. Let κ and λ be infinite cardinals. Prove each of the following:

   (i) $\kappa + \lambda = \max\{\kappa, \lambda\}$.

   (ii) $\kappa \cdot \lambda = \max\{\kappa, \lambda\}$.

   (iii) For each natural number $n \geq 1$, $\kappa^n = \kappa$.

2. Let κ, λ, and μ be infinite cardinals. Prove that $\kappa^\lambda \kappa^\mu = \kappa^{\lambda+\mu}$.

LEVEL 2

3. Let κ be an infinite cardinal and let $X = \bigcup\{\kappa^n \mid n \in \omega\}$. Prove that $|X| = \kappa$.

4. Let κ be an infinite cardinal and for each ordinal $\alpha < \kappa$ let X_α be a set such that $|X_\alpha| \leq \kappa$. Prove that $|\bigcup\{X_\alpha \mid \alpha < \kappa\}| \leq \kappa$.

LEVEL 3

5. Let X be a set of cardinals. Prove that $\bigcup X$ is a cardinal.

6. Let κ be an infinite cardinal. Define the relation $\lhd$ on $\kappa \times \kappa$ by $(\alpha, \beta) \lhd (\gamma, \delta)$ if and only if

   (i) $\max\{\alpha, \beta\} \in \max\{\gamma, \delta\}$; or

   (ii) $\max\{\alpha, \beta\} = \max\{\gamma, \delta\}$ and $\alpha \in \gamma$; or

   (iii) $\max\{\alpha, \beta\} = \max\{\gamma, \delta\}$ and $\alpha = \gamma$ and $\beta \in \delta$.

   Prove that $(\kappa \times \kappa, \lhd)$ is a well-ordered set.

LEVEL 4

7. Prove that every infinite successor cardinal is regular.

8. Prove that for any ordinal α, there exists a strictly increasing cofinal function $f : cf(\alpha) \to \alpha$.

LEVEL 5

9. Let α be a limit ordinal and let $f : \alpha \to \beta$ be a strictly increasing cofinal function. Prove that $cf(\alpha) = cf(\beta)$.

10. Prove that for any ordinal α, $cf\big(cf(\alpha)\big) = cf(\alpha)$.

CHALLENGE PROBLEMS

11. Assume that κ is a cardinal greater than ω. Prove that $cf(\kappa)$ is the smallest ordinal α such that there exist sets A_η, $\eta < \alpha$, each of cardinality less than κ, such that $\kappa = \bigcup\{A_\eta \mid \eta < \alpha\}$.

12. The **Generalized Continuum Hypothesis (GCH)** is the statement $\forall \kappa \geq \omega (2^\kappa = \kappa^+)$. Assuming GCH, compute κ^λ for all cardinals λ and κ.

LESSON 14
MARTIN'S AXIOM

Dominating Functions

Martin's Axiom, abbreviated as **MA**, is an example of a statement that is independent of ZFC + CH. Informally, MA says "all infinite cardinals less than 2^ω behave a lot like ω." I admit that this statement is quite vague—we will see the precise definition later in the lesson. For now, let's begin by looking at an example.

Let $f, g \in {}^\omega\omega$. We say that g **dominates** f (or f is **dominated** by g), written $f <^* g$, if and only if there is a natural number n such that for every natural number m greater than n, $f(m) < g(m)$. We can write this symbolically as follows:

$$\exists n \in \omega \; \forall m > n \big(f(m) < g(m) \big).$$

Example 14.1: Define $f, g : \omega \to \omega$ by $f(n) = n + 100$ and $g(n) = 2^n$. Observe that $f(m) < g(m)$ for $m > 6$. It follows that $f <^* g$.

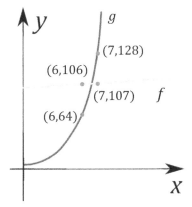

Notes: (1) $f(1) = 101$ and $g(1) = 2^1 = 2$, so that $f(1) > g(1)$. So, it's not true that $f(n) < g(n)$ for all n. In fact, $f(n) > g(n)$ for $n = 0, 1, 2, 3, 4, 5$, and 6. The definition of $<^*$ allows for this. $f <^* g$ means that the values of f are *eventually* less than the values of g.

(2) The figure to the right gives a visual representation of the functions f and g. Note that the solid curves are there only to help with the visualization. The actual graphs of f and g consist only of isolated points. Notice how initially the graph of f is above the graph of g, but *eventually* the graph of g is above the graph of f.

(3) $({}^\omega\omega, <^*)$ is a strict poset ($<^*$ is antireflexive, antisymmetric, and transitive on ${}^\omega\omega$). You were asked to prove this in part (i) of Problem 7 from Problem Set 6.

In part (iii) of Problem 7 from Problem Set 6, you were asked the following question:

Question 1: Given countably many functions from ω to ω, can we always find another function from ω to ω that dominates all the given functions?

Theorem 14.1 below will give us an answer to this question. To help us gain a better understanding of the question, let's first look at a specific example.

Example 14.2: Consider the family $\mathcal{F} = \{f_n\colon \omega \to \omega \mid n \in \omega\}$, where $f_n(k) = n$ for all $k \in \omega$. For each $n \in \omega$, f_n is a constant function. For example, f_0 is the function which gives an output of 0 for each natural number input. You can visualize this constant function as dots along the x-axis, as shown in the figure to the right. The figure also shows the functions f_1, f_2, and f_3. There is no function g such that for all $n \in \omega$, $f_n(k) < g(k)$ for all $k \in \omega$. However, there are functions which dominate every f_n. For example, let $g\colon \omega \to \omega$ be defined by $g(n) = n$. You can visualize g as the dots along the diagonal ray shown in the figure to the right. We have $f_0(k) < g(k)$ for all $k > 0$. We also have $f_1(k) < g(k)$ for all $k > 1$. In general, $f_n(k) < g(k)$ for all $k > n$. It follows that g dominates f_n for all $n \in \omega$.

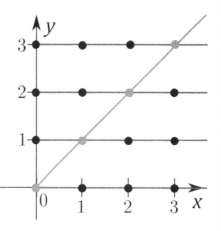

Note: Any function of the form $g(n) = mn + b$, where $m > 0$ would serve as a dominating function for all members of the family $\mathcal{F}$. Of course, there are many other functions that would work just as well (uncountably many, in fact!).

Theorem 14.1: Let $\mathcal{F} = \{f_n\colon \omega \to \omega \mid n \in \omega\}$ be a countable set of functions. Then there is a function $g \in {}^{\omega}\omega$ such that for all $n \in \omega$, $f_n <^* g$.

We can dominate each f_n as follows:

We let $g(0)$ be any number greater than $f_0(0)$. For example, we can let $g(0) = f_0(0) + 1$.

We then let $g(1)$ be any number greater than both $f_0(1)$ and $f_1(1)$. For example, we can let $g(1) = \max\{f_0(1) + 1, f_1(1) + 1\}$.

Next, we let $g(2)$ be any number greater than $f_0(2)$, $f_1(2)$, and $f_2(2)$. For example, we can let $g(2) = \max\{f_0(2) + 1, f_1(2) + 1, f_2(2) + 1\}$.

In general, we let $g(k)$ be any number greater than $f_0(k), f_1(k), \ldots, f_k(k)$. For example, we can let $g(k) = \max\{f_0(k) + 1, f_1(k) + 1, f_2(k) + 1, \ldots, f_k(k) + 1\} = \max\{f_n(k) + 1 \mid n \leq k\}$.

This definition gives us a function $g\colon \omega \to \omega$ that dominates every f_n.

Proof: Let $\mathcal{F} = \{f_n\colon \omega \to \omega \mid n \in \omega\}$ and define $g\colon \omega \to \omega$ by $g(k) = \max\{f_n(k) + 1 \mid n \leq k\}$.

Let $n \in \omega$. If $m > n$, then we have $f_n(m) < f_n(m) + 1 \leq g(m)$. So, $f_n <^* g$. Since $n \in \omega$ was arbitrary, it follows that for all $n \in \omega$, $f_n <^* g$. $\quad\square$

Question 2: Given ω_1 many functions from ω to ω, can we always find another function from ω to ω that dominates all the given functions?

We can state this a bit more precisely as follows:

Let $\mathcal{F} = \{f_\alpha\colon \omega \to \omega \mid \alpha < \omega_1\}$. Must there be a function $g \in {}^{\omega}\omega$ such that for all $\alpha < \omega_1$, $f_\alpha <^* g$?

Partial Answer: Maybe not! If CH holds ($2^\omega = \omega_1$), then $\mathcal{F}$ could be equal to $^\omega\omega$. Since no function can dominate itself, in this case there is no function that dominates all the functions in $\mathcal{F}$.

So, we see that if CH holds, the answer to Question 2 is NO!

But what if CH fails? Then $2^\omega > \omega_1$. It turns out that in this case, if we assume MA, the answer to Question 2 is YES! Of course, we will first need to give a formal definition of MA to prove this. We will get to this shortly.

Posets

Recall from Lesson 4 that a **poset** is a pair $(P, \leq)$, where P is a set and $\leq$ is reflexive, antisymmetric, and transitive on P.

If $\mathbb{P} = (P, \leq)$ is a poset, we will use $\mathbb{P}$ and P interchangeably if no confusion can arise. For example, we may say $p \in \mathbb{P}$ or $A \subseteq \mathbb{P}$ instead of $p \in P$ or $A \subseteq P$, respectively.

Let $\mathcal{F} \subseteq {}^\omega\omega$. We define a poset $\mathbb{P}_\mathcal{F} = (P, \leq)$ as follows:

1. P consists of pairs $(s, \mathcal{F}_0)$, where

    (i) $s: n \to \omega$ for some $n \in \omega$.

    (ii) $\mathcal{F}_0$ is a finite subset of $\mathcal{F}$.

2. If $(s, \mathcal{F}_0), (t, \mathcal{F}_1) \in P$, then $(t, \mathcal{F}_1) \leq (s, \mathcal{F}_0)$ if and only if each of the following holds:

    (i) $s \subseteq t$.

    (ii) $\mathcal{F}_0 \subseteq \mathcal{F}_1$.

    (iii) For all $k \in \text{dom } t \setminus \text{dom } s$ and all $f \in \mathcal{F}_0$, $f(k) < t(k)$.

Notes: (1) The partial order $\mathbb{P}_\mathcal{F}$ can be thought of as a collection of finite approximations to a function $g \in {}^\omega\omega$ that dominates all $f \in \mathcal{F}$. A typical element of $\mathbb{P}_\mathcal{F}$ has the form $(s, \mathcal{F}_0)$. The finite function $s: n \to \omega$ might possibly give the first few values of g, and $\mathcal{F}_0$ can be thought of as a finite set of promises: we promise that for all $n \in \omega \setminus \text{dom } s$, $f(n) < g(n)$ for all $f \in \mathcal{F}_0$.

(2) Set theorists often refer to the elements of a partial order as **conditions** and for p, q in the partial order, they say that q **extends** p if $q \leq p$. Informally, we see that if q extends p, then q gives more information than p (or at least as much information as p).

(3) We will refer to $\mathbb{P}_\mathcal{F}$ as a **dominating poset**.

Example 14.3: For each $k \in \omega$, let $f_k: \omega \to \omega$ be defined by $f_k(n) = kn$. Let $\mathcal{F} = \{f_k \mid k \in \omega\}$ and let $\mathbb{P}_\mathcal{F}$ be the corresponding dominating poset.

Now, let $s = \{(0,0), (1,1), (2,4), (3,5)\}$, let $\mathcal{F}_0 = \{f_1, f_2, f_3\}$, and let $p = (s, \mathcal{F}_0)$. Then $p \in \mathbb{P}_\mathcal{F}$.

Also, let $t = \{(0,0), (1,1), (2,4), (3,5), (4,21)\}$, let $\mathcal{F}_1 = \{f_1, f_2, f_3, f_{1000}, f_{2526}\}$, and let $q = (t, \mathcal{F}_1)$. Then $q \in \mathbb{P}_\mathcal{F}$.

Let's show that $q \le p$. It's clear that $s \subseteq t$ and $\mathcal{F}_0 \subseteq \mathcal{F}_1$. Observe that $\operatorname{dom} s = \{0, 1, 2, 3\}$ and $\operatorname{dom} t = \{0, 1, 2, 3, 4\}$. So, $\operatorname{dom} t \setminus \operatorname{dom} s = \{4\}$. We have $f_1(4) = 1 \cdot 4 = 4$, $f_2(4) = 2 \cdot 4 = 8$, $f_3(4) = 3 \cdot 4 = 12$, and $t(4) = 21$. Therefore, $f_1(4), f_2(4), f_3(4)$ are all less than $t(4)$. It follows that $\forall k \in \operatorname{dom} t \setminus \operatorname{dom} s \, \forall f \in \mathcal{F}_0\big(f(k) < t(k)\big)$, and therefore, $q \le p$.

Notes: (1) In this example, we have countably many functions $f_0, f_1, f_2, f_3, \dots$ defined by $f_0(n) = 0$, $f_1(n) = n$, $f_2(n) = 2n$, $f_3(n) = 3n$, and so on. These are the functions we would like to dominate.

(2) Notice how q has all the same information as p, plus a little more. We have $t = s \cup \{(4, 21)\}$ and $\mathcal{F}_1 = \mathcal{F}_0 \cup \{f_{1000}, f_{2526}\}$. We can throw whatever functions we want into $\mathcal{F}_0$ (but just finitely many) to form $\mathcal{F}_1$, but we need to be careful about what we throw into s to form t if we want q to extend p. For example, if we were to let $t = s \cup \{(4, 12)\}$, then q would **not** extend p because in this case, we would have $f_3(4) = t(4)$.

(3) Also, notice that in order for q to extend p, t has to agree with s on $\operatorname{dom} s$. For example, if we let $t = \{(0, 0), (1, 1), (2, 4), (3, 6), (4, 21)\}$, then $s \not\subseteq t$, and so, p and q are incomparable. If we try to take the union of s and t, we get $s \cup t = \{(0, 0), (1, 1), (2, 4), (3, 5), (3, 6), (4, 21)\}$. This is **not** a function, and so, $(s \cup t, \mathcal{F}_1) \notin \mathbb{P}_\mathcal{F}$.

Filters, Dense Sets, and the CCC

If $\mathbb{P}$ is a poset, then $\mathcal{G} \subseteq \mathbb{P}$ is a **filter** if and only if

1. $\forall p, q \in \mathcal{G} \, \exists r \in \mathcal{G}(r \le p \wedge r \le q)$.
2. $\forall p \in \mathcal{G} \, \forall q \in \mathbb{P}(p \le q \to q \in \mathcal{G})$.

Notes: (1) The first clause in the definition of a filter says that any two elements have a common extension inside the filter. If we think of p and q in $\mathcal{G}$ each providing some "information," then there must be an element of $\mathcal{G}$ that provides *at least* all the information that both p and q do.

(2) The second clause in the definition of a filter says that the filter is closed under "less information." Again, if we think of p in $\mathcal{G}$ as providing some "information," and q provides less information than p, then q must be an element of $\mathcal{G}$ as well.

Example 14.4: Let $\mathcal{F} = \{f_k \mid k \in \omega\}$ be as in Example 14.3. That is, for each $k \in \omega$, $f_k(n) = kn$ for all $n \in \omega$. Let $\mathcal{G} = \{(s_n, \emptyset) \mid n \in \omega \wedge \forall k < n(s_n(k) = 0)\}$. It is quite easy to see that $\mathcal{G}$ is a filter. If we let $g = \bigcup\{s_n \mid (s_n, \emptyset) \in \mathcal{G}\}$, we see that $g: \omega \to \omega$ is the constant zero function. That is, $g(k) = 0$ for all $k \in \omega$. To see this, let $k \in \omega$. Then if $n > k$, we have $s_n(k) = 0$ (if $n \le k$, $s_n(k)$ is not defined). Since $s_n \subseteq g$, we also have $g(k) = 0$. This isn't a particularly useful filter, as we can see from the fact that all it allowed us to do was to generate a trivial function. See Theorem 14.2 below for a nontrivial example.

If $\mathbb{P}$ is a poset, then $\mathcal{D} \subseteq \mathbb{P}$ is **dense** if for every $p \in \mathbb{P}$, there is $d \in \mathcal{D}$ such that $d \le p$.

In words, a dense subset contains extensions of all elements of the poset.

Example 14.5: Let $\mathcal{F} \subseteq {}^{\omega}\omega$ and let $\mathbb{P}_{\mathcal{F}}$ be the corresponding dominating poset.

1. For each $f \in \mathcal{F}$, let $\mathcal{D}_f = \{(s, \mathcal{F}_0) \mid f \in \mathcal{F}_0\}$. Then $\mathcal{D}_f$ is dense in $\mathbb{P}_{\mathcal{F}}$. Indeed, if $(s, \mathcal{F}_0) \in \mathbb{P}_{\mathcal{F}}$ is arbitrary, then $(s, \mathcal{F}_0 \cup \{f\}) \in \mathcal{D}_f$ because $f \in \mathcal{F}_0 \cup \{f\}$. Also, $(s, \mathcal{F}_0 \cup \{f\}) \leq (s, \mathcal{F}_0)$ because $s \subseteq s$, $\mathcal{F}_0 \subseteq \mathcal{F}_0 \cup \{f\}$, and $\text{dom } s \setminus \text{dom } s = \emptyset$ (so that clause 2(iii) in the definition of $\leq$ holds vacuously).

2. For each $k \in \omega$, let $\mathcal{E}_k = \{(s, \mathcal{F}_0) \mid k \in \text{dom } s\}$. Then $\mathcal{E}_k$ is dense in $\mathbb{P}_{\mathcal{F}}$. To see this, let $(s, \mathcal{F}_0) \in \mathbb{P}_{\mathcal{F}}$ be arbitrary. For each $j \leq k$ with $j \notin \text{dom } s$, let $n_j = \max\{f(j) + 1\} \mid f \in \mathcal{F}_0\}$. Let $t = s \cup \{(j, n_j) \mid j \leq k \wedge j \notin \text{dom } s\}$. Then $(t, \mathcal{F}_0) \in \mathcal{E}_k$ because $(k, n_k) \in t$ and therefore, $k \in \text{dom } t$. Let's check that $(t, \mathcal{F}_0) \leq (s, \mathcal{F}_0)$. Clearly, $s \subseteq t$ and $\mathcal{F}_0 \subseteq \mathcal{F}_0$. Now, let $j \in \text{dom } t \setminus \text{dom } s$ and $f \in \mathcal{F}_0$. Then $f(j) < f(j) + 1 \leq n_j = t(j)$. Thus, $(t, \mathcal{F}_0) \leq (s, \mathcal{F}_0)$.

Theorem 14.2: Let $\mathcal{F} \subseteq {}^{\omega}\omega$ and let $\mathbb{P}_{\mathcal{F}}$ be the corresponding dominating poset. Suppose there is a filter $\mathcal{G} \subseteq \mathbb{P}_{\mathcal{F}}$ such that $\mathcal{G} \cap \mathcal{D}_f \neq \emptyset$ for all $f \in \mathcal{F}$ and $\mathcal{G} \cap \mathcal{E}_k \neq \emptyset$ for all $k \in \omega$. Then there exists a function $g \in {}^{\omega}\omega$ such that $f <^* g$ for all $f \in \mathcal{F}$.

Proof: Let $g = \bigcup\{s \mid (s, \mathcal{F}_0) \in \mathcal{G} \text{ for some } \mathcal{F}_0\}$. We first show that $g \in {}^{\omega}\omega$. Let $k \in \omega$. By Example 14.5 (part 2), $\mathcal{E}_k$ is dense in $\mathbb{P}_{\mathcal{F}}$. So, by assumption, there is $p \in \mathcal{G} \cap \mathcal{E}_k$, say $p = (s, \mathcal{F}_0)$. Since $k \in \text{dom } s$ and $s \subseteq g$, $k \in \text{dom } g$. Suppose that $q = (t, \mathcal{F}_1) \in \mathcal{G}$ also satisfies $k \in \text{dom } t$. Since $\mathcal{G}$ is a filter, there is $r \in \mathcal{G}$ with $r \leq p$ and $r \leq q$. Let's say that $r = (u, \mathcal{F}_2)$. Since $s \subseteq u$, $t \subseteq u$, and u is a function with $k \in \text{dom } u$, we must have $s(k) = u(k) = t(k)$. It follows that g is a function with domain ω.

Now, we show that $f <^* g$ for all $f \in \mathcal{F}$. Let $f \in \mathcal{F}$. By assumption, there is $p \in \mathcal{G} \cap \mathcal{D}_f$, let's say $p = (s, \mathcal{F}_0)$. Let $k \in \omega \setminus \text{dom } s$. Again, by assumption, there is $q \in \mathcal{G} \cap \mathcal{E}_k$, say $q = (t, \mathcal{F}_1)$. Since $\mathcal{G}$ is a filter, there is $r \in \mathcal{G}$ with $r \leq p$ and $r \leq q$, let's say $r = (u, \mathcal{F}_2)$. Since $r \leq p$, $k \in \text{dom } r \setminus \text{dom } s$, and $f \in \mathcal{F}_0$, we have $f(k) < u(k)$. Since $u \subseteq g$, $u(k) = g(k)$. Therefore, $f(k) < g(k)$. Since $k \in \omega \setminus \text{dom } s$ was arbitrary, $f <^* g$. $\square$

So, the big question now is, "Does a filter satisfying the hypothesis of Theorem 14.2 exist?" Martin's Axiom will guarantee the existence of such a filter as long as the set $\mathcal{F}$ isn't "too big."

Martin's Axiom is a general statement about a class of posets. As long as a given poset doesn't get "too wide," Martin's Axiom provides a filter that intersects a fairly large (but not too large) collection of dense subsets of the poset. We will make this precise shortly. Let's begin by formalizing what we mean by "too wide."

Let $\mathbb{P}$ be a poset. We say that $p, q \in \mathbb{P}$ are **compatible** if there exists $r \in \mathbb{P}$ with $r \leq p$ and $r \leq q$. Otherwise, we say that p and q are **incompatible**, and we write $p \perp q$. A subset $A \subseteq \mathbb{P}$ is called an **antichain** if for all $p, q \in A$, $p \perp q$. We say that $\mathbb{P}$ has the **countable chain condition** (abbreviated **c.c.c**) if every antichain $A \subseteq \mathbb{P}$ is countable.

Note: The name "countable chain condition" was an odd choice. It would have been more appropriate to name this condition the "countable antichain condition." I have decided to follow the trend here, and continue using the name "countable chain condition."

Example 14.6: Let $\mathcal{F} \subseteq {}^{\omega}\omega$ and let $\mathbb{P}_{\mathcal{F}}$ be the corresponding dominating poset. We now show that $\mathbb{P}_{\mathcal{F}}$ has the c.c.c. To see this, assume towards contradiction that $\{p_i = (s_i, \mathcal{F}_i) \mid i \in I\}$ is an antichain, where I is an uncountable set. Since $\{s \mid \exists n \in \omega \ (s: n \to \omega)\}$ is a countable set, there must be $n \in \omega$, $s: n \to \omega$, and an uncountable set $J \subseteq I$ such that $s_i = s$ for all $i \in J$. So, the set $\{p_i = (s, \mathcal{F}_i) \mid i \in J\}$ is still an uncountable antichain. Let $i, j \in J$ and let $r = \left(s, \mathcal{F}_i \cup \mathcal{F}_j\right)$. Then $r \le p_i$ and $r \le p_j$, and so, p_i and p_j are compatible, contradicting our assumption that $\{p_i = (s_i, \mathcal{F}_i) \mid i \in I\}$ is an antichain. Therefore, $\mathbb{P}_{\mathcal{F}}$ has no uncountable antichains.

Martin's Axiom

We are now ready to state Martin's Axiom.

MA(κ) is the statement "Whenever $\mathbb{P}$ is a nonempty c.c.c. poset and $\mathcal{D}$ is a family of at most κ dense subsets of $\mathbb{P}$, then there is a filter $\mathcal{G} \subseteq \mathbb{P}$ such that $\mathcal{G} \cap A \ne \emptyset$ for all $A \in \mathcal{D}$."

MA is the statement "$\forall \kappa < 2^{\omega}\left(\text{MA}(\kappa)\right)$."

Theorem 14.3 (MA): Let $\mathcal{F} \subseteq {}^{\omega}\omega$ and $|\mathcal{F}| < 2^{\omega}$. Then there is $g \in {}^{\omega}\omega$ such that $f <^* g$ for all $f \in \mathcal{F}$.

Proof: Consider the dominating poset $\mathbb{P}_{\mathcal{F}}$ together with the sets $\mathcal{D}_f = \{(s, \mathcal{F}_0) \mid f \in \mathcal{F}_0\}$ for each $f \in \mathcal{F}$ and $\mathcal{E}_k = \{(s, \mathcal{F}_0) \mid k \in \text{dom } s\}$ for each $k \in \omega$. We showed in Example 14.5 that each of these sets is dense. We showed in Example 14.6 that $\mathbb{P}_{\mathcal{F}}$ has the c.c.c. By MA, there is a filter $\mathcal{G} \subseteq \mathbb{P}$ such that $\mathcal{G} \cap \mathcal{D}_f \ne \emptyset$ for all $f \in \mathcal{F}$ and $\mathcal{G} \cap \mathcal{E}_k \ne \emptyset$ for all $k \in \omega$. By Theorem 14.2, there is a function $g \in {}^{\omega}\omega$ such that $f <^* g$ for all $f \in \mathcal{F}$. $\qquad\square$

Theorem 14.3 provides an example showing how all infinite cardinals less than 2^{ω} behave a lot like ω. Using only ZFC, we can find a function that dominates any set of ω many functions. If $\omega < \kappa < 2^{\omega}$, then we cannot find a function that dominates any set of κ many functions using ZFC alone. However, if we assume MA, then we can do it.

In Example 13.4, we saw that $cf(2^{\omega})$ must be greater than ω. Also, since CH is consistent with ZFC, it is consistent that $2^{\omega} = \omega_1$. Since ω_1 is regular, we know that 2^{ω} **can** be regular. It is natural to ask if 2^{ω} **must** be regular. Using ZFC alone, we **cannot** prove that 2^{ω} is regular (it is in fact consistent with ZFC that 2^{ω} is singular). However, if we assume MA, then it is not too hard to show that 2^{ω} **is** regular. We will prove this in Theorem 14.5 below. We will need to use the following Lemma in the proof.

Lemma 14.4: For any ordinal α, there is a strictly increasing cofinal function $f: cf(\alpha) \to \alpha$.

This is Problem 8 from Problem Set 13.

Theorem 14.5 (MA): 2^{ω} is regular.

Proof: Let $\{f_\alpha \mid \alpha < 2^{\omega}\}$ be a well-ordering of ${}^{\omega}\omega$. For each $\alpha < 2^{\omega}$, we use MA to define $g_\alpha: \omega \to \omega$ so that $f_\alpha <^* g_\alpha$ and for all $\beta < \alpha$, $g_\beta <^* g_\alpha$. By Theorem 14.3, this can be done for each $\alpha < 2^{\omega}$ because $\left|\{g_\beta \mid \beta < \alpha\} \cup \{f_\alpha\}\right| < 2^{\omega}$.

Suppose toward contradiction that 2^ω is singular, so that $\kappa = cf(2^\omega) < 2^\omega$. By Lemma 14.4, there is a strictly increasing cofinal function $h \colon \kappa \to 2^\omega$. Let $\mathcal{H} = \{g_{h(\eta)} \mid \eta < \kappa\}$. Then $|\mathcal{H}| = \kappa < 2^\omega$. By Theorem 14.3, there is $f \in {}^\omega\omega$ such that $g_{h(\eta)} <^* f$ for all $\eta < \kappa$. Since $\{f_\alpha \mid \alpha < 2^\omega\}$ is a well-ordering of ${}^\omega\omega$, there is $\xi < 2^\omega$ such that $f = f_\xi$. By Theorem 12.2, $h(\xi) \geq \xi$. So, $g_{h(\xi)} <^* f_\xi <^* g_\xi <^* g_{h(\xi)}$ (or $g_\xi = g_{h(\xi)}$). Since $<^*$ is transitive on ${}^\omega\omega$ (see Note 3 after Example 14.1), we have $g_{h(\xi)} <^* g_{h(\xi)}$. This contradicts that $<^*$ is antireflexive on ${}^\omega\omega$ (once again, see Note 3 after Example 14.1). Therefore, 2^ω is regular. $\qquad\square$

Mad Families

Let $\mathcal{A} \subseteq \mathcal{P}(\omega)$. We will refer to $\mathcal{A}$ as a **family** of sets. We say that $\mathcal{A}$ is **almost disjoint** if and only if

1. $\forall A \in \mathcal{A}(|A| = \omega)$.

2. $\forall A, B \in \mathcal{A}(A \neq B \to |A \cap B| < \omega)$.

So, an almost disjoint family is a collection of infinite subsets of ω such that the intersection of any two distinct members of the family is finite.

Note: The expression "family of sets" is synonymous with "set of sets."

Example 14.7:

1. Let $\mathcal{A} = \{\mathbb{E}, \mathbb{O}\}$, where $\mathbb{E} = \{2k \mid k < \omega\}$ is the set of even natural numbers and $\mathbb{O} = \{2k + 1 \mid k < \omega\}$ is the set of odd natural numbers. Then $\mathcal{A}$ is an almost disjoint family. In fact, $\mathcal{A}$ is a pairwise disjoint family ($\mathbb{E} \cap \mathbb{O} = \emptyset$) consisting of two infinite subsets of ω.

2. Let $\mathcal{B}_n = \{[k] \mid k \in \omega\}$, where $k \sim t$ if and only if $n \mid k - t$. Then $\mathcal{B}_n$ is a partition of ω into n infinite sets. It follows that for each $n \geq 1$, $\mathcal{B}_n$ is an almost disjoint family of size n. As in part 1, in this case, the family $\mathcal{B}_n$ is pairwise disjoint (see part 4 of Example 5.1).

3. By part (i) of Problem 5 from Problem Set 7, there is a partition $\mathcal{C}$ of ω such that $|\mathcal{C}| = \omega$ and for each $X \in \mathcal{C}$, $|X| = \omega$. $\mathcal{C}$ is an almost disjoint family of size ω (once again, in this case, the family $\mathcal{C}$ is pairwise disjoint).

4. Let's show that there is an almost disjoint family of cardinality 2^ω. For each $X \subseteq \omega$ with $|X| = \omega$, let $D_X = \{X \cap n \mid n \in \omega\}$. Since $|X| = \omega$, $|D_X| = \omega$. Therefore, $\mathcal{D} = \{D_X \mid X \subseteq \omega\}$ satisfies clause 1 in the definition of almost disjoint set. We will now show that clause 2 is also satisfied. Let $X, Y \subseteq \omega$ with $X \neq Y$. Without loss of generality, assume that there is $n \in X \setminus Y$. If $j, k > n$, then $n \in X \cap j$, but $n \notin Y \cap k$. So, $X \cap j \neq Y \cap k$ Therefore, if $S \in D_X \cap D_Y$, then $S = X \cap m$ and $S = Y \cap m'$, where $m, m' \leq n$. Thus, $D_X \cap D_Y \subseteq \{X \cap m \mid m \leq n\}$. It follows that $|D_X \cap D_Y| \leq |\{X \cap m \mid m \leq n\}| \leq |n| < \omega$. So, Clause 2 holds. There is still one small issue. $\mathcal{D}$ is **not** a subset of $\mathcal{P}(\omega)$. Each element of $\mathcal{D}$ is a collection of finite subsets of ω. Therefore, $\mathcal{D} \subseteq \mathcal{P}\big(Q(\omega)\big)$, where $Q(\omega) = \{A \in \mathcal{P}(\omega) \mid A \text{ is finite}\}$. By Problem 11 in Problem Set 8, there is a bijection $f \colon Q(\omega) \to \omega$. Therefore, by Problem 6 in Problem Set 7, there is a bijection $F \colon \mathcal{P}\big(Q(\omega)\big) \to \mathcal{P}(\omega)$. It follows that $F[\mathcal{D}] = \{F[D_X] \mid X \subseteq \omega \wedge |X| = \omega\}$ is an almost disjoint family. By Problem 11 in Problem Set 8 again, we have that $|\mathcal{D}| = 2^\omega$. Since F is a bijection, $|F[\mathcal{D}]| = 2^\omega$.

Let $\mathcal{A} \subseteq \mathcal{P}(\omega)$ be an almost disjoint family. We say that $\mathcal{A}$ is a **maximal almost disjoint family** (or **mad** family) if whenever $\mathcal{A} \subset \mathcal{B} \subseteq \mathcal{P}(\omega)$, then $\mathcal{B}$ is **not** an almost disjoint family.

Example 14.8:

1. Let $\mathcal{A} = \{\mathbb{E}, \mathbb{O}\}$ be the almost disjoint family from part 1 of Example 14.7. Then $\mathcal{A}$ is a mad family. Indeed, if $X \subseteq \omega$ with $|X| = \omega$, then since $\mathcal{A} = \{\mathbb{E}, \mathbb{O}\}$ partitions ω, the intersection of X with either $\mathbb{E}$ or $\mathbb{O}$ must be infinite. Similarly, for each $n \geq 1$, the almost disjoint family $\mathcal{B}_n$ defined in part 2 of Example 14.7 is a mad family.

2. If $\mathcal{C}$ is a partition of ω such that $|\mathcal{C}| = \omega$ and for each $X \in \mathcal{C}$, $|X| = \omega$, then $\mathcal{C}$ is an almost disjoint family of size ω, but $\mathcal{C}$ is **not** a mad family. To see this, for each $X \in \mathcal{C}$, let y_X be an element of X. Then $Y = \{y_X \mid X \in \mathcal{C}\}$ is an infinite set such that $|Y \cap X| = 1$ for each $X \in \mathcal{C}$.

3. In part 4 of Example 14.7, we defined an almost disjoint family of size 2^ω. A standard application of Zorn's Lemma (see Lesson 11) can be used to extend this almost disjoint family to a mad family (see Problem 2 below). Since 2^ω is the maximum possible cardinality of an almost disjoint family, it follows that under ZFC, there is a mad family of size 2^ω.

In Example 14.8, we showed that there are mad families of size n for each $n \leq 1$ and also that there are mad families of size 2^ω. However, we failed to create a mad family of size ω. As it turns out, there is no mad family of size ω.

Theorem 14.6: Let $\mathcal{A}$ be an almost disjoint family with $|\mathcal{A}| = \omega$. Then $\mathcal{A}$ is **not** maximal.

You will be asked to prove this in Problem 5 below.

Question 3: Is there a mad family $\mathcal{A}$ such that $\omega < |\mathcal{A}| < 2^\omega$?

Partial Answer: Maybe not! If CH holds ($2^\omega = \omega_1$), then there are no cardinals between ω and 2^ω.

So, we see that if CH holds, the answer to Question 3 is NO!

But what if CH fails? Then $2^\omega > \omega_1$. It turns out that the answer to this question is independent of ZFC. However, if we assume MA, the answer to Question 3 is still NO!

Theorem 14.7 (MA): Every infinite mad family has cardinality 2^ω.

Proof: Let $\mathcal{A} \subseteq \mathcal{P}(\omega)$ be an infinite almost disjoint family with $|\mathcal{A}| < 2^\omega$. We define a poset $\mathbb{P}_\mathcal{A} = (P, \leq)$ as follows:

1. P consists of pairs $(s, \mathcal{A}_0)$, where
    (i) s is a finite subset of ω.
    (ii) $\mathcal{A}_0$ is a finite subset of $\mathcal{A}$.

2. If $(s, \mathcal{A}_0), (t, \mathcal{A}_1) \in P$, then $(t, \mathcal{A}_1) \leq (s, \mathcal{A}_0)$ if and only if each of the following holds:
    (i) $s \subseteq t$.
    (ii) $\mathcal{A}_0 \subseteq \mathcal{A}_1$.
    (iii) For all $A \in \mathcal{A}_0$, $t \cap A = s \cap A$.

We will refer to this poset as a **mad poset**.

By Problem 3 below, $\mathbb{P}_\mathcal{A}$ has the c.c.c. By Problem 1 below, for each $A \in \mathcal{A}$, the set $\mathcal{D}_A = \{(s, \mathcal{A}_0) \in \mathbb{P}_\mathcal{A} \mid A \in \mathcal{A}_0\}$ is dense. By Problem 4 below, for each $n \in \omega$, $\mathcal{E}_n = \{(s, \mathcal{A}_0) \in \mathbb{P}_\mathcal{A} \mid \exists m \in s(m > n)\}$ is dense.

By MA, there exists a filter $\mathcal{G} \subseteq \mathbb{P}_\mathcal{A}$ such that $\mathcal{G} \cap \mathcal{D}_A \neq \emptyset$ for all $A \in \mathcal{A}$ and $\mathcal{G} \cap \mathcal{E}_n \neq \emptyset$ for all $n \in \omega$. Let $B = \bigcup\{s \mid \exists p = (s, \mathcal{A}_0) \in \mathcal{G}\}$. We first show that B is an infinite subset of ω. Let $n \in \omega$. Since $\mathcal{E}_n$ is dense in $\mathbb{P}_\mathcal{A}$, there is $p \in \mathcal{G} \cap \mathcal{E}_n$, say $p = (s, \mathcal{A}_0)$. Since $\exists m \in s(m > n)$ and $s \subseteq B$, $\exists m \in B(m > n)$. Since $n \in \omega$ was arbitrary, B is infinite.

Now, we show that $|A \cap B| < \omega$ for all $A \in \mathcal{A}$. Let $A \in \mathcal{A}$. Since $\mathcal{D}_A$ is dense in $\mathbb{P}_\mathcal{A}$, there is $p \in \mathcal{G} \cap \mathcal{D}_A$, let's say $p = (s, \mathcal{A}_0)$. Let $n \in B \setminus s$. Then there is $q = (t, \mathcal{A}_0) \in \mathcal{G}$ with $n \in t$. Since $\mathcal{G}$ is a filter, there is $r \in \mathcal{G}$ with $r \leq p$ and $r \leq q$, let's say $r = (u, \mathcal{A}_2)$. Since $r \leq p$, $u \cap A = s \cap A$. Since $r \leq q$, $n \in u$. If $n \in A$, then $n \in u \cap A = s \cap A \subseteq s$, contradicting $n \notin s$. So, $n \notin A$. Since $n \in B \setminus s$ was arbitrary, we see that $|A \cap B| < \omega$. It follows that $\mathcal{A}$ is **not** a mad family. $\square$

In the beginning of this lesson we claimed that MA says "all infinite cardinals less than 2^ω behave a lot like ω." We now finish this lesson with a theorem that provides more justification for this claim.

Theorem 14.8 (MA): If $\omega \leq \kappa < 2^\omega$, then $2^\kappa = 2^\omega$.

Proof: Let $\mathcal{A} \subseteq \mathcal{P}(\omega)$ be an almost disjoint family of cardinality κ, say $\mathcal{A} = \{A_\alpha \mid \alpha < \kappa\}$. We define the function $F: \mathcal{P}(\omega) \to \mathcal{P}(\kappa)$ by $F(B) = \{\alpha < \kappa \mid |B \cap A_\alpha| < \omega\}$. Since $|\mathcal{P}(\kappa)| = 2^\kappa$, it suffices to show that F is surjective. Let $X \in \mathcal{P}(\kappa)$. We must find $C \subseteq \omega$ so that $\forall \alpha \in X(|C \cap A_\alpha| < \omega)$ and $\forall \alpha \in \kappa \setminus X(|C \cap A_\alpha| = \omega)$.

Let $\mathcal{B} = \{A_\alpha \mid \alpha \in X\}$ and let $\mathbb{P}_\mathcal{B} = (P, \leq)$ be the appropriate mad poset. In other words, we have:

1. P consists of pairs $(s, \mathcal{B}_0)$, where

    (i) s is a finite subset of ω.

    (ii) $\mathcal{B}_0$ is a finite subset of $\mathcal{B}$.

2. If $(s, \mathcal{B}_0), (t, \mathcal{B}_1) \in P$, then $(t, \mathcal{B}_1) \leq (s, \mathcal{B}_0)$ if and only if each of the following holds:

    (i) $s \subseteq t$.

    (ii) $\mathcal{B}_0 \subseteq \mathcal{B}_1$.

    (iii) For all $B \in \mathcal{B}_0$, $t \cap B = s \cap B$.

As in the proof of Theorem 14.7, $\mathbb{P}_\mathcal{B}$ has the c.c.c., for each $B \in \mathcal{B}$, $\mathcal{D}_B = \{(s, \mathcal{B}_0) \in \mathbb{P}_\mathcal{B} \mid B \in \mathcal{B}_0\}$ is dense, and for each $A \in \mathcal{A} \setminus \mathcal{B}$ and $n \in \omega$, $\mathcal{E}_{A,n} = \{(s, \mathcal{A}_0) \in \mathbb{P}_\mathcal{B} \mid \exists m \in s \cap A(m > n)\}$ is dense.

By MA, there is a filter $\mathcal{G} \subseteq \mathbb{P}_\mathcal{B}$ such that $\mathcal{G} \cap \mathcal{D}_B \neq \emptyset$ for all $B \in \mathcal{B}$ and $\mathcal{G} \cap \mathcal{E}_{A,n} \neq \emptyset$ for all $A \in \mathcal{A} \setminus \mathcal{B}$ and $n \in \omega$. Let $C = \bigcup\{s \mid \exists p = (s, \mathcal{B}_0) \in \mathcal{G}\}$. It is straightforward to show that $\forall \alpha \in X(|C \cap A_\alpha| < \omega)$ and $\forall \alpha \in \kappa \setminus X(|C \cap A_\alpha| = \omega)$. Therefore, $f(C) = X$, as desired. $\square$

Problem Set 14

Full solutions to these problems are available for free download here:
www.SATPrepGet800.com/STFBYKG

LEVEL 1

1. Let $\mathcal{A}$ be an infinite almost disjoint family with $|\mathcal{A}| < 2^\omega$ and let $\mathbb{P}_{\mathcal{A}}$ be the corresponding mad poset. Prove that for each $A \in \mathcal{A}$, $\mathcal{D}_A = \{(s, \mathcal{A}_0) \in \mathbb{P}_{\mathcal{A}} \mid A \in \mathcal{A}_0\}$ is dense.

2. Use Zorn's Lemma to prove that any almost disjoint family can be extended to a mad family.

LEVEL 2

3. Let $\mathcal{A}$ be an infinite almost disjoint family with $|\mathcal{A}| < 2^\omega$ and let $\mathbb{P}_{\mathcal{A}}$ be the corresponding mad poset. Prove that $\mathbb{P}_{\mathcal{A}}$ has the c.c.c.

4. Let $\mathcal{A}$ be an infinite almost disjoint family with $|\mathcal{A}| < 2^\omega$ and let $\mathbb{P}_{\mathcal{A}}$ be the corresponding mad poset. Prove that for each $n \in \omega$, $\mathcal{E}_n = \{(s, \mathcal{A}_0) \in \mathbb{P}_{\mathcal{A}} \mid \exists m \in s (m > n)\}$ is dense.

LEVEL 3

5. Prove that there does not exist a denumerable mad family.

6. Prove that $\text{MA}(2^\omega)$ is false.

LEVEL 4

7. Prove that $\text{MA}(\omega)$ is true.

8. Let $\mathbb{P} = \{f \mid f: n \to \omega_1 \text{ for some } n < \omega\}$ ordered by $f \leq h$ if and only if $h \subseteq f$. Let $\mathcal{G} \subseteq \mathbb{P}$ be a filter intersecting each of the sets $E_k = \{f \mid k \in \text{dom } f\}$ for each $k < \omega$ and $D_\alpha = \{f \mid \alpha \in \text{ran } f\}$ for each $\alpha < \omega_1$. Assume that CH is false. Prove that $g = \bigcup \mathcal{G}$ is a surjective function from ω to ω_1 and explain why this does not prove that MA is inconsistent.

LEVEL 5

9. We will say that A is **almost a subset** of B, written $A \subseteq^* B$ if $B \setminus A$ is finite. If $\mathcal{A}$ is a family of sets, then a **pseudointersection** of $\mathcal{A}$ is an infinite set that is almost a subset of every member of $\mathcal{A}$. A **tower** is a collection $\{T_\alpha \mid \alpha < \lambda\}$ such that (a) Each T_α is an infinite subset of ω, (b) $\alpha < \beta < \lambda \to T_\alpha \subseteq^* T_\beta$, and (c) $\{T_\alpha \mid \alpha < \lambda\}$ has no pseudointersection. Prove that a countably infinite tower is not maximal.

10. Prove that if MA holds, then every maximal infinite tower has cardinality 2^ω.

11. If $X \subseteq \omega$ and $Y \subseteq \omega$ with $|Y| = \omega$, then we say that X **splits** Y if $|Y \cap X| = |Y \setminus X| = \omega$. $\mathcal{S} \subseteq \mathcal{P}(\omega)$ is called a **splitting family** if $\forall Y \subseteq \omega \exists X \in \mathcal{S}(X \text{ splits } Y)$. Prove that if MA holds, then a maximal splitting family has cardinality 2^{ω}.

LESSON 15
THE FIELD OF REAL NUMBERS

Groups, Rings, and Fields

Let's review the definitions of group, ring, and field that we introduced in Lesson 10.

First recall that a **binary operation** on a set is a rule that combines two elements of the set to produce another element of the set.

Example 15.1: Let $S = \{0, 1\}$. Multiplication on S is a binary operation, whereas addition on S is **not** a binary operation (here we are thinking of multiplication and addition in the "usual" sense, meaning the way we would think of them in elementary school or middle school).

To see that multiplication is a binary operation on S, observe that $0 \cdot 0 = 0$, $0 \cdot 1 = 0$, $1 \cdot 0 = 0$, and $1 \cdot 1 = 1$. Each of the four computations produces 0 or 1, both of which are in the set S.

To see that addition is not a binary operation on S, just note that $1 + 1 = 2$, and $2 \notin S$.

Formally, a **binary operation** $\star$ on a set S is a **function** $\star : S \times S \to S$. So, if $a, b \in S$, then we have $\star(a, b) \in S$. For easier readability, we usually write $\star(a, b)$ as $a \star b$.

When $\star$ is a binary operation on S, we say that S is **closed** under $\star$.

Example 15.2:

1. Let $S = \{u, v, w\}$ and define $\star$ using the following table:

$\star$	u	v	w
u	v	w	w
v	w	u	u
w	u	v	v

   The table given above is called a **multiplication table**. For $a, b \in S$, we evaluate $a \star b$ by taking the entry in the row given by a and the column given by b. For example, $v \star w = u$.

$\star$	u	v	w
u	v	w	w
v	w	u	u
w	u	v	v

   $\star$ is a binary operation on S because the only possible "outputs" are u, v, and w.

2. The operation of addition on the set of natural numbers is a binary operation because whenever we add two natural numbers we get another natural number (we proved this in Theorem 8.2 from Lesson 8). Here, the set S is $\mathbb{N}$ and the operation $\star$ is $+$.

3. Similarly, the operation of multiplication on the set of natural numbers is a binary operation because whenever we multiply two natural numbers we get another natural number (you were asked to prove this in part (ii) of Problem 3 from Problem Set 8). Here, the set S is $\mathbb{N}$ and the operation $\star$ is $\cdot$.

4. The operation of addition on the set of integers is a binary operation because whenever we add two integers we get another integer. Here, the set S is $\mathbb{Z} = \{[(a,b)] \mid (a,b) \in \mathbb{N} \times \mathbb{N}\}$, where $(a,b) \sim (c,d)$ if and only if $a + d = b + c$. The operation $\star$ is $+$, which is defined by $[(a,b)] + [(c,d)] = [(a+c, b+d)]$. You were asked to prove that this operation is well-defined in Problem 7 from Problem Set 5. By 2 above, if $a, b \in \mathbb{N}$, then $a + c, b + d \in \mathbb{N}$. So, $[(a,b)], [(c,d)] \in \mathbb{Z}$ implies that $[(a,b)] + [(c,d)] = [(a+c, b+d)] \in \mathbb{Z}$, showing that $\mathbb{Z}$ is closed under addition.

5. Similarly, the operation of multiplication on the set of integers is also a binary operation. The operation $\star$ is $\cdot$, which is defined by $[(a,b)] \cdot [(c,d)] = [(ac + bd, ad + bc)]$. You were asked to prove that this operation is well-defined in Problem 12 from Problem Set 5. By 2 and 3 above, if $a, b, c, d \in \mathbb{N}$, then $ac + bd, ad + bc \in \mathbb{N}$. So, $[(a,b)], [(c,d)] \in \mathbb{Z}$ implies that $[(a,b)] \cdot [(c,d)] = [(ac + bd, ad + bc)] \in \mathbb{Z}$, showing that $\mathbb{Z}$ is closed under multiplication.

6. The operation of addition on the set of rational numbers is a binary operation because whenever we add two rational numbers we get another rational number. Here, the set S is $\mathbb{Q} = \left\{ \frac{a}{b} \mid a \in \mathbb{Z} \wedge b \in \mathbb{Z}^* \right\}$, where $\frac{a}{b} = \frac{c}{d}$ if and only if $ad = bc$. The operation $\star$ is $+$, which is defined by $\frac{a}{b} + \frac{c}{d} = \frac{ad+bc}{bd}$. You were asked to prove that this operation is well-defined in Problem 8 from Problem Set 5. By 4 and 5 above, if $a, b, c, d \in \mathbb{Z}$, then $ad + bc, bd \in \mathbb{Z}$. We need to show that for integers $b, d \neq 0$, we have $bd \neq 0$. Let $b = [(m,n)]$ and $d = [(s,t)]$ and assume that $b \cdot d = [(m,n)] \cdot [(s,t)] = [(0,0)]$ and $b = [(m,n)] \neq [(0,0)]$. We must show that $d = [(s,t)] = [(0,0)]$. Since $b \cdot d = [(0,0)]$, we have $[(ms + nt, mt + ns)] = [(0,0)]$. So, $ms + nt = mt + ns$. Since $b \neq [(0,0)]$, we have $m \neq n$. Without loss of generality, assume that $m < n$, then by part (ix) of Problem 3 from Problem Set 8, there is a natural number $k > 0$ such that $n = m + k$. Using associativity of addition, commutativity of multiplication, and distributivity of multiplication over addition in $\mathbb{N}$, we have

$$ms + mt + kt = ms + (m+k)t = ms + nt = mt + ns = mt + (m+k)s = mt + ms + ks$$

By part (vii) of Problem 3 from Problem Set 8, $kt = ks$. By part (viii) of Problem 3 from Problem Set 8, $t = s$. So, $d = [(s,t)] = [(0,0)]$. Thus, $\mathbb{Q}$ is closed under addition.

7. Similarly, the operation of multiplication on the set of rational numbers is also a binary operation. The operation $\star$ is $\cdot$, which is defined by $\frac{a}{b} \cdot \frac{c}{d} = \frac{ac}{bd}$. You were asked to prove that this operation is well-defined in Problem 8 from Problem Set 5. By 5 above, if $a, b, c, d \in \mathbb{Z}$, then $ac, bd \in \mathbb{Z}$. Also, if $b, d \neq 0$, then $bd \neq 0$ by the same argument given in 6 above. Thus, $\mathbb{Q}$ is closed under multiplication.

8. The operation of addition on the set of real numbers is a binary operation because whenever we add two real numbers we get another real number. Here, the set S is $\mathbb{R} = \{[(x_n)] \mid (x_n) \text{ is a Cauchy sequence of rational numbers}\}$, where $(x_n) \sim (y_n)$ if and only if for every $k \in \mathbb{N}^+$, there is $K \in \mathbb{N}$ such that $n > K$ implies $|x_n - y_n| < \frac{1}{k}$. The operation $\star$ is $+$, which is defined by $[(x_n)] + [(y_n)] = [(x_n + y_n)]$. You were asked to prove that this operation is well-defined and that the sum of two real numbers is a real number in Problem 10 from Problem Set 6. Thus, $\mathbb{R}$ is closed under addition.

9. Similarly, the operation of multiplication on the set of real numbers is also a binary operation. The operation $\star$ is $\cdot$, which is defined by $[(x_n)] \cdot [(y_n)] = [(x_n \cdot y_n)]$. You were asked to prove that this operation is well-defined and that the product of two real numbers is a real number in Problem 11 from Problem Set 6. Thus, $\mathbb{R}$ is closed under multiplication.

10. Subtraction on the set of natural numbers is **not** a binary operation. To see this, we just need to provide a single **counterexample**. Recall from Lesson 8 that for natural numbers m, n, and t, we say that $m - n = t$ if and only if $m = t + n$. It is straightforward to prove by induction on $t \in \mathbb{N}$ that $1 \subset t + 2$ (1 is a *proper* subset of $t + 2$) for all $t \in \mathbb{N}$. In particular, for all $t \in \mathbb{N}$, $1 \neq t + 2$. Therefore, $1 - 2$ is not defined in $\mathbb{N}$.

Some authors refer to a binary operation $\star$ on a set S even when the binary operation is not defined on all pairs of elements $a, b \in S$. We will always refer to these "false operations" as **partial binary operations**.

We say that the set S is **closed** under the partial binary operation $\star$ if whenever $a, b \in S$, we have $a \star b \in S$.

In Example 15.2, part 10 above, we saw that subtraction is a partial binary operation on $\mathbb{N}$ that is not a binary operation. In other words, $\mathbb{N}$ is not **closed** under subtraction.

A **group** is a pair $(G, \star)$ consisting of a set G together with a binary operation $\star$ on G satisfying:

(1) **(Associativity)** For all $x, y, z \in G$, $(x \star y) \star z = x \star (y \star z)$.

(2) **(Identity)** There exists an element $e \in G$ such that for all $x \in G$, $e \star x = x \star e = x$.

(3) **(Inverse)** For each $x \in G$, there is $y \in G$ such that $x \star y = y \star x = e$.

Notes: (1) If $y \in G$ is an inverse of $x \in G$, we will usually write $y = x^{-1}$.

(2) Recall that the definition of a binary operation already implies closure. However, many books on groups will mention this property explicitly:

(**Closure**) For all $x, y \in G$, $x \star y \in G$.

(3) A group is **commutative** or **Abelian** if for all $x, y \in G$, $x \star y = y \star x$.

(4) The properties that define a group are called the **group axioms**. These are the statements that are **given** to be true in all groups. There are many other statements that are true in groups. However, any additional statements need to be **proved** using the axioms.

(5) If properties (1) and (2) hold, we get a **monoid**. So, a group is a monoid with the inverse property.

(6) If property (1) holds, we get a **semigroup**. So, a monoid is semigroup with an identity element.

Example 15.3:

1. Is $(\mathbb{N}, +)$ a group? By Theorem 8.2 from Lesson 8, $+$ is a binary operation on $\mathbb{N}$ (or equivalently, $\mathbb{N}$ is closed under $+$). By Theorem 8.4, $+$ is associative in $\mathbb{N}$. By Theorem 8.3, together with the definition of addition (see Note 1 following Theorem 8.3), 0 is an additive identity for $\mathbb{N}$. It follows that $(\mathbb{N}, +)$ is a monoid.

    However, $(\mathbb{N}, +)$ is **not** a group. The inverse property fails. For example, 1 has no inverse (and in fact, the only natural number with an additive inverse is 0). Indeed, suppose toward contradiction that $n \in \mathbb{N}$ with $n + 1 = 0$. Since $n + 1 = n^+ = n \cup \{n\}$, and $n \in n \cup \{n\}$, we must have $n \in 0 = \emptyset$. But the empty set has no elements. This contradiction proves that there is no natural number n such that $n + 1 = 0$. So, 1 has no additive inverse in $\mathbb{N}$. Therefore, the inverse property fails and $(\mathbb{N}, +)$ is **not** a group. It's worth mentioning that $(\mathbb{N}, +)$ is commutative. This follows from part (i) of Problem 3 from Problem Set 8. So, $(\mathbb{N}, +)$ is a commutative monoid that is **not** a group.

2. Similarly, $(\mathbb{N}, \cdot)$ is a commutative monoid with identity 1 that is not a group. I leave the details that $(\mathbb{N}, \cdot)$ is a commutative monoid to the reader. Let's prove that 2 has no multiplicative inverse in $\mathbb{N}$. We have $2 \cdot 0 = 0 \neq 1$. We now prove by induction that for all $n \geq 1$, $2n > 1$. The base case is $2 \cdot 1 = 2 > 1$. Assuming $2k > 1$, by parts (iv) and (x) of Problem 3 from Problem Set 8, we have $2(k + 1) = 2k + 2 > 1 + 2 > 1$. In particular, we showed that for all $n \in \mathbb{N}$, $2n \neq 1$. Therefore, 2 has no multiplicative inverse in $\mathbb{N}$.

3. $(\mathbb{Z}, +)$ is a commutative group with identity $0 = [(0, 0)]$. We showed that $+$ is a binary operation on $\mathbb{Z}$ in part 4 of Example 15.2 above. To see that $+$ is associative in $\mathbb{Z}$, observe that for $a, b, c, d, e, f \in \mathbb{N}$, we have

$$([(a, b)] + [(c, d)]) + [(e, f)] = [(a + c, b + d)] + [(e, f)] = [((a + c) + e, (b + d) + f)]$$
$$= [(a + (c + e), b + (d + f))] = [(a, b)] + [(c + e, d + f)] = [(a, b)] + ([(c, d)] + [(e, f)])$$

    For the first, second, fourth and fifth equalities, we simply used the definition of addition of integers. For the third equality, we used the associativity of addition in $\mathbb{N}$. I leave it to the reader to verify that $[(0, 0)]$ is an additive identity, that the inverse of $[(a, b)]$ is $[(b, a)]$, and that $+$ is commutative in $\mathbb{Z}$.

4. $(\mathbb{Z}, \cdot)$ is a commutative monoid with identity $1 = [(1, 0)]$ that is not a group. I leave it to the reader to verify that $(\mathbb{Z}, \cdot)$ is a commutative monoid. Let's prove that $2 = [(2, 0)]$ has no multiplicative inverse. If $[(a, b)]$ is a multiplicative inverse of 2, then we have $2a + 0b = 1$ and $2b + 0a = 0$. The first equation is equivalent to $2a = 1$. However, by 2 above, 2 has no multiplicative Inverse in $\mathbb{N}$. Therefore, the equation $2a = 1$ has no solution, and so, 2 has no multiplicative inverse in $\mathbb{Z}$.

5. $(\mathbb{Q}, +)$ is a commutative group with identity $0 = \frac{0}{1}$. You will need to prove this as part of Problem 17 below.

178

6. $(\mathbb{R}, +)$ is a commutative group with identity $[(0)]$. We showed that $+$ is a binary operation on $\mathbb{R}$ in part 8 of Example 15.2 above. To see that $+$ is associative in $\mathbb{R}$, we use the associativity of $+$ in $\mathbb{Q}$. If $[(x_n)], [(y_n)], [(z_n)] \in \mathbb{R}$, then

$$([(x_n)] + [(y_n)]) + [(z_n)] = [(x_n + y_n)] + [(z_n)] = [((x_n + y_n) + z_n)]$$
$$= [(x_n + (y_n + z_n))] = [x_n] + [(y_n + z_n)] = [(x_n)] + ([(y_n)] + [(z_n)]).$$

To see that $[(0)]$ is the additive identity, using the fact that 0 is the additive identity in $\mathbb{Q}$, we have for $[(x_n)] \in \mathbb{R}$,

$$[(0)] + [(x_n)] = [(0 + x_n)] = [(x_n)] \text{ and } [(x_n)] + [(0)] = [(x_n + 0)] = [(x_n)].$$

The inverse of the real number $[(x_n)]$ is $[(-x_n)]$, where for each $n \in \mathbb{N}$, $-x_n$ is the additive inverse of x_n in $\mathbb{Q}$. To see this, simply observe that

$$[(x_n)] + [(-x_n)] = [(x_n + (-x_n))] = [(0)] \text{ and } [(-x_n)] + [(x_n)] = [(-x_n + x_n)] = [(0)].$$

Finally, to see that $+$ is commutative in $\mathbb{R}$, we use the commutativity of $+$ in $\mathbb{Q}$. If $[(x_n)], [(y_n)] \in \mathbb{R}$, then

$$[(x_n)] + [(y_n)] = [(x_n + y_n)] = [(y_n + x_n)] = [(y_n)] + [(x_n)].$$

7. $(\mathbb{Q}, \cdot)$ and $(\mathbb{R}, \cdot)$ fail to be groups, but only because 0 has no inverse (this follows immediately from part (iii) of Problem 7 below). However, $(\mathbb{Q}^*, \cdot)$ and $(\mathbb{R}^*, \cdot)$ are both commutative groups. You will need to prove this as part of Problem 17 below.

A **field** is a triple $(F, +, \cdot)$, where F is a set and $+$ and $\cdot$ are binary operations on F satisfying

(1) $(F, +)$ is a commutative group.

(2) $(F^*, \cdot)$ is a commutative group.

(3) $\cdot$ is **distributive** over $+$ in F. That is, for all $x, y, z \in F$, we have

$$x \cdot (y + z) = x \cdot y + x \cdot z \qquad \text{and} \qquad (y + z) \cdot x = y \cdot x + z \cdot x.$$

(4) $0 \neq 1$ (where 0 is the identity of $(F, +)$ and 1 is the identity of $(F^*, \cdot)$).

We will refer to the operation $+$ as addition, the operation $\cdot$ as multiplication, the additive identity as 0, the multiplicative identity as 1, the additive inverse of an element $x \in F$ as $-x$, and the multiplicative inverse of an element $x \in F^*$ as x^{-1}. We will often abbreviate $x \cdot y$ as xy.

Notes: (1) $(F, +)$ a commutative group means the following:

- **(Closure)** For all $x, y \in F$, $x + y \in F$.

- **(Associativity)** For all $x, y, z \in F$, $(x + y) + z = x + (y + z)$.

- **(Commutativity)** For all $x, y \in F$, $x + y = y + x$.

- **(Identity)** There exists an element $0 \in F$ such that for all $x \in F$, $0 + x = x + 0 = x$.

- **(Inverse)** For each $x \in F$, there is $-x \in F$ such that $x + (-x) = (-x) + x = 0$.

(2) Similarly, $(F^*, \cdot)$ a commutative group means the following:

- **(Closure)** For all $x, y \in F^*$, $xy \in F^*$.
- **(Associativity)** For all $x, y, z \in F^*$, $(xy)z = x(yz)$.
- **(Commutativity)** For all $x, y \in F^*$, $xy = yx$.
- **(Identity)** There exists an element $1 \in F^*$ such that for all $x \in F^*$, $1x = x \cdot 1 = x$.
- **(Inverse)** For each $x \in F^*$, there is $x^{-1} \in F^*$ such that $xx^{-1} = x^{-1}x = 1$.

(3) Recall that F^* is the set of nonzero elements of F. We can write $F^* = \{x \in F \mid x \neq 0\}$ (pronounced "the set of x in F such that x is not equal to 0") or $F^* = F \setminus \{0\}$ (pronounced "F with 0 removed").

(4) The properties that define a field are called the **field axioms**. These are the statements that are **given** to be true in all fields. There are many other statements that are true in fields. However, any additional statements need to be **proved** using the axioms.

(5) If we replace the condition that "$(F^*, \cdot)$ is a commutative group" by "$(F, \cdot)$ is a monoid," then the resulting structure is called a **ring**. The most well-known example of a ring is $\mathbb{Z}$, the ring of integers.

We also do not require 0 and 1 to be distinct in the definition of a ring. If $0 = 1$, we get the zero ring, which consists of just one element, namely 0 (Why?). The operations of addition and multiplication are defined by $0 + 0 = 0$ and $0 \cdot 0 = 0$. The reader may want to verify that the zero ring is in fact a ring.

The main difference between a ring and a field is that in a ring, there can be nonzero elements that do not have multiplicative inverses. For example, in $\mathbb{Z}$, 2 has no multiplicative inverse (see part 4 of Example 15.3 above). So, the equation $2x = 1$ has no solution.

(6) If we also replace "$(F, +)$ is a commutative group" by "$(F, +)$ is a commutative monoid," then the resulting structure is a **semiring**. The most well-known example of a semiring is $\mathbb{N}$, the semiring of natural numbers.

The main difference between a semiring and a ring is that in a semiring, there can be elements that do not have additive inverses. For example, in $\mathbb{N}$, 1 has no additive inverse (see part 1 of Example 15.3). Thus, the equation $x + 1 = 0$ has no solution.

Technical note: For a semiring, we include one additional axiom: For all $x \in F$, $0 \cdot x = x \cdot 0 = 0$. This statement follows from the ring axioms (see part (iii) of Problem 7 below), but **not** from the other semiring axioms. We need the additive inverse property to prove it.

(7) Every field is a commutative ring. Although this is not too hard to show (you will be asked to show this in Problem 12 below), it is worth observing that this is not completely obvious. For example, if $(F, +, \cdot)$ is a ring, then since $(F, \cdot)$ is a monoid with identity 1, it follows that $1 \cdot 0 = 0 \cdot 1 = 0$. However, in the definition of a field given above, this property of 0 is not given as an axiom. We **are** given that $(F^*, \cdot)$ is a commutative group, and so, it follows that 1 is an identity for F^*. But $0 \notin F^*$, and so, $1 \cdot 0 = 0 \cdot 1 = 0$ needs to be proved.

Similarly, in the definition of a field given above, 0 is excluded from associativity and commutativity. These need to be checked.

Example 15.4:

1. $(\mathbb{Z}, +, \cdot)$ is a ring that is **not** a field. In parts 3 and 4 of Example 15.3 above, we saw that $(\mathbb{Z}, +)$ is a commutative group and $(\mathbb{Z}, \cdot)$ is a monoid. All that is left to check is distributivity. We first check left distributivity. For $a, b, c, d, e, f \in \mathbb{N}$, we have

$$[(a,b)]([(c,d)] + [(e,f)]) = [(a,b)] \cdot [(c+e, d+f)]$$
$$= [(a(c+e) + b(d+f), a(d+f) + b(c+e))]$$
$$= [((ac+ae) + (bd+bf), (ad+af) + (bc+be))]$$
$$= [((ac+bd) + (ae+bf), (ad+bc) + (af+be))]$$
$$= [(ac+bd, ad+bc)] + [(ae+bf, af+be)] = [(a,b)] \cdot [(c,d)] + [(a,b)] \cdot [(e,f)].$$

For the first, second, fifth and sixth equalities, we simply used the definitions of addition and multiplication of integers. For the third equality, we used the distributivity of multiplication over addition in $\mathbb{N}$. For the fourth equality, we used the associativity and commutativity of addition in $\mathbb{N}$. Since multiplication is commutative in $\mathbb{Z}$, right distributivity follows immediately from left distributivity.

$$([(c,d)] + [(e,f)])[(a,b)] = [(a,b)]([(c,d)] + [(e,f)])$$
$$= [(a,b)] \cdot [(c,d)] + [(a,b)] \cdot [(e,f)] = [(c,d)] \cdot [(a,b)] + [(e,f)] \cdot [(a,b)].$$

Therefore, $(\mathbb{Z}, +, \cdot)$ is a ring. We already showed in part 4 of Example 15.3 that 2 has no multiplicative inverse in $\mathbb{Z}$. So, $(\mathbb{Z}, +, \cdot)$ is **not** a field.

2. $(\mathbb{Q}, +, \cdot)$ and $(\mathbb{R}, +, \cdot)$ are both fields. You will need to prove this as part of Problem 17 below.

Subtraction and Division: If $a, b \in F$, we define $a - b = a + (-b)$ and for $b \neq 0, \frac{a}{b} = ab^{-1}$.

Ordered Rings and Fields

An **ordered ring** is a quadruple $(R, +, \cdot, \leq)$, where $(R, +, \cdot)$ is a ring, and $(R, \leq)$ is a linearly ordered set such that:

(1) If $a, b, c \in R$, then $a \leq b \rightarrow a + c \leq b + c$.

(2) If $a, b \in R$ with $0 \leq a$ and $0 \leq b$, then $0 \leq ab$.

Example 15.5:

1. $(\mathbb{Z}, +, \cdot, \leq)$ is an ordered ring. We already showed that $(\mathbb{Z}, +, \cdot)$ is a ring in part 1 of Example 15.4.

   In Problem 5 from Problem Set 5, you were asked to show that $<$ is a well-defined strict linear ordering on $\mathbb{Z}$. $\leq$ is the corresponding linear ordering given by Theorem 4.3 from Lesson 4.

   Let's check that properties (1) and (2) above are satisfied.

For (1), let $a, b, c, d, e, f \in \mathbb{N}$, and assume that $[(a, b)] \leq [(c, d)]$. Then $a + d \leq b + c$, and so, by part (x) of Problem 3 from Problem Set 8, $(a + d) + (e + f) \leq (b + c) + (e + f)$. We can then use associativity and commutativity of addition in $\mathbb{N}$, to get the inequality $(a + e) + (d + f) \leq (b + f) + (c + e)$. By definition, $[(a + e, b + f)] \leq [(c + e, d + f)]$. Therefore, $[(a, b)] + [(e, f)] \leq [(c, d)] + [(e, f)]$. For (2), let $a, b, c, d \in \mathbb{N}$, and assume that $[(0, 0)] \leq [(a, b)]$ and $[(0, 0)] \leq [(c, d)]$. Then $b \leq a$, and $d \leq c$. By part (ix) of Problem 3 from Problem Set 8, there are natural numbers $k > 0$ and $t > 0$ such that $a = b + k$ and $c = d + t$. Then we have

$$ad + bc = (b + k)d + b(d + t) = bd + kd + bd + bt.$$

$$ac + bd = (b + k)(d + t) + bd = (b + k)d + (b + k)t + bd = bd + kd + bt + kt + bd.$$

It follows that $ac + bd = (ad + bc) + kt$. Therefore, again by part (ix) of Problem 3 from Problem Set 8, we have $ad + bc \leq ac + bd$. Thus, $[(0, 0)] \leq [(ac + bd, ad + bc)]$. Therefore, $[(0, 0)] \leq [(a, b)] \cdot [(c, d)]$.

2. $(\mathbb{Q}, +, \cdot, \leq)$ and $(\mathbb{R}, +, \cdot, \leq)$ are ordered fields. You will be asked to prove this in Problem 17 below.

If $(R, +, \cdot, \leq)$ is an ordered ring, we will write $a < b$ if $a \leq b$ and $a \neq b$. By Theorem 4.2 in Lesson 4, $<$ is a strict linear ordering on R. We may also write $b \geq a$ in place of $a \leq b$ and $b > a$ in place of $a < b$.

In general, we may just use the name of the underlying set for a whole structure when there is no danger of confusion. For example, we may refer to the ring R or the ordered field F instead of the ring $(R, +, \cdot)$ or the ordered field $(F, +, \cdot, \leq)$.

Fields are particularly nice to work with because all the arithmetic and algebra we've learned through the years can be used in fields. For example, in the field of rational numbers, we can solve the equation $2x = 1$. The multiplicative inverse property allows us to do this. Indeed, the multiplicative inverse of 2 is $\frac{1}{2}$, and therefore, $x = \frac{1}{2}$ is a solution to the given equation. Compare this to the ring of integers. If we restrict ourselves to the integers, then the equation $2x = 1$ has no solution.

Working with ordered fields is very nice as well. In the problem set below, you will be asked to derive some additional properties of fields and ordered fields that follow from the axioms. We will prove a few of these properties now as examples.

Theorem 15.1: Let $(F, \leq)$ be an ordered field. Then for all $x \in F^*$, $x \cdot x > 0$.

Proof: There are two cases to consider:

Case 1: If $x > 0$, then $x \geq 0$ and $x \neq 0$. By property (2) of an ordered field, $x \cdot x \geq 0$. If $x \cdot x = 0$, then since x has an inverse, $x = x \cdot 1 = x \cdot (x \cdot x^{-1}) = (x \cdot x) \cdot x^{-1} = 0 \cdot x^{-1} = 0$ (by part (iii) of Problem 7 below), contrary to our assumption that $x \in F^*$. So, $x \cdot x \neq 0$, and therefore, $x \cdot x > 0$.

Case 2: If $x < 0$, then $x \leq 0$. By property (1) of an ordered field, $x + (-x) \leq 0 + (-x)$, and so, $0 \leq -x$. Therefore, $(-x)(-x) \geq 0$, by property (2) of an ordered field. Now, using Problem 7 (parts (vi) and (vii)) in the problem set below, together with commutativity and associativity of multiplication, and the multiplicative identity property, we have

$$(-x)(-x) = (-1x)(-1x) = (-1)(-1)x \cdot x = 1(x \cdot x) = x \cdot x.$$

So, again we have $x \cdot x \geq 0$. The same argument in case 1 can be used to rule out $x \cdot x = 0$. Therefore, $x \cdot x > 0$. $\qquad\qquad\square$

Theorem 15.2: Every ordered field $(F, +, \cdot, \leq)$ contains a copy of the natural numbers. Specifically, F contains a subset $\overline{\mathbb{N}} = \{\overline{n} \mid n \in \mathbb{N}\}$ such that for all $n, m \in \mathbb{N}$, we have $\overline{n + m} = \overline{n} + \overline{m}, \overline{n \cdot m} = \overline{n} \cdot \overline{m}$, and $n < m \leftrightarrow \overline{n} < \overline{m}$.

Proof: Let $(F, +, \cdot, \leq)$ be an ordered field. By the definition of a field, $0, 1 \in F$ and $0 \neq 1$.

We let $\overline{0} = 0$ and $\overline{n} = 1 + 1 + \cdots + 1$, where 1 appears n times. Let $\overline{\mathbb{N}} = \{\overline{n} \mid n \in \mathbb{N}\}$. Then $\overline{\mathbb{N}} \subseteq F$.

We first prove by induction on m that for all $n, m \in \mathbb{N}, \overline{n + m} = \overline{n} + \overline{m}$.

Base case $(k = 0)$: $\overline{n + 0} = \overline{n} = \overline{n} + 0 = \overline{n} + \overline{0}$.

Inductive step: Suppose that $\overline{n + k} = \overline{n} + \overline{k}$. Then we have

$$\overline{n + (k + 1)} = \overline{(n + k) + 1} = \overline{n + k} + 1 = \left(\overline{n} + \overline{k}\right) + 1 = \overline{n} + \left(\overline{k} + 1\right) = \overline{n} + \overline{k + 1}.$$

By the Principle of Mathematical Induction, for all natural numbers $m, \overline{n + m} = \overline{n} + \overline{m}$.

Similarly, we prove by induction on m that for all $n, m \in \mathbb{N}, \overline{n \cdot m} = \overline{n} \cdot \overline{m}$.

Base case $(k = 0)$: $\overline{n \cdot 0} = \overline{0} = \overline{n} \cdot \overline{0}$.

Inductive step: Suppose that $\overline{n \cdot k} = \overline{n} \cdot \overline{k}$. Then we have

$$\overline{n \cdot (k + 1)} = \overline{nk + n} = \overline{nk} + \overline{n} = \overline{n} \cdot \overline{k} + \overline{n} = \overline{n}(\overline{k} + 1) = \overline{n}(\overline{k} + \overline{1}) = \overline{n}(\overline{k + 1}).$$

By the Principle of Mathematical Induction, for all natural numbers $m, \overline{n \cdot m} = \overline{n} \cdot \overline{m}$.

We now wish to prove that for all $n, m \in \mathbb{N}, n < m \leftrightarrow \overline{n} < \overline{m}$.

We first note that since $1 > 0$ (because $1 = 1 \cdot 1 > 0$ by Theorem 15.1), we have for any natural number $n, \overline{n + 1} = \overline{n} + 1 > \overline{n} + 0 = \overline{n}$ by property (1) of an ordered field.

We now prove by induction on $m \in \mathbb{N}$ that $n < m \to \overline{n} < \overline{m}$.

The base case $k = 0$ is vacuously true because $n < 0$ never occurs. For the inductive step, let $k \in \mathbb{N}$ and assume that $n < k \to \overline{n} < \overline{k}$. Now, suppose that $n < k + 1 = k \cup \{k\}$. Then $n < k$ or $n = k$. If $n < k$, then $\overline{n} < \overline{k}$ by the inductive hypothesis. By property (1) of an ordered field and $0 < 1$, we have $\overline{k} = \overline{k} + 0 < \overline{k} + 1 = \overline{k + 1}$. By the transitivity of $<, \overline{n} < \overline{k + 1}$. If $n = k$, then by the same reasoning in the last sentence, $\overline{k} < \overline{k + 1}$. By the Principle of Mathematical Induction, we have for all $m, n \in \mathbb{N}$, $n < m \to \overline{n} < \overline{m}$.

Finally, we need to prove that $\overline{n} < \overline{m} \rightarrow n < m$. By the law of the contrapositive, this statement is equivalent to $m \leq n \rightarrow \overline{m} \leq \overline{n}$. The proof of this statement is similar to the argument given in the last paragraph (but not identical), and so, the details are left to the reader. $\qquad\square$

Note: Recall from Lesson 10 that the function that sends $n \in \mathbb{N}$ to $\overline{n} \in \overline{\mathbb{N}}$ is called an **isomorphism**. It has the following properties: (i) $\overline{n+m} = \overline{n} + \overline{m}$; (ii) $\overline{n \cdot m} = \overline{n} \cdot \overline{m}$; (iii) $n < m$ if and only if $\overline{n} < \overline{m}$; (iv) the function provides a bijection between the elements of $\mathbb{N}$ and the elements of $\overline{\mathbb{N}}$.

So, when we say that every field contains a "copy" of the natural numbers, we mean that there is a subset $\overline{\mathbb{N}}$ of the field so that $\left(\overline{\mathbb{N}}, +, \cdot, \leq\right)$ is isomorphic to $(\mathbb{N}, +, \cdot, \leq)$.

Theorem 15.3: Let $(F, \leq)$ be an ordered field and let $x \in F$ with $x > 0$. Then $\frac{1}{x} > 0$.

Proof: Since $x \neq 0, \frac{1}{x} = x^{-1}$ exists and is nonzero.

Assume toward contradiction that $\frac{1}{x} < 0$. Then $\frac{1}{x} \leq 0$, and so, by property (1) of an ordered field, $\frac{1}{x} + \left(-\frac{1}{x}\right) \leq -\frac{1}{x}$, or equivalently, $0 \leq -\frac{1}{x}$. Using Problem 7 (part (vi)) from the problem set below, together with commutativity and associativity of multiplication, the multiplicative inverse property, and the multiplicative identity property, $x\left(-\frac{1}{x}\right) = x(-1)x^{-1} = -1xx^{-1} = -1 \cdot 1 = -1$. Since $x > 0$ and $-\frac{1}{x} \geq 0$, by property (2) of an ordered field, $-1 = x\left(-\frac{1}{x}\right) \geq 0$. So, by property (1) of an ordered field, $0 = 1 + (-1) \geq 1$. But by Theorem 15.1, $1 = 1 \cdot 1 > 0$. This is a contradiction. Thus, $\frac{1}{x} > 0$. $\qquad\square$

Why Isn't $\mathbb{Q}$ Enough?

At first glance, it would appear that the ordered field of rational numbers would be sufficient to solve all "real world" problems. However, a long time ago, a group of people called the Pythagoreans showed that this is not the case. The problem was first discovered when applying the now well-known Pythagorean Theorem.

Theorem 15.4 (Pythagorean Theorem): In a right triangle with legs of lengths a and b, and a hypotenuse of length c, $c^2 = a^2 + b^2$.

The picture to the right shows a right triangle. The vertical and horizontal segments (labeled a and b, respectively) are called the **legs** of the right triangle, and the side opposite the right angle (labeled c) is called the **hypotenuse** of the right triangle.

There are many ways to prove the Pythagorean Theorem. Here, we will provide a simple geometric argument. For the proof we will want to recall that the area of a square with side length s is $A = s^2$, and the area of a triangle with base b and height h is $A = \frac{1}{2}bh$. Notice that in our right triangle drawn here, the base is labeled b (how convenient), and the height is labeled a. So, the area of this right triangle is $A = \frac{1}{2}ba = \frac{1}{2}ab$.

Proof of Theorem 15.4: We draw 2 squares, each of side length $a + b$, by rearranging 4 copies of the given triangle in 2 different ways:

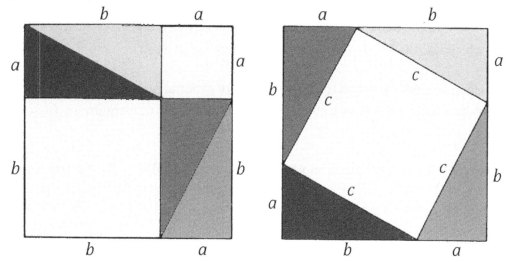

We can get the area of each of these squares by adding the areas of all the figures that comprise each square.

The square on the left consists of 4 copies of the given right triangle, a square of side length a and a square of side length b. It follows that the area of this square is $4 \cdot \frac{1}{2}ab + a^2 + b^2 = 2ab + a^2 + b^2$.

The square on the right consists of 4 copies of the given right triangle, and a square of side length c. It follows that the area of this square is $4 \cdot \frac{1}{2}ab + c^2 = 2ab + c^2$.

Since the areas of both squares of side length $a + b$ are equal (both areas are equal to $(a + b)^2$), $2ab + a^2 + b^2 = 2ab + c^2$. Cancelling $2ab$ from each side of this equation yields $a^2 + b^2 = c^2$. □

Question: In a right triangle where both legs have length 1, what is the length of the hypotenuse?

Let's try to answer this question. If we let c be the length of the hypotenuse of the triangle, then by the Pythagorean Theorem, we have $c^2 = 1^2 + 1^2 = 1 + 1 = 2$. Since $c^2 = c \cdot c$, we need to find a number with the property that when you multiply that number by itself you get 2. The Pythagoreans showed that if we use only numbers in $\mathbb{Q}$, then no such number exists.

Theorem 15.5: There does not exist a rational number a such that $a^2 = 2$.

Analysis: We will prove this Theorem by assuming that there is a rational number a such that $a^2 = 2$, and arguing until we reach a contradiction. A first attempt at a proof would be to let $a = \frac{m}{n} \in \mathbb{Q}$ satisfy $\left(\frac{m}{n}\right)^2 = 2$. It follows that $\boldsymbol{m^2 = 2n^2}$ ($\frac{m^2}{n^2} = \frac{m \cdot m}{n \cdot n} = \frac{m}{n} \cdot \frac{m}{n} = \left(\frac{m}{n}\right)^2$ and $2 = \frac{2}{1} \Rightarrow \frac{m^2}{n^2} = \frac{2}{1} \Rightarrow m^2 = 2n^2$), showing that $\boldsymbol{m^2}$ **is even**. We will then use this information to show that both m and n are even (we will need a preliminary Lemma to help us with this).

Now, in our first attempt, the fact that m and n both turned out to be even did not produce a contradiction. However, we can modify the beginning of the argument to make this happen.

Remember that every rational number has infinitely many representations. For example, $\frac{6}{12}$ is the same rational number as $\frac{2}{4}$ (because $6 \cdot 4 = 12 \cdot 2$). Notice that in both representations, the numerator (number on the top) and the denominator (number on the bottom) are even. However, they are both equivalent to $\frac{1}{2}$, which has the property that the numerator is not even.

In Problem 16 below, you will be asked to show that every rational number can be written in the form $\frac{m}{n}$, where at least one of m or n is **not** even. We can now adjust our argument to get the desired contradiction.

Recall that an integer n is **even** if there is another integer b such that $n = 2b$. For example, 6 and -22 are even because $6 = 2 \cdot 3$ and $-22 = 2 \cdot (-11)$. An integer n is **odd** if there is another integer b such that $n = 2b + 1$. For example, 7 and -23 are odd because $7 = 2 \cdot 3 + 1$ and $-22 = 2 \cdot (-12) + 1$.

Lemma 15.6: Every integer is even or odd, but not both.

Proof: We already proved in Theorem 8.9 from Lesson 8 that every natural number is even or odd. If $n < 0$ is an integer, then $-n > 0$, and so, there is a natural number j such that $-n = 2j$ or $-n = 2j + 1$. If $-n = 2j$, then $n = 2(-j)$ (and since $j \in \mathbb{N}$, $-j \in \mathbb{Z}$). If $-n = 2j + 1$, then it follows that $n = -(2j + 1) = -2j - 1 = -2j - 1 - 1 + 1$ (SACT) $= -2j - 2 + 1 = 2(-j - 1) + 1$. Here we used the fact that $(\mathbb{Z}, +, \cdot)$ is a ring. Since $\mathbb{Z}$ is closed under addition, $-j - 1 = -j + (-1) \in \mathbb{Z}$.

Now, if $n = 2j$ and $n = 2k + 1$, then $2j = 2k + 1$. So, we have
$$2(j - k) = 2j - 2k = (2k + 1) - 2k = 2k + (1 - 2k) = 2k + (-2k + 1)$$
$$= (2k - 2k) + 1 = 0 + 1 = 1.$$

So, $2(j - k) = 1$. But by part 4 of Example 15.3, 2 does not have a multiplicative inverse in $\mathbb{Z}$, and so, this is a contradiction. □

Lemma 15.7: The product of two odd integers is odd.

Proof: Let m and n be odd integers. Then there are integers j and k such that $m = 2j + 1$ and $n = 2k + 1$. So,
$$m \cdot n = (2j + 1) \cdot (2k + 1) = (2j + 1)(2k) + (2j + 1)(1) = (2k)(2j + 1) + (2j + 1)$$
$$= \big((2k)(2j) + 2k\big) + (2j + 1) = \big(2\big(k(2j)\big) + 2k\big) + (2j + 1) = 2(k(2j) + k) + (2j + 1)$$
$$= (2(k(2j) + k) + 2j) + 1 = 2\big((k(2j) + k) + j\big) + 1.$$

Here we used the fact that $(\mathbb{Z}, +, \cdot)$ is a ring. (Which properties did we use?) Since $\mathbb{Z}$ is closed under addition and multiplication, we have $(k(2j) + k) + j \in \mathbb{Z}$. Therefore, mn is odd. □

Proof of Theorem 15.5: Assume, toward contradiction, that there is a rational number a such that $a^2 = 2$. Since a is a rational number, there are $m \in \mathbb{Z}$ and $n \in \mathbb{Z}^*$, **not both even**, so that $a = \frac{m}{n}$.

So, we have $\frac{m^2}{n^2} = \frac{m \cdot m}{n \cdot n} = \frac{m}{n} \cdot \frac{m}{n} = a \cdot a = a^2 = 2 = \frac{2}{1}$. Thus, $m^2 \cdot 1 = n^2 \cdot 2$. So, $m^2 = 2n^2$. Therefore, m^2 is even. If m were odd, then by Lemma 15.7, $m^2 = m \cdot m$ would be odd. So, **m is even**.

Since m is even, there is $k \in \mathbb{Z}$ such that $m = 2k$. Replacing m by $2k$ in the equation $m^2 = 2n^2$ gives us $2n^2 = m^2 = (2k)^2 = (2k)(2k) = 2\big(k(2k)\big)$. So, using part (viii) of Problem 3 from Problem Set 8 (the analogous result for the integers – Prove this!), $n^2 = k(2k)$. Using associativity and commutativity of multiplication in $\mathbb{Z}$, we have $k(2k) = (k \cdot 2)k = (2k)k = 2(k \cdot k)$. So, $n^2 = 2(k \cdot k)$, and we see that n^2 is even. Again, by Lemma 15.7, **n is even**.

So, we have m even and n even, contrary to our original assumption that m and n are not both even. Therefore, there is no rational number a such that $a^2 = 2$. $\qquad\qquad\square$

It turns out that $\mathbb{Q}$ fails to have an element a such that $a^2 = 2$ because $\mathbb{Q}$ is not complete. Luckily $\mathbb{R}$ doesn't have this deficiency, as we will show shortly.

Completeness

Let F be an ordered field and let S be a nonempty subset of F. We say that S is **bounded above** if there is $M \in F$ such that for all $s \in S$, $s \leq M$. Each such number M is called an **upper bound** of S.

In words, an upper bound of a set S is simply an element from the field that is at least as big as every element in S.

Similarly, we say that S is **bounded below** if there is $K \in F$ such that for all $s \in S$, $K \leq s$. Each such number K is called a **lower bound** of S.

In words, a lower bound of a set S is simply an element from the field that is no bigger than any element in S.

We will say that S is **bounded** if it is both bounded above and bounded below. Otherwise S is **unbounded**.

A **least upper bound** of a set S is an upper bound that is smaller than any other upper bound of S, and a **greatest lower bound** of S is a lower bound that is larger than any other lower bound of S.

Example 15.6: Let F be an ordered field with $\mathbb{Q} \subseteq F$.

Note: The only two examples of F that we are interested in are $\mathbb{Q}$ (the set of rational numbers) and $\mathbb{R}$ (the set of real numbers). As you look at the set in each example below, think about what it looks like as a subset of $\mathbb{Q}$ and as a subset of $\mathbb{R}$.

1. $S = \{1, 2, 3, 4, 5\}$ is bounded.

   5 is an upper bound of S, as is any number larger than 5. The number 5 is special in the sense that there are no upper bounds smaller than it. So, 5 is the **least** upper bound of S.

   Similarly, 1 is a lower bound of S, as is any number smaller than 1. The number 1 is the **greatest** lower bound of S because there are no lower bounds larger than it.

Notice that the least upper bound and greatest lower bound of S are inside the set S itself. This will always happen when the set S is finite.

2. $T = \{x \in F \mid -2 < x \leq 2\}$ is also bounded. Any number greater than or equal to 2 is an upper bound of T, and any number less than or equal to -2 is a lower bound of T.

   2 is the least upper bound of T and -2 is the greatest lower bound of T.

   Note that the least upper bound of T is in T, whereas the greatest lower bound of T is not in T.

3. $U = \{x \in F \mid x < -3\}$ is bounded above by any number greater than or equal to -3, and -3 is the least upper bound of U. The set U is not bounded below, and therefore, U is unbounded.

4. $V = \{x \in F \mid x^2 < 2\}$ is bounded above by 2. To see this, note that if $x > 2$, then $x^2 > 4 \geq 2$ (the reader should verify that for all $a, b \in F^+$, $a > b \rightarrow a^2 > b^2$), and therefore, $x \notin V$. Any number greater than 2 is also an upper bound. Is 2 the least upper bound of V? It's not! For example, $\frac{3}{2}$ is also an upper bound. Indeed, if $x > \frac{3}{2}$, then $x^2 > \frac{9}{4} \geq 2$.

   Does V have a least upper bound? A moment's thought might lead you to suspect that a least upper bound M would satisfy $M^2 = 2$. And it turns out that you are right! (Proving this, however, is quite difficult—see Problem 21 below). Clearly, this least upper bound M is not in the set V. The big question is "Does M exist at all?"

   Well, if $F = \mathbb{Q}$, then by Theorem 15.5, M **does not** exist in F. In this case, V is an example of a set which is bounded above in $\mathbb{Q}$, but has no least upper bound in $\mathbb{Q}$.

   So, if we want an ordered field F containing $\mathbb{Q}$ where M does exist, we can insist that F has the property that any set which is bounded above in F has a least upper bound in F. It turns out that $\mathbb{R}$ is such an ordered field.

Many authors use the term **supremum** for "least upper bound" and **infimum** for "greatest lower bound," and they may write sup A and inf A for the supremum and infimum of a set A, respectively (if they exist).

In the examples above, we stated the least upper bound and greatest lower bound of the sets $S, T, U,$ and V without proof. Intuitively, it seems reasonable that those numbers are correct. Let's do one of the examples carefully.

Theorem 15.8: Let $U = \{x \in F \mid x < -3\}$. Then sup $U = -3$.

Analysis: We need to show that -3 is an upper bound of U, and that any number less than -3 is **not** an upper bound of U. That -3 is an upper bound of U follows immediately from the definition of U.

The harder part of the argument is showing that a number less than -3 is not an upper bound of U. However, conceptually it's not hard to see that this is true. If $a < -3$, we simply need to find some number x between a and -3. Here is a picture of the situation.

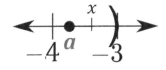

Notice that a can be very close to -3 and we don't know exactly what a is—we know only that it's less than -3. So, we need to be careful how we choose x. The most natural choice for x would be to go midway between a and -3. In other words, we can take the average of a and -3. So, we will let $x = \frac{1}{2}(a + (-3))$. Then we just need to verify that $a < x$ and that $x \in U$ (that is, $x < -3$).

Proof of Theorem 15.8: If $x \in U$, then $x < -3$ by definition, and so, -3 is an upper bound of U.

Suppose that $a < -3$ (or equivalently, $-a - 3 > 0$). We want to show that a is **not** an upper bound of U. To do this, we let $x = \frac{1}{2}(a - 3) = 2^{-1}(a + (-3))$. $x \in F$ because F is closed under addition and multiplication, and the multiplicative inverse property holds in F^*. We will show that $a < x < -3$.

$$x - a = \frac{1}{2}(a - 3) - a = \frac{1}{2}(a - 3) - \frac{1}{2}(2a) = \frac{1}{2}(a - 3 - 2a) = \frac{1}{2}(a - 2a - 3) = \frac{1}{2}(-a - 3).$$

Since $\frac{1}{2} > 0$ (by Theorem 15.3) and $-a - 3 > 0$, it follows that $x - a > 0$, and therefore, $x > a$.

$$-3 - x = -3 - \frac{1}{2}(a - 3) = \frac{1}{2}(-6) - \frac{1}{2}a + \frac{1}{2} \cdot 3 = \frac{1}{2}(-6 - a + 3) = \frac{1}{2}(-a - 3).$$

Again, since $\frac{1}{2} > 0$ and $-a - 3 > 0$, it follows that $-3 - x > 0$, and therefore, $x < -3$. Thus, $x \in U$.

So, we found an element $x \in U$ (because $x < -3$) with $a < x$. This shows that a is **not** an upper bound of U. It follows that $-3 = \sup U$. $\qquad\square$

An ordered field F has the **Completeness Property** if every nonempty subset of F that is bounded above in F has a least upper bound in F. In this case, we say that F is a **complete ordered field**.

Our next goal is to provide an outline for a proof that the ordered field $\mathbb{R}$ is complete. In order to do this, we will need a few preliminary results.

Theorem 15.9: Every Cauchy sequence of rational numbers is bounded by a rational number.

Proof: Let (x_n) be a Cauchy sequence. Then for every $k \in \mathbb{N}^+$, there is $K \in \mathbb{N}$ such that $m \geq n > K$ implies $|x_m - x_n| < \frac{1}{k}$. In particular, by letting $k = 1$, we see that there is $K \in \mathbb{N}$ such that $m \geq n > K$ implies $|x_m - x_n| < 1$. By the Triangle Inequality (and SACT), we have

$$|x_m| = |(x_m - x_n) + x_n| \leq |x_m - x_n| + |x_n|.$$

Therefore, $m \geq n > K$ implies $|x_m| - |x_n| \leq |x_m - x_n| < 1$. Letting $n = K + 1$, we see that $m > K$ implies $|x_m| - |x_{K+1}| < 1$, or equivalently, $|x_m| < 1 + |x_{K+1}|$.

Let $M = \max\{|x_0|, |x_1|, \ldots, |x_K|, 1 + |x_{K+1}|\}$. Then for all $m \in \mathbb{N}$, $|x_m| \leq M$. $\qquad\square$

By Theorem 15.2, every ordered field F contains an isomorphic copy of $\mathbb{N}$. For example, $\mathbb{Q}$ contains $\left\{\frac{n}{1} \,\middle|\, n \in \mathbb{N}\right\}$ and $\mathbb{R}$ contains $\left\{\left[\left(\frac{n}{1}\right)\right] \,\middle|\, n \in \mathbb{N}\right\}$. To avoid using messy notation, we will usually abuse notation just a bit and use the name $\mathbb{N}$ for the isomorphic copy of $\mathbb{N}$. So, if F is an ordered field, we can write $\mathbb{N} \subseteq F$.

We say that an ordered field F has the **Archimedean Property** if $\mathbb{N}$ is unbounded in F. Symbolically, we write $\forall x \in F \exists n \in \mathbb{N} (n > x)$.

Theorem 15.10: $\mathbb{Q}$ and $\mathbb{R}$ both have the Archimedean Property.

Proof: We first show that $\mathbb{Q}$ has the Archimedean Property. Let $q \in \mathbb{Q}$. If $q \leq 0$, then since $0 < 1$, by the transitivity of $<$, we have $q < 1$. If $q > 0$, then there are $a, b \in \mathbb{Z}^+$ with $q = \frac{a}{b}$. We have

$$(a+1) - \frac{a}{b} = \frac{(a+1)}{1} + \left(\frac{-a}{b}\right) = \frac{(a+1)b + 1 \cdot (-a)}{1b} = \frac{ab + b - a}{b} = \frac{a(b-1)+b}{b}.$$

Since $b \in \mathbb{Z}^+$, $b - 1 \geq 0$, and so, $a(b-1) \geq 0$. Therefore, $a(b-1) + b \geq 0 + b > 0$. Thus, $(a+1) - \frac{a}{b} = \frac{a(b-1)+b}{b} > 0$. Therefore, we have $a + 1 > \frac{a}{b} = q$. Since $a, 1 \in \mathbb{N}$ and $\mathbb{N}$ is closed under addition, it follows that $a + 1 \in \mathbb{N}$. Since $q \in \mathbb{Q}$ was arbitrary, we have shown that $\mathbb{Q}$ has the Archimedean Property.

Next, we show that $\mathbb{R}$ has the Archimedean Property. Let $[(x_n)] \in \mathbb{R}$. We want to find a natural number $[(t)]$ such that $[(t)] > [(x_n)]$. Suppose toward contradiction, that for all $t \in \mathbb{N}$, $[(t)] \leq [(x_n)]$. Then for each $t \in \mathbb{N}$, there is K_t such that $n > K_t$ implies $t \leq x_n$. Since (x_n) is a Cauchy sequence, by Theorem 15.9, (x_n) is bounded by a rational number M. So, for all $n \in \mathbb{N}$, $x_n \leq M$. Let $t \in \mathbb{N}$ and choose K_t such that $n > K_t$ implies $t \leq x_n$. Since $x_n \leq M$, by the transitivity of $\leq$, we have $t \leq M$. Since $t \in \mathbb{N}$ was arbitrary, we see that $\mathbb{N}$ is bounded by the rational number M, contradicting that $\mathbb{Q}$ has the Archimedean Property. This contradiction proves that $\mathbb{R}$ has the Archimedean Property. $\square$

Theorem 15.11 (The Density Theorem): If $x, y \in \mathbb{R}$ with $x < y$, then there is $q \in \mathbb{Q}$ with $x < q < y$.

In other words, the Density Theorem says that between any two real numbers we can always find a rational number. We say that $\mathbb{Q}$ is **dense** in $\mathbb{R}$.

To help understand the proof, let's first run a simple simulation using a specific example. Let's let $x = \frac{16}{3}$ and $y = \frac{17}{3}$. We begin by subtracting to get $y - x = \frac{1}{3}$. This is the distance between x and y. We wish to find a natural number n such that $\frac{1}{n}$ is smaller than this distance. In other words, we want $\frac{1}{n} < \frac{1}{3}$, or equivalently, $n > 3$. So, we can let n be any natural number greater than 3, say $n = 4$. We now want to "shift" $\frac{1}{n} = \frac{1}{4}$ to the right to get a rational number between x and y. We can do this as follows. We multiply n times x to get $nx = 4 \cdot \frac{16}{3} = \frac{64}{3}$. We then let m be the **least** integer greater than nx. So, $m = \frac{66}{3} = 22$. Finally, we let $q = \frac{m}{n} = \frac{22}{4} = \frac{11}{2}$. And we did it! Indeed, we have $\frac{16}{3} < \frac{11}{2} < \frac{17}{3}$. The reader should confirm that these inequalities hold. Let's write out the details of the proof.

Proof: Let's first consider the case where $0 \leq x < y$. Let $z = y - x = y + (-x)$. Since $\mathbb{R}$ has the additive inverse property and is closed under addition, $z \in \mathbb{R}$. Also, $z > 0$. By the Archimedean Property, there is $n \in \mathbb{N}$ such that $n > \frac{1}{z}$. Using Problem 11 (part (i)) in the problem set below, we have $\frac{1}{n} < z$.

By the Archimedean Property once again, there is $m \in \mathbb{N}$ such that $m > nx$. Therefore, $\frac{m}{n} > x$ (Check this!). So, $\left\{ m \in \mathbb{N} \mid \frac{m}{n} > x \right\} \neq \emptyset$. By the Well Ordering Principle, $\left\{ m \in \mathbb{N} \mid \frac{m}{n} > x \right\}$ has a least element, let's call it k. Since $k > 0$, (because $x \geq 0$ and $n > 0$) and k is the **least** natural number such that $\frac{k}{n} > x$, it follows that $k - 1 \in \mathbb{N}$ and $\frac{k-1}{n} \leq x$, or equivalently, $\frac{k}{n} - \frac{1}{n} \leq x$. Therefore, we have $\frac{k}{n} \leq x + \frac{1}{n} < x + z = x + (y - x) = y$. Thus, $x < \frac{k}{n} < y$. Since $k, n \in \mathbb{N}$, we have $\frac{k}{n} \in \mathbb{Q}$.

Now, we consider the case where $x < 0$ and $x < y$. By the Archimedean Property, there is $t \in \mathbb{N}$ such that $t > -x$. Then, we have $0 < x + t < y + t$. So, $x + t$ and $y + t$ satisfy the first case above. Thus, there is $q \in \mathbb{Q}$ with $x + t < q < y + t$. It follows that $x < q - t < y$. Since $t \in \mathbb{N}$, $-t \in \mathbb{Z}$. Since $\mathbb{Z} \subseteq \mathbb{Q}$, $-t \in \mathbb{Q}$. So, we have $q, -t \in \mathbb{Q}$. Since $\mathbb{Q}$ is closed under addition, $q - t = q + (-t) \in \mathbb{Q}$. □

Theorem 15.12: $\mathbb{R}$ is a complete ordered field.

The proof of this theorem requires several steps. I will give a brief outline of these steps and leave the details as an exercise for the reader (see Problem 22 below).

Proof outline for Theorem 15.12: We already know that $\mathbb{R}$ is an ordered field. All that's left to show is that $\mathbb{R}$ is complete. So, let $S \subseteq \mathbb{R}$ with $S \neq \emptyset$ be bounded above. Then there is $b_0 \in \mathbb{R}$ such that $\forall s \in S, s \leq b_0$ (b_0 is an upper bound of S). Since $S \neq \emptyset$, there is $a_0 \in S$. Let $c_0 = \frac{1}{2}(a_0 + b_0)$. If c_0 is an upper bound of S, let $a_1 = a_0$ and $b_1 = c_0$. If c_0 is **not** an upper bound of S, let $a_1 = c_0$ and $b_1 = b_0$. We continue in this fashion to inductively create sequences of real numbers (a_n), (b_n), and (c_n), where $c_n = \frac{1}{2}(a_n + b_n)$, if c_n is an upper bound of S, $a_{n+1} = a_n$ and $b_{n+1} = c_n$, and if c_n is **not** an upper bound of S, $a_{n+1} = c_n$ and $b_{n+1} = b_n$. Then let $c_{n+1} = \frac{1}{2}(a_n + b_n)$.

Step 1: Use induction on $\mathbb{N}$ to prove that for all $n \in \mathbb{N}$, $a_{n+1} \geq a_n$ and $b_{n+1} \leq b_n$.

Step 2: Use Step 1 to prove that (a_n) and (b_n) are real-valued Cauchy sequences.

Step 3: Use Theorems 15.10 and 15.11 to prove that there is $x \in \mathbb{R}$ such that the following holds:

$$\text{for every } k \in \mathbb{N}^+, \text{ there is } K \in \mathbb{N} \text{ such that } n > K \text{ implies } |b_n - x| < \frac{1}{k}.$$

In this case, we say that (b_n) converges to x and we write $b_n \to x$.

Step 4: Use Theorem 15.10 to prove that $a_n \to x$.

Step 5: Use the sequence (b_n) to prove that x is an upper bound of S.

Step 6: Use the sequence (a_n) to prove that if $y < x$, then y is **not** an upper bound of S.

Completing these steps will prove the theorem. □

Problem Set 15

Full solutions to these problems are available for free download here:
www.SATPrepGet800.com/STFBYKG

LEVEL 1

1. Show that there are exactly two monoids on the set $S = \{e, a\}$, where e is the identity. Which of these monoids are groups? Which of these monoids are commutative?

2. The addition and multiplication tables below are defined on the set $S = \{0, 1\}$. Show that $(S, +, \cdot)$ does **not** define a ring.

+	0	1
0	0	1
1	1	0

$\cdot$	0	1
0	1	0
1	0	1

3. The addition and multiplication tables below are defined on the set $S = \{0, 1, 2\}$. Show that $(S, +, \cdot)$ does **not** define a field.

+	0	1	2
0	0	1	2
1	1	2	0
2	2	0	1

$\cdot$	0	1	2
0	0	0	0
1	0	1	2
2	0	2	2

4. Let $F = \{0, 1\}$, where $0 \neq 1$. Show that there is exactly one field $(F, +, \cdot)$, where 0 is the additive identity and 1 is the multiplicative identity.

LEVEL 2

5. Let $G = \{e, a, b\}$ and let $(G, \star)$ be a group with identity element e. Draw a multiplication table for $(G, \star)$.

6. Prove that in any monoid $(M, \star)$, the identity element is unique.

7. Let $(F, +, \cdot)$ be a field. Prove each of the following:

   (i)   If $a, b \in F$ with $a + b = b$, then $a = 0$.

   (ii)   If $a \in F$, $b \in F^*$, and $ab = b$, then $a = 1$.

   (iii)   If $a \in F$, then $a \cdot 0 = 0$.

   (iv)   If $a \in F^*$, $b \in F$, and $ab = 1$, then $b = \frac{1}{a}$.

   (v)   If $a, b \in F$ and $ab = 0$, then $a = 0$ or $b = 0$.

   (vi)   If $a \in F$, then $-a = -1a$.

   (vii) $(-1)(-1) = 1$.

192

8. Let $(F, +, \cdot)$ be a field with $\mathbb{N} \subseteq F$. Prove that $\mathbb{Q} \subseteq F$.

LEVEL 3

9. Assume that a group $(G, \star)$ of order 4 exists with $G = \{e, a, b, c\}$, where e is the identity, $a^2 = b$ and $b^2 = e$. Construct the multiplication table for the operation of such a group.

10. Prove that in any group $(G, \star)$, each element has a unique inverse.

11. Let $(F, +, \cdot, \leq)$ be an ordered field. Prove each of the following:

    (i)   If $a, b \in F^+$ and $a > b$, then $\frac{1}{a} < \frac{1}{b}$.

    (ii) If $a, b \in F$, then $a \geq b$ if and only if $-a \leq -b$.

12. Let $(F, +, \cdot)$ be a field. Show that $(F, \cdot)$ is a commutative monoid.

LEVEL 4

13. Let $(G, \star)$ be a group with $a, b \in G$, and let a^{-1} and b^{-1} be the inverses of a and b, respectively. Prove

    (i) $(a \star b)^{-1} = b^{-1} \star a^{-1}$.

    (ii) the inverse of a^{-1} is a.

14. Prove that there is no smallest positive real number.

15. Let a be a nonnegative real number. Prove that $a = 0$ if and only if a is less than every positive real number. (Note: a nonnegative means $a \geq 0$.)

16. Prove that every rational number can be written in the form $\frac{m}{n}$, where $m \in \mathbb{Z}$, $n \in \mathbb{Z}^*$, and at least one of m or n is **not** even.

LEVEL 5

17. Prove that $(\mathbb{Q}, +, \cdot, \leq)$ and $(\mathbb{R}, +, \cdot, \leq)$ are ordered fields.

18. Prove that every nonempty set of real numbers that is bounded below has a greatest lower bound in $\mathbb{R}$.

19. Show that between any two real numbers there is a real number that is **not** rational.

20. Let $T = \{x \in F \mid -2 < x \leq 2\}$. Prove $\sup T = 2$ and $\inf T = -2$.

21. Let $V = \{x \in F \mid x^2 < 2\}$ and let $a = \sup V$. Prove that $a^2 = 2$.

22. Prove that $\mathbb{R}$ is a complete ordered field.

23. Prove that any two complete ordered fields are isomorphic.

24. Let $D = \{A, B\}$ be a partition of $\mathbb{Q}$ such that $A \neq \emptyset$, $A \neq \mathbb{Q}$, A has no greatest element, and every element of A is less than every element of B. D is called a **Dedekind cut**. Let $X = \{D \mid D \text{ is a Dedekind cut}\}$. Prove that $+$, $\cdot$, and $\leq$ can be defined on X so that $(X, +, \cdot, \leq)$ is a complete ordered field that is isomorphic to $\mathbb{R}$.

LESSON 16
CLUBS AND STATIONARY SETS

Dense Linearly Ordered Sets Without Endpoints

Let $\mathcal{L} = \{<\}$. That is, $\mathcal{L}$ is the language consisting of a single binary relation symbol denoted by $<$. Recall from Lesson 10 that the theory of **dense linear orders without endpoints** (abbreviated as **DLO**) consists of the following sentences:

(1) **(Transitivity)** $\forall x \forall y \forall z \big((x < y \wedge y < z) \to x < z\big)$

(2) **(Antireflexivity)** $\forall x(x \not< x)$

(3) **(Antisymmetry)** $\forall x \forall y \big((x < y \wedge y < x) \to x = y\big)$

(4) **(Trichotomy)** $\forall x \forall y (x < y \vee x = y \vee y < x)$

(5) **(Density)** $\forall x \forall y \big(x < y \to \exists z(x < z \wedge z < y)\big)$

(6) **(No endpoints)** $\forall x \exists y \exists z(y < x \wedge x < z)$

$(\mathbb{Q}, <)$ (the set of rational numbers together with its usual ordering) is an example of a model of DLO. In Problem 13 from Problem Set 10, you were asked to prove that any two countable models of DLO are isomorphic. In other words, there is essentially just one countable model of DLO.

What about uncountable models of DLO? Specifically, in this section we will look at models of DLO of cardinality ω_1. How many are there? As it turns out, the situation is exactly the opposite of the case ω.

For convenience, from now on, we will call a model of DLO a DLO. For example, we will refer to $(\mathbb{Q}, <)$ as a DLO. We may also refer to the underlying set A of $(A, <)$ as a DLO (for example, we may say that $\mathbb{Q}$ is a DLO). It is of course implied that we are really talking about the model $(A, <)$.

Notes: (1) Although there is really just one countable DLO, there are many different ways to visualize this set. The most natural visualization of this is as $\mathbb{Q}$ together with its usual order. However, another way to visualize this set is as a bounded open interval of rational numbers such as $(0, 1) \cap \mathbb{Q}$ (Note that we use the notation $(0, 1) \cap \mathbb{Q}$, as opposed to simply $(0, 1)$ so that we do not confuse intervals of rational numbers with intervals of real numbers).

(2) $(0, 1) \cap \mathbb{Q}$ has an interesting relationship with $\mathbb{Q}$. On the one hand, it is a proper subset of $\mathbb{Q}$. On the other hand, the DLO $\big((0, 1) \cap \mathbb{Q}, <\big)$ is isomorphic to the DLO $(\mathbb{Q}, <)$.

(3) The DLO $\big((0, \sqrt{2}) \cap \mathbb{Q}, <\big)$ is another DLO and therefore, it is isomorphic to both $\big((0, 1) \cap \mathbb{Q}, <\big)$ and $(\mathbb{Q}, <)$. However, as subsets of $\mathbb{Q}$, the sets $(0, 1) \cap \mathbb{Q}$ and $\big(0, \sqrt{2}\big) \cap \mathbb{Q}$ behave slightly differently as we will see in Note 5 below.

(4) Let $(C, <)$ be an ordered set and let $A \subseteq C$. Recall that A is **bounded above** if there is $M \in C$ such that for all $a \in A$, $a \leq M$. Each such number M is called an **upper bound** of A. A **least upper bound** of a set A is an upper bound that is smaller than any other upper bound of A.

(5) Let's let $A = (0,1) \cap \mathbb{Q}$, $B = \left(0, \sqrt{2}\right) \cap \mathbb{Q}$, and $C = \mathbb{Q}$. Now, A and B are both proper subsets of C. However, the set A has a least upper bound in C (namely, 1), whereas B does **not** have a least upper bound in C. We say that C is a **rational extension** of A and an **irrational extension** of B. Observe that B is also a rational extension of A. In general, if A, B, and C are countable DLOs with $A \subseteq B \subseteq C$ (where all three orderings agree on A), then B is a rational extension of A if and only if C is a rational extension of A (and similarly for irrational extensions).

Our goal is to show that there are exactly 2^{ω_1} pairwise nonisomorphic DLOs of cardinality ω_1. First, let's prove that 2^{ω_1} is the maximum possible cardinal value.

Theorem 16.1: Let $X = \{(\omega_1, <) \mid (\omega_1, <)$ is a DLO$\}$. Then $|X| \leq 2^{\omega_1}$.

Proof: Let $(\omega_1, <)$ be a DLO. Then $(\omega_1, <) \in \mathcal{P}(\omega_1) \times \mathcal{P}(\omega_1 \times \omega_1)$. So, $X \subseteq \mathcal{P}(\omega_1) \times \mathcal{P}(\omega_1 \times \omega_1)$. By Theorem 13.2 from Lesson 13, $|(\omega_1 \times \omega_1)| = \omega_1 \cdot \omega_1 = \omega_1$. So, $|\mathcal{P}(\omega_1 \times \omega_1)| = |\mathcal{P}(\omega_1)|$. By the same theorem, we have that $|\mathcal{P}(\omega_1) \times \mathcal{P}(\omega_1)| = |\mathcal{P}(\omega_1)| \cdot |\mathcal{P}(\omega_1)| = |\mathcal{P}(\omega_1)|$. Therefore, $|\mathcal{P}(\omega_1) \times \mathcal{P}(\omega_1 \times \omega_1)| = |\mathcal{P}(\omega_1)|$. By part 4 of Example 6.8 from Lesson 6, we have $|\mathcal{P}(\omega_1)| = 2^{\omega_1}$. It follows that $|X| \leq 2^{\omega_1}$. $\qquad\square$

Before we begin trying to construct 2^{ω_1} pairwise nonisomorphic DLOs of cardinality ω_1, let's start by constructing just 2 such DLOs.

Theorem 16.2: There exist DLOs $(A, <_A)$ and $(B, <_B)$ such that $|A| = |B| = 2^{\omega_1}$ and $(A, <_A)$ is **not** isomorphic to $(B, <_B)$

To prove Theorem 16.2, we will need the following Lemma.

Lemma 16.3: Every countable DLO A can be extended to a countable DLO B so that B is a rational extension of A. Similarly, every countable DLO A can be extended to a countable DLO C so that C is an irrational extension of A.

Analysis: For the rational extension, we will identify A with $(0,1) \cap \mathbb{Q}$ and essentially "build the rest of $\mathbb{Q}$" around it. We will let $B = Y \cup A \cup X$, where Y is *essentially* $(-\infty, 0] \cap \mathbb{Q}$ and X is *essentially* $[1, \infty) \cap \mathbb{Q}$. We can visualize this identification as follows:

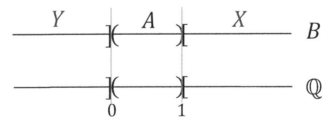

For the irrational extension, we will identify A with $\left(0, \sqrt{2}\right) \cap \mathbb{Q}$ and let $C = Y \cup A \cup X$, where Y is *essentially* $(-\infty, 0] \cap \mathbb{Q}$ and X is *essentially* $\left(\sqrt{2}, \infty\right) \cap \mathbb{Q}$. The reader may want to draw a picture similar to the one above for this case.

Proof of Lemma 16.3: Let $(A, <_A)$ be a DLO, let X and Y be denumerable sets such that A, X, and Y are pairwise disjoint, let $f : A \to (0, 1) \cap \mathbb{Q}$ be an isomorphism, and let $g : X \to [1, \infty) \cap \mathbb{Q}$ and $h : Y \to (-\infty, 0] \cap \mathbb{Q}$ be bijections. Let $B = Y \cup A \cup X$ and define an ordering $<_B$ on B by $x <_B y$ if and only if one of the following conditions is met:

(i) $x \in Y$ and $y \in A$

(ii) $x \in Y$ and $y \in X$

(iii) $x \in A$ and $y \in X$

(iv) $x, y \in Y$ and $h(x) < h(y)$

(v) $x, y \in A$ and $x <_A y$ (or equivalently, $f(x) < f(y)$)

(vi) $x, y \in X$ and $g(x) < g(y)$

It is straightforward (although a bit tedious) to check that $(B, <_B)$ is a DLO that extends $(A, <_A)$. We claim that $g^{-1}(1)$ is a least upper bound of A in B. First note that $g^{-1}(1) \in X$ and $X \subseteq B$, and so $g^{-1}(1) \in B$. If $x \in A$, then since $g^{-1}(1) \in X$, by clause (iii), $x <_B g^{-1}(1)$. Therefore, $g^{-1}(1)$ is an upper bound of A. Now suppose that $z <_B g^{-1}(1)$. Then $z \notin X$. If $z \in Y$, then since $A \neq \emptyset$, by clause (i), there is $y \in A$ with $z <_B y$. If $z \in A$, then since A has no endpoints, there is $y \in A$ with $z <_B y$. Thus, z is **not** an upper bound of A. It follows that $g^{-1}(1)$ is the least upper bound of A in B.

To extend A to a DLO C so that C is an irrational extension of A, use $\left(0, \sqrt{2}\right) \cap \mathbb{Q}$ in place of $(0, 1) \cap \mathbb{Q}$ and $\left[\sqrt{2}, \infty\right) \cap \mathbb{Q}$ (or equivalently, $\left(\sqrt{2}, \infty\right) \cap \mathbb{Q}$) in place of $[1, \infty) \cap \mathbb{Q}$ in the above paragraph. The rest of the argument is similar, and so, I leave it to the reader. $\square$

Let's now attempt to construct nonisomorphic DLOs $(H, <_H)$ and $(K, <_K)$ such that $|H| = |K| = 2^{\omega_1}$.

For each ordinal $\alpha < w_1$, we define countable DLOs H_α and K_α as follows:

We begin by letting $H_0 = \mathbb{Q}$ and $K_0 = \mathbb{Q}$.

Now, assume that H_β and K_β have been defined for all $\beta < \alpha$ so that each H_β and K_β are countable DLOs, if $\gamma < \beta$, then $H_{\gamma+1}$ is a rational extension of H_γ and $K_{\gamma+1}$ is an irrational extension of K_γ, and if β is a limit ordinal, then $H_\beta = \bigcup\{H_\delta \mid \delta < \beta\}$ and $K_\beta = \bigcup\{K_\delta \mid \delta < \beta\}$.

We now define H_α and K_α.

If $\alpha = \beta + 1$, extend H_β to a countable DLO H_α so that H_α is a rational extension of H_β and extend K_β to a countable DLO K_α so that K_α is an irrational extension of K_β (this can be done by Lemma 16.3).

If α is a limit ordinal, let $H_\alpha = \bigcup\{H_\beta \mid \beta < \alpha\}$ and $K_\alpha = \bigcup\{K_\beta \mid \beta < \alpha\}$. By part (ii) of Problem 5 from Problem Set 7, H_α and K_α are countable.

We now let $H = \bigcup\{H_\alpha \mid \alpha < \omega_1\}$ and $K = \bigcup\{K_\alpha \mid \alpha < \omega_1\}$.

It is easy to check that H and K are DLOs of cardinality ω_1 (see Problem 2 below). So, all that's left to show is that H and K are nonisomorphic.

Lemma 16.4: Suppose that $f: H \to K$ is a bijection and there is $\alpha < \omega_1$ such that $f[H_\alpha] = K_\alpha$. Then f is not an isomorphism.

Proof: Let $f: H \to K$ be a bijection and suppose that $f[H_\alpha] = K_\alpha$ for some $\alpha < \omega_1$. Suppose toward contradiction that f is an isomorphism. Let x be the least upper bound of H_α in H. So, for all $a \in H_\alpha$, $a \leq x$. Since f is an isomorphism, for all $a \in H_\alpha$, $f(a) \leq f(x)$. So, $f(x)$ is an upper bound of K_α in K. Since K_α has no least upper bound in K, there is $z < f(x)$ such that for all $b \in K_\alpha$, $b < z$. So, for all $a \in H_\alpha$, $f(a) < z$. Since f is an isomorphism, for all $a \in H_\alpha$, $a < f^{-1}(z)$. So $f^{-1}(z)$ is an upper bound of H_α. But $f^{-1}(z) < x$, contradicting that x is the least upper bound of H_α in H. Therefore, f cannot be an isomorphism. $\square$

So, to finish the proof of Theorem 16.2, we need to show that if $f: H \to K$ is a bijection, then there is $\alpha < \omega_1$ such that $f[H_\alpha] = K_\alpha$. Not only will be able to find such an ordinal α, but we will show that there are "many" such α.

By "many" such α, we mean that we can find a **club (closed unbounded set)** $C \subseteq \omega_1$ such that for all $\alpha \in C$, $f[H_\alpha] = K_\alpha$. A club can be thought of as a "quite large" set. This notion of "quite large" will be explored next.

Clubs

Let κ be a regular uncountable cardinal. A subset $C \subseteq \kappa$ is a **club** if and only if the following two properties hold:

   (i) **(C is unbounded)** For all $\alpha < \kappa$, there is $\beta \in C$ such that $\alpha < \beta$.

   (ii) **(C is closed)** Let $\delta < \kappa$ be a limit ordinal and suppose that $\{\alpha_\eta \mid \eta < \delta\}$ satisfies (a) for all η, ζ with $\eta < \zeta < \delta$, $\alpha_\eta < \alpha_\zeta$ and (b) for all $\eta < \delta$, $\alpha_\eta \in C$. Then $\bigcup\{\alpha_\eta \mid \eta < \delta\} \in C$.

Example 16.1: Let κ be a regular uncountable cardinal and let $\alpha < \kappa$ be an ordinal. Then it is easy to see that $C = \{\eta \mid \alpha < \eta < \kappa\}$ is a club. To see that C is unbounded, let $\gamma < \kappa$ and let $\beta = \max\{\alpha + 1, \gamma + 1\}$. Since κ is a limit ordinal, $\beta < \kappa$. Since we also have $\beta > \alpha$, $\beta \in C$. To see that C is closed, let $\delta < \kappa$ be a limit ordinal and suppose that $\{\alpha_\eta \mid \eta < \delta\}$ satisfies (a) for all η, ζ with $\eta < \zeta < \delta$, $\alpha_\eta < \alpha_\zeta$ and (b) for all $\eta < \delta$, $\alpha_\eta \in C$. Then $\bigcup\{\alpha_\eta \mid \eta < \delta\} > \alpha_0$ and since κ is regular and $\delta < \kappa$, $\bigcup\{\alpha_\eta \mid \eta < \delta\} < \kappa$. Therefore, $\bigcup\{\alpha_\eta \mid \eta < \delta\} \in C$.

Lemma 16.5: Let $\kappa > \omega$ be a regular cardinal. Suppose that for each $\alpha < \kappa$, A_α and B_α are defined such that (i) for each $\alpha < \kappa$, $|A_\alpha|, |B_\alpha| < \kappa$, (ii) $\alpha < \beta$ implies $A_\alpha \subseteq A_\beta$ and $B_\alpha \subseteq B_\beta$, and (iii) if α is a limit ordinal, then $A_\alpha = \bigcup\{A_\beta \mid \beta < \alpha\}$ and $B_\alpha = \bigcup\{B_\beta \mid \beta < \alpha\}$. Let $A = \bigcup\{A_\alpha \mid \alpha < \kappa\}$, $B = \bigcup\{B_\alpha \mid \alpha < \kappa\}$, and let $f: A \to B$ be a bijection. Then $C = \{\alpha < \kappa \mid f[A_\alpha] = B_\alpha\}$ is a club in κ.

Proof: We first show that C is **closed** in κ. To see this, let $\delta < \kappa$ be a limit ordinal and let $\{\alpha_\eta \mid \eta < \delta\}$ satisfy (a) for all η, ζ with $\eta < \zeta < \delta$, $\alpha_\eta < \alpha_\zeta$ and (b) for all $\eta < \delta$, $\alpha_\eta \in C$ (so that $f\left[A_{\alpha_\eta}\right] = B_{\alpha_\eta}$). Let $\alpha = \bigcup\{\alpha_\eta \mid \eta < \delta\}$. Then $f[A_\alpha] = f\left[\bigcup\left\{A_{\alpha_\eta} \mid \eta < \delta\right\}\right] = \bigcup\left\{f\left[A_{\alpha_\eta}\right] \mid \eta < \delta\right\} = \bigcup\left\{B_{\alpha_\eta} \mid \eta < \delta\right\} = B_\alpha$. For the second equality, we used part (i) of Problem 9 from Problem Set 6. Since $f[A_\alpha] = B_\alpha$, $\alpha \in C$. Therefore, C is closed.

We now wish to show that C is **unbounded** in κ.

First, we will show that for any $\alpha < \kappa$, there is $\beta < \kappa$ such that $f[A_\alpha] \subseteq B_\beta$. To see this, let $\alpha < \kappa$ and let $\lambda = |A_\alpha|$. We can then write $A_\alpha = \{\alpha_\eta \mid \eta < \lambda\}$. By (i), $\lambda < \kappa$. Define the function $g: \lambda \to \kappa$ by $g(\eta) = \min\{\gamma \mid \gamma < \kappa \wedge f(\alpha_\eta) \in B_\gamma\}$. Since κ is regular and $\lambda < \kappa$, there is $\beta < \kappa$ such that for all $\eta < \lambda$, $g(\eta) \leq \beta$. Let's show that $f[A_\alpha] \subseteq B_\beta$. To see this, let $\delta \in f[A_\alpha]$. Then there is $\eta < \lambda$ such that $f(\alpha_\eta) = \delta$. By definition of g, $f(\alpha_\eta) \in B_{g(\eta)}$. Since $g(\eta) \leq \beta$, by (ii), $B_{g(\eta)} \subseteq B_\beta$. Thus, $\delta = f(\alpha_\eta) \in B_\beta$. Since $\delta \in f[A_\alpha]$ was arbitrary, $f[A_\alpha] \subseteq B_\beta$.

Next, we show that for any $\beta < \kappa$, there is $\alpha < \kappa$ such that $B_\beta \subseteq f[A_\alpha]$. To see this, consider the bijection $f^{-1}: B \to A$. Using the same argument in the last paragraph, there is $\alpha < \kappa$ such that $f^{-1}[B_\beta] \subseteq A_\alpha$. Then $B_\beta = f\left[f^{-1}[B_\beta]\right] \subseteq f[A_\alpha]$.

Now, let $\alpha < \kappa$, and let $\alpha_0 = \alpha$. Choose $\alpha_1 > \alpha_0$ so that $f[A_{\alpha_0}] \subseteq B_{\alpha_1}$. Then choose $\alpha_2 > \alpha_1$ so that $B_{\alpha_1} \subseteq f[A_{\alpha_0}]$. In general, assuming that α_{2k} ($k \in \omega$) has been chosen, choose $\alpha_{2k+1} > \alpha_{2k}$ so that $f[A_{\alpha_{2k}}] \subseteq B_{\alpha_{2k+1}}$ and $\alpha_{2k+2} > \alpha_{2k+1}$ so that $B_{\alpha_{2k+1}} \subseteq f[A_{\alpha_{2k+2}}]$. Let $\beta = \bigcup\{\alpha_n \mid n < \omega\}$. Then $f[A_\beta] = f[\bigcup\{A_{\alpha_{2n}} \mid n < \omega\}] = \bigcup\{f[A_{\alpha_{2n}}] \mid n < \omega\} = \bigcup\{B_{\alpha_{2n+1}} \mid n < \omega\} = B_\beta$. So, $\beta \in C$ and clearly $\beta > \alpha$.

Since C is closed and unbounded, it follows that C is a club in κ. $\qquad\square$

To finish the proof of Theorem 16.2, let $\kappa = \omega_1$, define H and K as we did before Lemma 16.4, and let $f: H \to K$ be a bijection. By Lemma 16.5, $C = \{\alpha < \kappa \mid f[H_\alpha] = K_\alpha\}$ is a club in ω_1. In particular, there exists $\alpha < \kappa$ such that $f[H_\alpha] = K_\alpha$. By Lemma 16.4, f is **not** an isomorphism. Since f was an arbitrary bijection from H to K, it follows that A and B are **not** isomorphic. $\qquad\square$

Stationary Sets

Earlier, we made the bold claim that there are 2^{ω_1} pairwise nonisomorphic DLOs of cardinality ω_1. How do we make the leap from 2 nonisomorphic DLOs to 2^{ω_1} pairwise nonisomorphic DLOs? To do this, we need to understand stationary sets.

Let κ be a regular uncountable cardinal. A subset $S \subseteq \kappa$ is **stationary** if and only if for every club $C \subseteq \kappa$, $C \cap S \neq \emptyset$.

Example 16.2: Let κ be a regular uncountable cardinal and let $S = \{\alpha < \kappa \mid cf(\alpha) = \omega\}$. Then S is a stationary subset of κ. To see this, let $C \subseteq \kappa$ be a club and let $\{\alpha_n \mid n < \omega\}$ be the first ω elements of C. Let $\alpha = \bigcup\{\alpha_n \mid n < \omega\}$. By clause (ii) of the definition of a club, $\alpha \in C$. Also, $cf(\alpha) = \omega$ (the function $f: \omega \to \alpha$ defined by $f(n) = \alpha_n$ is cofinal), and so, $\alpha \in S$. Thus, $\alpha \in C \cap S$. Therefore, $C \cap S \neq \emptyset$. Since $C \subseteq \kappa$ was an arbitrary club, we see that S is a stationary subset of κ.

We will now state Ulam's Theorem, which says that there are "many" pairwise disjoint stationary sets. Since a club intersects every stationary set, this theorem supports our claim that clubs are "quite large."

Theorem 16.6 (Ulam's Theorem): Let $\kappa = \lambda^+$ be an uncountable cardinal. There are κ pairwise disjoint stationary subsets of κ.

Before proving Ulam's Theorem, let's use the theorem to prove our claim that we made toward the beginning of this lesson.

Theorem 16.7: There are 2^{ω_1} pairwise nonisomorphic DLOs of cardinality ω_1.

Proof: Since $\omega_1 = \omega^+$, by Ulam's Theorem, there are ω_1 pairwise disjoint stationary subsets of ω_1, let's say $\{S_\beta \mid \beta < \omega_1\}$ is such a collection. For each subset $X \subseteq \omega_1$, we define $H(X) = \bigcup\{H_\alpha(X) \mid \alpha < \omega_1\}$, where (i) for each $\alpha < \omega_1$, $H_\alpha(X)$ is a countable DLO, (ii) if α is a limit ordinal, $H_\alpha(X) = \bigcup\{H_\beta \mid \beta < \alpha\}$, and (iii) if $\alpha = \beta + 1$ then $H_\alpha(X)$ is an irrational extension of $H_\beta(X)$ if and only if $\alpha \in \bigcup\{S_\beta \mid \beta \in X\}$ (otherwise $H_\alpha(X)$ is a rational extension of $H_\beta(X)$). This construction can be carried out in similar fashion to the constructions of H and K that we made right before Lemma 16.4.

We now show that if $X \neq Y$, then $H(X)$ is not isomorphic to $H(Y)$. Suppose that $f : H(X) \to H(Y)$ is a bijection. By Lemma 16.5, $C = \{\alpha < \omega_1 \mid f[H_\alpha(X)] = H_\alpha(Y)\}$ is a club in ω_1. Since $X \neq Y$, there is $\beta \in X \setminus Y$ or $\beta \in Y \setminus X$. Without loss of generality, assume that there is $\beta \in X \setminus Y$. Since C is a club and S_β is a stationary set, $C \cap S_\beta \neq \emptyset$. So, there is $\alpha < \omega_1$ with $\alpha \in C \cap S_\beta$. Then $H_\alpha(X)$ has no least upper bound in $H(X)$, $H_\alpha(Y)$ has a least upper bound in $H(Y)$, and $f[H_\alpha(X)] = H_\alpha(Y)$. By the proof of Lemma 16.4, f is **not** an isomorphism. Since $f : H(X) \to H(Y)$ was an arbitrary bijection, $H(X)$ and $H(Y)$ are not isomorphic.

It follows that $Z = \{H(X) \mid X \subseteq \omega_1\}$ is a collection of pairwise nonisomorphic DLOs of cardinality ω_1. Finally, $|Z| = |\mathcal{P}(\omega_1)| = 2^{\omega_1}$. $\qquad\square$

We conclude this lesson with a proof of Ulam's Theorem. Before we begin, the following results will be helpful for the proof. You will be asked to prove these results in Problems 3, 4, and 5 below.

Lemma 16.8: Let κ be a regular uncountable cardinal, let $\lambda < \kappa$ be a cardinal, for each $\alpha < \lambda$, let $C_\alpha \subseteq \kappa$ be a club in κ, and let $C = \bigcap\{C_\alpha \mid \alpha < \lambda\}$. Then C is also a club in κ.

Corollary 16.9: Every club is a stationary set.

Corollary 16.10: Let κ be a regular uncountable cardinal, let $\lambda < \kappa$ be a cardinal, for each $\alpha < \lambda$, let $X_\alpha \subseteq \kappa$ be nonstationary, and let $X = \bigcup\{X_\alpha \mid \alpha < \lambda\}$. Then X is also nonstationary.

Proof of Theorem 16.6: Let $\kappa = \lambda^+$ be an uncountable cardinal. For each ordinal $\eta < \kappa$, let $f_\eta : \eta \to \lambda$ be an injective function and for each $\alpha < \kappa$ and $\gamma < \lambda$, let $X_\alpha^\gamma = \{\eta > \alpha \mid f_\eta(\alpha) = \gamma\}$.

We first show that if $\alpha \neq \beta$, then $X_\alpha^\gamma \cap X_\beta^\gamma = \emptyset$. To see this, suppose that $\eta \in X_\alpha^\gamma \cap X_\beta^\gamma$. Then we have $f_\eta(\alpha) = \gamma$ and $f_\eta(\beta) = \gamma$. So, $f_\eta(\alpha) = f_\eta(\beta)$. Since f_η is injective, $\alpha = \beta$.

Next, note that for all $\alpha < \kappa$, $\bigcup\{X_\alpha^\gamma \mid \gamma < \lambda\} = \{\beta \mid \alpha < \beta < \kappa\}$. To see this, let $\beta \in \bigcup\{X_\alpha^\gamma \mid \gamma < \lambda\}$. Then there is $\gamma < \lambda$ so that $\beta \in X_\alpha^\gamma$. So, $\beta > \alpha$. Conversely, let $\alpha < \beta < \kappa$. Then $\beta \in X_\alpha^{f_\beta(\alpha)}$, and so, $\beta \in \bigcup\{X_\alpha^\gamma \mid \gamma < \lambda\}$.

By Example, 16.1 $\bigcup\{X_\alpha^\gamma \mid \gamma < \lambda\}$ is a club in κ. By Corollary 16.9, $\bigcup\{X_\alpha^\gamma \mid \gamma < \lambda\}$ is a stationary set. By Corollary 16.10, there is $g(\alpha) < \lambda$ such that $X_\alpha^{g(\alpha)}$ is stationary. Note that $g : \kappa \to \lambda$. Therefore, $\kappa = \bigcup\{g^{-1}(\gamma) \mid \gamma < \lambda\}$. Since κ is regular, by Problem 11 in Problem Set 13, there is $\gamma < \lambda$ so that $|g^{-1}(\gamma)| = \kappa$. It follows that $\{X_\alpha^\gamma \mid g(\alpha) = \gamma\}$ is a set of κ pairwise disjoint stationary subsets of κ. $\quad\square$

Problem Set 16

Full solutions to these problems are available for free download here:

www.SATPrepGet800.com/STFBYKG

LEVEL 1

1. Let $C = \{\alpha < \omega_1 \mid \alpha$ is a limit ordinal$\}$. Prove that C is a club in ω_1.

2. Suppose that for each $\alpha < \omega_1$, (i) H_α is a countable DLO, and (ii) for each $\alpha, \beta < \omega_1$, $\alpha < \beta$ implies $H_\alpha \subseteq H_\beta$ and the orderings of H_α and H_β agree on elements of H_α. Let $H = \bigcup\{H_\alpha \mid \alpha < \omega_1\}$. Prove that H is a DLO.

LEVEL 2

3. Let κ be a regular uncountable cardinal and let C and D be clubs in κ. Prove that $C \cap D$ is a club in κ. Use this result to conclude that every club is a stationary set.

4. Let κ be a regular uncountable cardinal, let $\lambda < \kappa$ be a cardinal, for each $\alpha < \lambda$, let $C_\alpha \subseteq \kappa$ be a club in κ, and let $C = \bigcap\{C_\alpha \mid \alpha < \lambda\}$. Prove that C is a club in κ.

LEVEL 3

5. Let κ be a regular uncountable cardinal, let $\lambda < \kappa$ be a cardinal, for each $\alpha < \lambda$, let $X_\alpha \subseteq \kappa$ be nonstationary, and let $X = \bigcup\{X_\alpha \mid \alpha < \lambda\}$. Prove that X is nonstationary.

6. Let κ be a regular uncountable cardinal and let C_η be a club in κ for each $\eta < \kappa$. Prove that $D = \{\eta \mid \forall \beta < \eta (\eta \in C_\beta)\}$ is a club in κ (D is called the **diagonal intersection** of $\{C_\eta \mid \eta < \kappa\}$).

LEVEL 4

7. Let κ be a regular uncountable cardinal and let $S \subseteq \kappa$. A function $f: S \to \kappa$ is said to be **regressive** if $\forall \alpha (\alpha \neq 0 \to f(\alpha) < \alpha)$. Suppose that every regressive function $f: S \to \kappa$ is constant on an unbounded subset of S. Prove that S is stationary.

8. Let κ be a regular uncountable cardinal, let $S \subseteq \kappa$ be a stationary set, and let $f: S \to \kappa$ be regressive. Prove that there is a stationary set $A \subseteq S$ and $\beta < \kappa$ such that $f[A] = \{\beta\}$.

LEVEL 5

9. Prove that there is a set $S \subseteq \omega_1$ such that both S and $\omega_1 \setminus S$ are stationary.

10. Let D be the following statement: There is a family $\{A_\alpha \mid \alpha < \omega_1\}$, such that for each $\alpha < \omega_1$, $A_\alpha \subseteq \alpha$ and for every $A \subseteq \omega_1$, the set $\{\alpha < \omega_1 \mid A \cap \alpha = A_\alpha\}$ is stationary. Prove that D implies CH. (D stands for **diamond**.)

11. Let D^- be the following statement: There is a family $\{\mathcal{A}_\alpha \mid \alpha < \omega_1\}$, such that for each $\alpha < \omega_1$, $\mathcal{A}_\alpha \subseteq \mathcal{P}(\alpha)$, $|\mathcal{A}_\alpha| \leq \omega$, and for every $A \subseteq \omega_1$, the set $\{\alpha < \omega_1 \mid A \cap \alpha \in \mathcal{A}_\alpha\}$ is stationary. Prove that D^- is equivalent to D.

About the Author

Dr. Steve Warner, a New York native, earned his Ph.D. at Rutgers University in Pure Mathematics in May 2001. While a graduate student, Dr. Warner won the TA Teaching Excellence Award.

After Rutgers, Dr. Warner joined the Penn State Mathematics Department as an Assistant Professor and in September 2002, he returned to New York to accept an Assistant Professor position at Hofstra University. By September 2007, Dr. Warner had received tenure and was promoted to Associate Professor. He has taught undergraduate and graduate courses in Precalculus, Calculus, Linear Algebra, Differential Equations, Mathematical Logic, Set Theory, and Abstract Algebra.

From 2003 – 2008, Dr. Warner participated in a five-year NSF grant, "The MSTP Project," to study and improve mathematics and science curriculum in poorly performing junior high schools. He also published several articles in scholarly journals, specifically on Mathematical Logic.

Dr. Warner has nearly two decades of experience in general math tutoring and tutoring for standardized tests such as the SAT, ACT, GRE, GMAT, and AP Calculus exams. He has tutored students both individually and in group settings.

In February 2010, Dr. Warner released his first SAT prep book "The 32 Most Effective SAT Math Strategies," and in 2012 founded Get 800 Test Prep. Since then Dr. Warner has written books for the SAT, ACT, SAT Math Subject Tests, AP Calculus exams, and GRE. In September 2018, Dr. Warner released his first advanced math book "Pure Mathematics for Beginners."

Dr. Steve Warner can be reached at

steve@SATPrepGet800.com

BOOKS BY DR. STEVE WARNER

   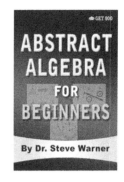

  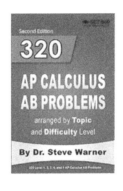 

Made in the USA
Coppell, TX
27 August 2020

35190657R00116